The HYMNAL

for Worship & Celebration

Containing Scriptures from the
King James Version of the Holy Bible

This hymnal is available in two editions: one has Scripture readings
from *The King James Version of the Holy Bible;* the second contains
readings taken from a combination of four translations—*New American
Standard Bible, Revised Standard Version, The Holy Bible, New
International Version,* and *The New King James Version.*

All musical selections from *The Hymnal* have been fully orchestrated:
part books and score are available for any size ensemble.

WORD MUSIC

NASHVILLE, TENNESSEE

0001020304 **QPH** 27262524

FOREWORD

I love to sing! Of greater importance, I love to sing with others.

I can think of no more glorious sound than a body of people who love their Lord, singing and making melody in their hearts. Whether the voices are blending together in harmonious a cappella or accompanied by a grand pipe organ or even a full orchestra, there is no sound on earth more heavenly than the sound of singing saints. As my minister of music has often said, "If you don't love to sing, then why in the world would you ever want to go to heaven?"

Music has its own international language, breaking down cultural barriers, cutting across age differences, and erasing denominational lines. For long centuries its soothing strains have calmed anxious hearts, incited courage in the fainthearted, comforted the grieving, healed the wounded, rescued the perishing, and drawn wanderers home.

Throughout my Christian life I have treasured the historic hymns of the church, having committed many of them to memory. They have been my dearest companions in dark hours of loneliness and discouragement and my greatest encouragers in times of celebration and adoration. In ministry, both at home and abroad, I have never failed to find new strength from these strong, timeless statements of faith.

The church will continue to sing her stately hymns, but, in addition to these, each new generation will continue to compose fresh choruses of worship and new psalms of praise. These songs give the church a relevant expression of her message. No longer is the singing of these current melodies and lyrics limited to the young. All of God's people are now joining the song . . . and when such singing is enjoyed alongside great preaching, it is a contagious combination.

The old Wittenberg monk, Martin Luther, was right:

> *Next to the Word of God, music deserves the highest praise. The gift of language combined with the gift of song was given to man that he should proclaim the Word of God through music.*

I commend Word, Incorporated, for its commitment to the church for providing this new collection of psalms, hymns, and spiritual songs, *The Hymnal for Worship and Celebration.* This fine volume maintains the continuity of history by including the hymns God's people have sung for centuries. But there is also variety in that the more recent songs of praise have been included, giving us a balanced blend of music so needed among congregations en route to the twenty-first century. All of this has been accomplished without the loss of theological integrity.

But there is more, so much more. *The Hymnal for Worship and Celebration* offers pastors, worship leaders, and ministers of music many tools for worship, prompting creativity, unpredictable ideas, and stimulating suggestions that enhance spontaneity. The *Brief Services* are designed to intensify the congregation's praise. They cover an abundance of relevant themes and each crafted arrangement possesses a natural flow that is easily understood and expressed. Even the indexes have been compiled and designed to prompt creative ideas for arranging one's own sequences of readings and musical selections.

Of special interest to leaders of worship and ministers of music is the provision of materials which fuse choir with congregation. The two work together as one—which they are—and yet the distinct presence of each is not ignored. And for those who have become weary of frequent repetition, due to a limited selection, you will be encouraged to discover a greater quantity of hymns and songs than in most other hymnals available today. And best of all, each selection is meaningful and singable.

As a minister I love to preach. I would be at a loss in the pulpit without my Bible. Nothing could or should replace the Scriptures in the church of Jesus Christ. This hymnal does not attempt to do that. The Bible is essential for the sowing of the seed. But over the years I have come to realize that nothing can or will prepare the soil of the heart like the hymns and the songs of faith. True worship therefore calls for companion volumes: a Bible and a hymnal. The two are as inseparable as the sword of the Spirit and the shield of faith. Christians need both to stand firm in the strength of His might.

If you love preaching there is no substitute for the Bible. If you love singing there is no substitute for the hymnal . . . and I know of none better today than *The Hymnal for Worship and Celebration.*

Charles R. Swindoll
Pastor, Radio Bible Teacher, Author

ACKNOWLEDGEMENTS

SENIOR EDITOR
Tom Fettke

ASSOCIATE EDITOR
Ken Barker

EXECUTIVE COMMITTEE
Tom Fettke—Chairman, Ken Barker, James C. Gibson, Bruce Howe, Dan Johnson and Kurt Kaiser

SCRIPTURE EDITOR AND THEOLOGICAL CONSULTANT
Dr. Kenneth L. Barker

ADVISORY BOARD
Cliff Barrows, C. Harry Causey, Dr. D. George Dunbar, Wilbur C. Ellsworth, Dr. Don Finto, Don G. Fontana, Richard M. Freeman, Gary Hallberg, Jack W. Hayford, Jr., Stan Jantz, Peter Kobe, Joseph Linn, Roger G. McMurrin, Thad Roberts, Jr., Tom Russell, Marshall J. Sanders, Barry Swanson and Dr. Edwin M. Willmington

CONSULTANTS
Neal Doty, Sean Doty, Donald W. Felice, Camp Kirkland, Anthony V. Klucznik, Jacquelyn Murray, Ronald Murray, Dr. Terry C. Terry and David S. Winkler

LOGO DESIGN
Dennis Hill, Patrick Pollei and Roger Sanders

COPYRIGHT ADMINISTRATION
Waverly Conlan and Cathy L. Donaldson

PRODUCTION ASSISTANTS
Mildred Burkett, Jenna L. Caraway, Jan Fettke, Ronald E. Garman, Jean Norwood and Kristin E. Payne

MUSIC TYPOGRAPHY
Musictype, Inc., Omaha, Arkansas; Don Ellingson

WORD INCORPORATED
Jarrell McCracken, Founder; Roland Lundy, President; Tom Ramsey, Executive Vice-President: Word Record and Music Group; Don Cason, Vice-President: Word Music

The Publisher gratefully acknowledges permission received from other publishers, organizations and individuals to reprint texts, music, and arrangements contained in this book.

PREFACE

At the heart of Christian worship, our songs and hymns are a treasure house of wisdom and beauty. They express praise, wonder, and awe. They contemplate the majesty, the mystery and the mercy of God, and in a profound way they express the depth of our response to God.

The Hymnal for Worship and Celebration combines the dignity of our musical heritage with the need for a worship resource book that speaks to the hearts of the 'people'—we who daily proclaim Him as Savior and Lord.

The Hymnal for Worship and Celebration possesses a number of unique characteristics which will enable pastors, ministers of music and worship leaders to create, plan and implement more effective and meaningful times of worship and celebration. Included in *The Hymnal* are 23 *Brief Services*—worship sequences that consist of a reading by a worship leader and/or congregation and two or more hymns, all relating to a central theme. Appropriate stanzas are clearly marked, and transitional or modulatory material is provided in the book, thereby allowing an uninterrupted flow from stanza to stanza and from one hymn to another. Each hymn is presented in a traditional format and can be used apart from the context of the *Brief Service*. By using the transitional material, any two of the selections in the *Brief Services* may be combined to form a medley. *The Hymnal* also includes a number of two-selection medleys on various themes (modulatory material is provided).

The Hymnal for Worship and Celebration includes optional choral introductions and endings for over 40 hymns and songs. Others have descants, while some include tastefully-arranged, optional last stanza harmonizations. Also included are many canons and rounds, which integrate individual and corporate worship very effectively.

The Hymnal for Worship and Celebration is fully orchestrated. Every selection is arranged in an interesting, yet accessible manner. The arrangements may be used in two different applications: to accompany congregational singing or to stand alone as preludes, postludes or offertories. Suggested keyboard introductions are bracketed in *The Hymnal*. These introductions are coordinated with suggested introductions in the orchestrations.

The Hymnal for Worship and Celebration includes the most comprehensive set of indexes ever assembled in one hymnal volume. I would encourage you to explore these vast resources. They are designed to provide you with the tools and the information necessary to create worship experiences tailored to meet the needs of your congregation.

I am convinced that you will find this volume to be one of quality, quantity, utility, and integrity. May it enable us to *Worship* and *Celebrate* the greatness of our God with more excitement and enthusiasm than ever before!

Soli Deo Gloria - **To God Alone Be the Glory**

Tom Fettke
Senior Editor

CONTENTS

BRIEF SERVICES

A more descriptive listing may be found at page 678.

Worship the Lord
in the beauty of holiness!
Celebrate His abundant
goodness and joyfully sing
of His righteousness.

Joyful, Joyful, We Adore Thee 1

Marvelous are Thy works; and that my soul knoweth right well. Ps. 139:14

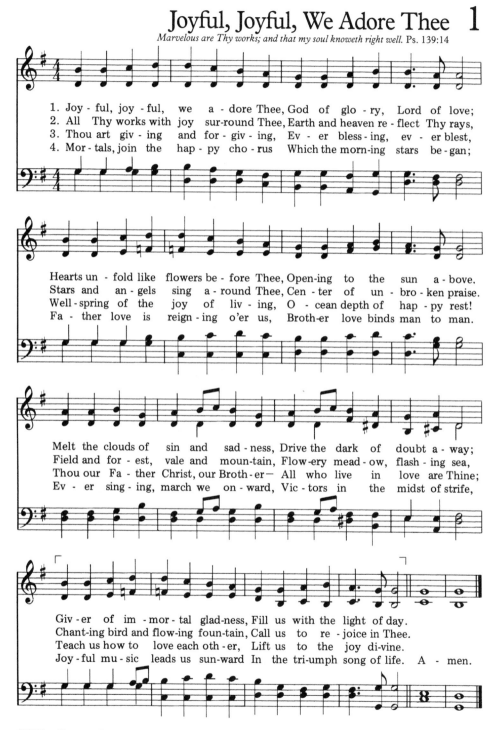

1. Joy - ful, joy - ful, we a - dore Thee, God of glo - ry, Lord of love;
2. All Thy works with joy sur-round Thee, Earth and heaven re - flect Thy rays,
3. Thou art giv - ing and for - giv - ing, Ev - er bless - ing, ev - er blest,
4. Mor - tals, join the hap - py cho - rus Which the morn-ing stars be - gan;

Hearts un - fold like flowers be - fore Thee, Open-ing to the sun a - bove.
Stars and an - gels sing a - round Thee, Cen - ter of un - bro - ken praise.
Well - spring of the joy of liv - ing, O - cean depth of hap - py rest!
Fa - ther love is reign - ing o'er us, Broth-er love binds man to man.

Melt the clouds of sin and sad - ness, Drive the dark of doubt a - way;
Field and for - est, vale and moun-tain, Flow-ery mead - ow, flash - ing sea,
Thou our Fa - ther Christ, our Broth-er— All who live in love are Thine;
Ev - er sing - ing, march we on - ward, Vic - tors in the midst of strife,

Giv - er of im - mor - tal glad-ness, Fill us with the light of day.
Chant-ing bird and flow-ing foun-tain, Call us to re - joice in Thee.
Teach us how to love each oth - er, Lift us to the joy di - vine.
Joy - ful mu - sic leads us sun-ward In the tri-umph song of life. A - men.

TEXT: Henry van Dyke
MUSIC: Ludwig van Beethoven; melody from *Ninth Symphony*;
adapted by Edward Hodges

HYMN TO JOY
8.7.8.7.D.

2 Come, Thou Fount of Every Blessing

The blessing of the Lord, it maketh rich. Prov. 10:22

1. Come, Thou Fount of ev-ery bless-ing, Tune my heart to sing Thy grace;
2. Hith-er-to Thy love has blest me; Thou hast bro't me to this place;
3. O to grace how great a debt-or Dai-ly I'm con-strained to be!

Streams of mer-cy, nev-er ceas-ing, Call for songs of loud-est praise.
And I know Thy hand will bring me Safe-ly home by Thy good grace.
Let Thy good-ness, like a fet-ter, Bind my wan-dering heart to Thee:

Teach me some me-lo-dious son-net, Sung by flam-ing tongues a-bove;
Je-sus sought me when a stran-ger, Wan-dering from the fold of God;
Prone to wan-der, Lord, I feel it, Prone to leave the God I love;

Praise His name—I'm fixed up-on it— Name of God's re-deem-ing love.
He, to res-cue me from dan-ger, Bought me with His precious blood.
Here's my heart, O take and seal it; Seal it for Thy courts a-bove. A-men.

TEXT: Robert Robinson; adapted by Margaret Clarkson
MUSIC: Traditional American melody; John Wyeth's *Repository of Sacred Music,* 1813

NETTLETON
8.7.8.7.D.

Praise, My Soul, the King of Heaven 3

Bless the Lord, O my soul . . . bless His holy name. Ps. 103:1

Unison

1. Praise, my soul, the King of heav-en, To His feet thy
2. Praise Him for His grace and fa-vor To our fa-thers
3. Frail as sum-mer's flow'r we flour-ish; Blows the wind and
4. An-gels in the height, a-dore Him; Ye be-hold Him

trib-ute bring; Ran-somed, healed, re-stored, for-giv-en,
in dis-tress; Praise Him, still the same as ev-er,
it is gone; But, while mor-tals rise and per-ish,
face to face; Saints tri-um-phant, bow be-fore Him;

Ev-er-more His prais-es sing; Al-le-lu-ia!
Slow to chide, and swift to bless; Al-le-lu-ia!
God en-dures un-chang-ing on: Al-le-lu-ia!
Gath-ered in from ev-ery race; Al-le-lu-ia!

Al-le-lu-ia! Praise the ev-er-last-ing King.
Al-le-lu-ia! Glo-rious in His faith-ful-ness.
Al-le-lu-ia! Praise the high E-ter-nal One.
Al-le-lu-ia! Praise with us the God of grace.

TEXT: Henry F. Lyte; based on Psalm 103
MUSIC: Mark Andrews
Alternate tune: REGENT SQUARE, No. 241

LAUDA ANIMA (Andrews)
8.7.8.7.8.7.

Music used by permission of G. Schirmer, Inc. All Rights Reserved.

4 How Great Thou Art

Great is the Lord, and greatly to be praised. Ps. 48:1

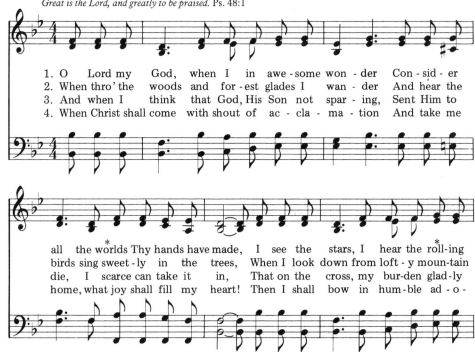

1. O Lord my God, when I in awe-some won-der Con-sid-er
2. When thro' the woods and for-est glades I wan-der And hear the
3. And when I think that God, His Son not spar-ing, Sent Him to
4. When Christ shall come with shout of ac-cla-ma-tion And take me

all the worlds* Thy hands have made, I see the stars, I hear the roll-ing*
birds sing sweet-ly in the trees, When I look down from loft-y moun-tain
die, I scarce can take it in, That on the cross, my bur-den glad-ly
home, what joy shall fill my heart! Then I shall bow in hum-ble ad-o-

Refrain

thun-der, Thy pow'r thro'-out the u-ni-verse dis-played.
gran-deur, And hear the brook and feel the gen-tle breeze. Then sings my
bear-ing, He bled and died to take a-way my sin.
ra-tion, And there pro-claim, my God, how great Thou art.

soul, my Sav-ior God, to Thee; How great Thou art, how great Thou art! Then sings my

*Translator's original words are "works" and "mighty."

TEXT and MUSIC: Stuart K. Hine;
Last stanza setting by Eugene Thomas

HOW GREAT THOU ART
11.10.11.10. with Refrain

soul, my Sav - ior God, to Thee: How great Thou art, how great Thou art!

Optional last stanza setting **Broader**

art! When Christ shall come with shout of ac - cla - ma - tion

8va *8va* *8va*

And take me home, what joy shall fill my heart! Then I shall bow in hum-ble ad-o-

Refrain

ra - tion, And there pro - claim, my God, how great Thou art! Then sings my

soul, my Sav-ior God, to Thee; How great Thou art, how great Thou art! Then sings my

continued on next page

5 Be Exalted, O God

Thy mercy is great . . . Be Thou exalted, O God, above the heavens. Ps. 57:10-11

TEXT and MUSIC: Brent Chambers; based on Psalm 57:9-11

BE EXALTED
Irregular meter

And Thy faith-ful-ness, Thy faith-ful-ness to the clouds.

Be ex - alt - ed, O God, a - bove the heav - ens;

Let Thy glo - ry be o - ver all the earth.

Be ex - alt - ed, O God, a - bove the heav - ens;

Let Thy glo - ry be o - ver all the earth.

6 Sing Praise to God Who Reigns Above

Ascribe ye greatness unto our God. Deut. 32:3

1. Sing praise to God who reigns a-bove, The God of all cre - a - tion, The God of pow'r, the God of love, The God of our sal - va - tion. With heal-ing balm my soul He fills, And ev - 'ry faith-less mur-mur stills: To God all praise and glo - ry!

2. What God's al-might-y pow'r hath made His gra-cious mer - cy keep-eth, By morn-ing glow or eve - ning shade His watch-ful eye ne'er sleep - eth. With-in the king-dom of His might, Lo! all is just and all is right: To God all praise and glo - ry!

3. The Lord is nev - er far a - way, But, thru all grief dis - tress-ing, An ev - er - pres-ent help and stay, Our peace and joy and bless - ing. As with a moth - er's ten - der hand He leads His own, His cho - sen band: To God all praise and glo - ry!

4. Thus all my toil - some way a - long I sing a - loud His prais - es, That men may hear the grate-ful song My voice un - wea - ried rais - es. Be joy - ful in the Lord, my heart! Both soul and bod - y bear your part: To God all praise and glo - ry! A - men.

TEXT: Johann J. Schütz; translated by Frances E. Cox
MUSIC: Bohemian Brethren's *Kirchengesänge*, Berlin, 1566

MIT FREUDEN ZART
8.7.8.7.8.8.7.

PRAISE GOD IN HIS SANCTUARY

A Brief Service of Worship and Exaltation

Suggested Hymn Stanzas

To facilitate an uninterrupted flow from stanza to stanza,
the suggested stanzas have been marked with an arrow: ▶

Praise to the Lord, the Almighty, stanzas 1, 4
Praise the Lord! Ye Heavens, Adore Him, stanzas 1, 3
O Worship the King, stanzas 1, 2, 4

WORSHIP LEADER:
Praise ye the Lord.

PEOPLE:
Praise ye the Lord.

WORSHIP LEADER:
Praise God in His sanctuary:
   praise Him in the firmament of His power.
Praise Him for His mighty acts:
   praise Him according to His excellent greatness.
Praise Him with the sound of the trumpet:
   praise Him with the psaltery.
Praise Him with the timbrel and dance:
   praise Him with stringed instruments and organs.
Praise Him upon the loud cymbals:
   praise Him upon the high sounding cymbals.
Let every thing that hath breath praise the Lord.

ALL:
Praise ye the Lord.

Psalm 150.

Optional introduction to "Praise to the Lord, the Almighty"

8 Praise to the Lord, the Almighty

Praise and extol and honour the King of heaven. Dan. 4:37

1. Praise to the Lord, the Al - might-y, the King of cre - a - tion!
2. Praise to the Lord, who o'er all things so won-drous-ly reign - eth,
3. Praise to the Lord, who doth pros - per thy work and de - fend thee;
4. Praise to the Lord! O let all that is in me a - dore Him!

O my soul, praise Him, for He is thy health and sal - va - tion!
Shel - ters thee un - der His wings, yes, so gen - tly sus - tain - eth!
Sure - ly His good - ness and mer - cy here dai - ly at - tend thee.
All that hath life and breath, come now with prais - es be - fore Him.

All ye who hear, Now to His tem - ple draw near; Join me in
Hast thou not seen How all thy long - ings have been Grant-ed in
Pon - der a - new What the Al - might - y can do, If with His
Let the A - men Sound from His peo - ple a - gain: Glad-ly for

Optional transition to "Praise the Lord!"

glad ad - o - ra - tion!
what He or - dain - eth?
love He be - friend thee.
aye we a - dore Him. A - men. Him.

TEXT: Joachim Neander; translated by Catherine Winkworth
MUSIC: *Stralsund Gesangbuch,* 1665

LOBE DEN HERREN
14.14.4.7.8.

Praise the Lord! Ye Heavens, Adore Him 9

Praise ye the Lord from the heavens . . . Praise the Lord from the earth. Ps. 148:1,7

1. Praise the Lord! ye heav'ns, a-dore Him; Praise Him an - gels in the height;
2. Praise the Lord! for He is glo - rious; Nev - er shall His prom-ise fail;
3. Wor -ship, hon - or, glo - ry, bless-ing, Lord, we of - fer un - to Thee;

Sun and moon, re - joice be - fore Him; Praise Him, all ye stars of light.
God hath made His saints vic - to - rious; Sin and death shall not pre - vail.
Young and old, Thy praise ex-press - ing, In glad hom-age bend the knee.

Praise the Lord! for He hath spo - ken; Worlds His might-y voice o-beyed;
Praise the God of our sal - va - tion! Hosts on high, His pow'r pro-claim;
All the saints in heav'n a-dore Thee; We would bow be - fore Thy throne:

Laws which nev-er shall be bro-ken For their guid-ance He hath made.
Heav'n and earth and all cre - a - tion, Laud and mag-ni - fy His name.
As Thine an - gels serve be-fore Thee, So on earth Thy will be done.* A - men.

*Optional segue to "O Worship the King"
no transition is needed

TEXT: *Foundling Hospital Collection,* 1796; Edward Osler, stanza 3;
based on Psalm 148
MUSIC: Franz Joseph Haydn
A higher setting may be found at No. 278; Alternate tune: HYFRYDOL, No. 89

AUSTRIAN HYMN
8.7.8.7.D.

10 O Worship the King

Bless the Lord . . . clothed with honour and majesty. Ps. 104:1

1. O wor-ship the King, all glo-rious a-bove, And grate-ful-ly sing
2. O tell of His might, O sing of His grace, Whose robe is the light,
3. Thy boun-ti-ful care what tongue can re-cite? It breathes in the air,
4. Frail chil-dren of dust, and fee-ble as frail, In Thee do we trust,

His won-der-ful love; Our Shield and De-fend-er, the An-cient of
whose can-o-py space! His char-iots of wrath the deep thun-der-clouds
it shines in the light, It streams from the hills, it de-scends to the
nor find Thee to fail: Thy mer-cies how ten-der, how firm to the

Days, Pa-vil-ioned in splen-dor, and gird-ed with praise.
form, And dark is His path on the wings of the storm.
plain, And sweet-ly dis-tills in the dew and the rain.
end, Our Mak-er, De-fend-er, Re-deem-er, and Friend. A-men.

Optional last stanza harmonization
Descant

Broaden
Unison

storm.   4. Frail chil-dren of dust, and

4. Frail chil-dren of dust, and

TEXT: Robert Grant
MUSIC: William Gardiner's *Sacred Melodies,* 1815; arranged from Johann M. Haydn;
Last stanza harmonization and descant by Herbert Colvin

LYONS
10.10.11.11.

feeble as frail, In Thee do we trust, nor find Thee to

feeble as frail, In Thee do we trust, nor find Thee to

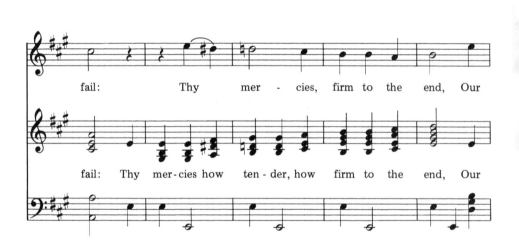

fail: Thy mer - cies, firm to the end, Our

fail: Thy mer - cies how ten - der, how firm to the end, Our

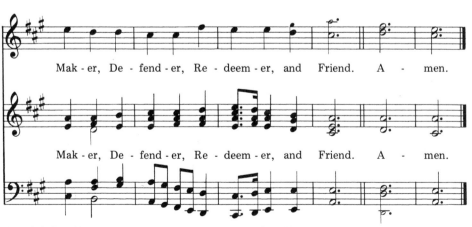

Mak - er, De - fend - er, Re - deem - er, and Friend. A - men.

Mak - er, De - fend - er, Re - deem - er, and Friend. A - men.

The end of "PRAISE GOD IN HIS SANCTUARY—A Brief Service of Worship and Exaltation"

11 My Tribute

Not unto us, O Lord . . . but unto Thy name give glory. Ps. 115:1

How can I say thanks for the things You have done for me— Things
so un-de-served, yet You give to prove Your love for me? The voic-es
of a mil-lion an-gels could not ex-press my grat-i-tude— All
that I am and ev-er hope to be, I owe it all to Thee. To

Refrain

God be the glo-ry, To God be the glo-ry; To

TEXT and MUSIC: Andraé Crouch

MY TRIBUTE
Irregular meter

God be the glo - ry for the things He has done. With His

blood He has saved me; With His pow'r He has raised me; To

Fine

God be the glo - ry For the things He has done.

On introduction, hold 4 beats.

Just let me live my life; Let it be pleas-ing, Lord, to Thee. And

D.S. al Fine

should I gain an - y praise, Let it go to Cal - va - ry. With His

12 Holy God, We Praise Thy Name

I will bless Thy name for ever and ever. Ps. 145:1

Descant, last stanza

3. Ho-ly   Fa - ther,   ho - ly   Son,   Ho-ly   Spir - it:

1. Ho - ly   God,   we   praise   Thy   name;   Lord   of   all,   we
2. Hark,   the   glad   ce - les - tial   hymn   An - gel   choirs   a-
3. Ho - ly   Fa - ther,   ho - ly   Son,   Ho - ly   Spir - it:

three   we   name   Thee,   Though   in   es - sence   on - ly   one;

bow   be - fore   Thee;   All   on   earth   Thy   scep - ter   claim,
bove   are   rais - ing;   Cher - u - bim   and   ser - a - phim,
three   we   name   Thee,   Though   in   es - sence   on - ly   one;

Un - di - vid - ed   God   we   claim   Thee,   And   a - dor - ing,   bend   the   knee.

All   in   heaven   a - bove   a - dore   Thee: In - fi - nite   Thy   vast   do-
In   un - ceas - ing   cho - rus   prais - ing;   Fill   the   heavens   with   sweet   ac-
Un - di - vid - ed   God   we   claim   Thee,   And   a - dor - ing,   bend   the

TEXT: Attributed to Ignace Franz; translated by Clarence A. Walworth;
based on *Te Deum*

MUSIC: Melody in *Katholisches Gesangbuch*, Vienna, c. 1774;
Descant by Ken Barker

GROSSER GOTT
7.8.7.8.7.7.

Al - le - lu - ia! Praise to Thee. A - men.

main, Ev - er - last - ing is Thy reign.
cord: Ho - ly, ho - ly, ho - ly Lord.
knee While we sing our praise to Thee. A - men.

Bless His Holy Name 13

Bless the Lord, O my soul. Ps. 103:22

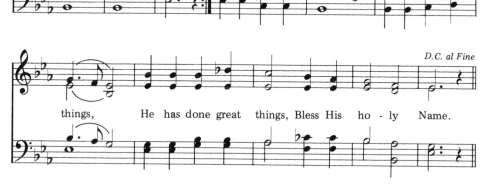

Bless the Lord, O my soul, and all that is with - in me, Bless His

Fine

ho - ly Name. He has done great things, He has done great

D.C. al Fine

things, He has done great things, Bless His ho - ly Name.

TEXT and MUSIC: Andraé Crouch; based on Psalm 103

BLESS HIS HOLY NAME
Irregular meter

14 Come, Let Us Worship and Bow Down

O come, let us worship and bow down. Ps. 95:6

Come, let us wor-ship and bow down, let us kneel be-fore the Lord, our God, our

accompaniment

Mak - er. Mak - er. For He is our

God, and we are the peo-ple of His pas - ture, and the

TEXT: Psalm 95:6, 7; adapted by Dave Doherty
MUSIC: Dave Doherty

WORSHIP AND BOW DOWN
Irregular meter

sheep of His hand, just the sheep of His hand.

Abba Father 15

Ye have received the Spirit of adoption, whereby we cry, Abba Father. Rom. 8:15

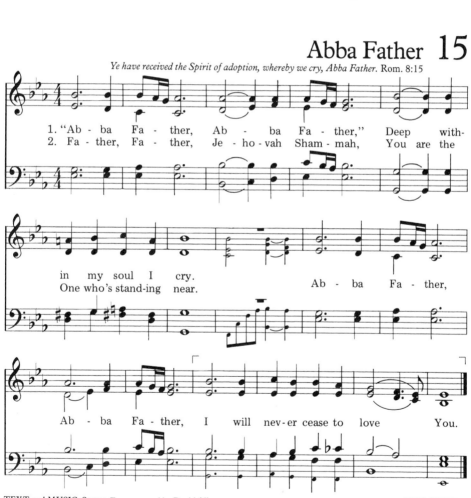

1. "Ab - ba Fa - ther, Ab - ba Fa - ther," Deep with-
2. Fa - ther, Fa - ther, Je - ho - vah Sham - mah, You are the

in my soul I cry.
One who's stand-ing near. Ab - ba Fa - ther,

Ab - ba Fa - ther, I will nev-er cease to love You.

TEXT and MUSIC: Steven Fry; arranged by David Allen

ABBA FATHER
Irregular meter

16 We Praise Thee, O God, Our Redeemer

Great is the Lord, and greatly to be praised. 1 Chr. 16:25

3. With voic-es u-nit-ed our prais-es we of-fer To Thee, great Je-

1. We praise Thee, O God, our Re- deem-er, Cre-a-tor In grate-ful de-
2. We wor-ship Thee, God of our fa-thers, we bless Thee Thru life's storm and
3. With voic-es u-nit-ed our prais-es we of-fer To Thee, great Je-

ho-vah, glad an-thems we raise; Thy strong arm will guide us,

vo-tion our trib-ute we bring; We lay it be-fore Thee, we kneel
tem-pest our Guide hast Thou been; When per-ils o'er-take us, es-cape
ho-vah, glad an-thems we raise; Thy strong arm will guide us, our God

and our God is be-side us, great Re- deem-er, for-ev-er be praise!

and a-dore Thee, We bless Thy ho-ly Name, glad prais-es we sing.
Thou wilt make us, And with Thy help, O Lord, our bat-tles we win.
is be-side us, To Thee, our great Re-deem-er, for-ev-er be praise!

TEXT: Julia Cady Cory
MUSIC: Netherlands Folk song; arranged by Edward Kremser;
Descant and choral ending by Steve Holcomb
A lower setting may be found at No. 561

KREMSER
12.11.12.11.

Optional choral ending

praise!

rit.

praise! A - men! A - men.

Ye Servants of God 17

Salvation to our God which sitteth upon the throne, and unto the Lamb. Rev. 7:10

1. Ye ser - vants of God, your Mas - ter pro - claim, And pub - lish a -
2. God rul - eth on high, al - might - y to save, And still He is
3. "Sal - va - tion to God, who sits on the throne!" Let all cry a -
4. Then let us a - dore, and give Him His right— All glo - ry and

broad His won - der - ful name; The name, all - vic - to - rious, of Je - sus
nigh, His pres - ence we have; The great con - gre - ga - tion His tri - umph
loud, and hon - or the Son; The prais - es of Je - sus the an - gels
pow'r, all wis - dom and might, All hon - or and bless - ing, with an - gels

ex - tol: His king - dom is glo - rious, He rules o - ver all.
shall sing, As - crib - ing sal - va - tion to Je - sus, our King.
pro - claim, Fall down on their fac - es and wor - ship the Lamb.
a - bove, And thanks nev - er - ceas - ing, and in - fi - nite love. A - men.

TEXT: Charles Wesley
MUSIC: William Croft

HANOVER
10.10.11.11.

18 Come, We That Love the Lord

Praise ye the Lord. Sing unto the Lord a new song. Ps. 149:1

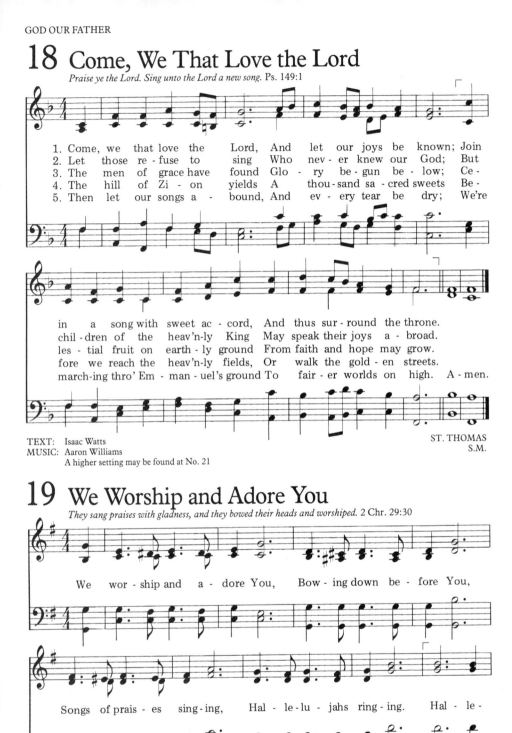

1. Come, we that love the Lord, And let our joys be known; Join
2. Let those re-fuse to sing Who nev-er knew our God; But
3. The men of grace have found Glo-ry be-gun be-low; Ce-
4. The hill of Zi-on yields A thou-sand sa-cred sweets Be-
5. Then let our songs a-bound, And ev-ery tear be dry; We're

in a song with sweet ac-cord, And thus sur-round the throne.
chil-dren of the heav'n-ly King May speak their joys a-broad.
les-tial fruit on earth-ly ground From faith and hope may grow.
fore we reach the heav'n-ly fields, Or walk the gold-en streets.
march-ing thro' Em-man-uel's ground To fair-er worlds on high. A-men.

TEXT: Isaac Watts
MUSIC: Aaron Williams
A higher setting may be found at No. 21

ST. THOMAS
S.M.

19 We Worship and Adore You

They sang praises with gladness, and they bowed their heads and worshiped. 2 Chr. 29:30

We wor-ship and a-dore You, Bow-ing down be-fore You,

Songs of prais-es sing-ing, Hal-le-lu-jahs ring-ing. Hal-le-

TEXT and MUSIC: Traditional

WORSHIP AND ADORE
7.6.6.6.8.6.

lu - jah, hal - le - lu - jah, hal - le - lu - jah, A - men.

All People That on Earth Do Dwell 20

Make a joyful noise unto the Lord, all ye lands. Ps. 100:1

1. All peo - ple that on earth do dwell, Sing to the
2. The Lord, ye know, is God in - deed; With - out our
3. O en - ter then His gates with praise, Ap - proach with
4. For why? The Lord our God is good, His mer - cy
5. To Fa - ther, Son, and Ho - ly Ghost, the God whom

Lord with cheer - ful voice; Him serve with fear, His praise forth
aid He did us make; We are His flock, He doth us
joy His courts un - to; Praise, laud, and bless His name al -
is for - ev - er sure; His truth at all times firm - ly
heaven and earth a - dore, From earth and from the an - gel

tell, Come ye be - fore Him and re - joice.
feed, And for His sheep He doth us take.
ways, For it is seem - ly so to do.
stood, And shall from age to age en - dure.
host Be praise and glo - ry ev - er - more. A - men.

TEXT: William Kethe and *Scottish Psalter*, 1565; based on Psalm 100
MUSIC: *Genevan Psalter*, 1551; attributed to Louis Bourgeois

OLD HUNDREDTH
L.M.

21 Stand Up and Bless the Lord

Stand up and bless the Lord your God. Neh. 9:5

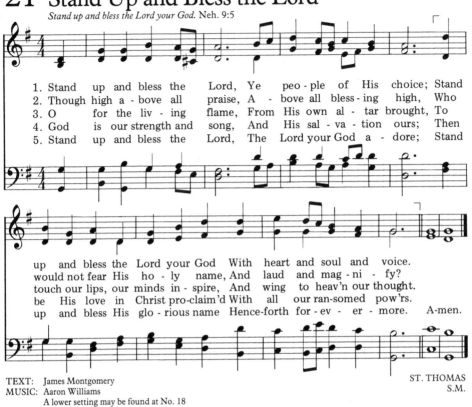

1. Stand up and bless the Lord, Ye peo-ple of His choice; Stand
2. Though high a-bove all praise, A-bove all bless-ing high, Who
3. O for the liv-ing flame, From His own al-tar brought, To
4. God is our strength and song, And His sal-va-tion ours; Then
5. Stand up and bless the Lord, The Lord your God a-dore; Stand

up and bless the Lord your God With heart and soul and voice.
would not fear His ho-ly name, And laud and mag-ni-fy?
touch our lips, our minds in-spire, And wing to heav'n our thought.
be His love in Christ pro-claim'd With all our ran-somed pow'rs.
up and bless His glo-rious name Hence-forth for-ev-er-more. A-men.

TEXT: James Montgomery
MUSIC: Aaron Williams
    A lower setting may be found at No. 18

ST. THOMAS
S.M.

22 Isaiah 6:3

Holy, holy, holy is the Lord of hosts: the whole earth is full of His glory. Isa. 6:3

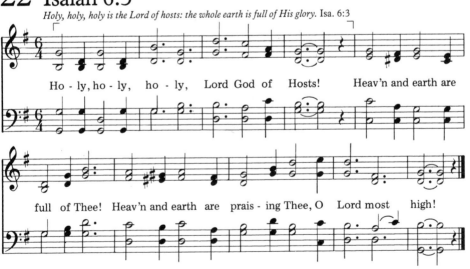

Ho-ly, ho-ly, ho-ly, Lord God of Hosts! Heav'n and earth are

full of Thee! Heav'n and earth are prais-ing Thee, O Lord most high!

TEXT: Mary A. Lathbury; from Isaiah 6:3
MUSIC: William F. Sherwin

CHAUTAUQUA (Refrain only)
Irregular meter

Make a Joyful Noise 23

Make a joyful noise unto the Lord, all the earth. Ps. 98:4

4 Part Canon

Make a joyful noise unto the Lord, all the earth! Make a joyful noise unto the Lord!

Make a joyful noise unto the Lord, all the earth! Make a joyful noise unto the Lord! Make a

loud noise and re - joice! Sing prais-es! Make a joyful noise unto the Lord! Make a

loud noise and re - joice! Sing prais-es! Make a joy-ful noise un-to the Lord!

TEXT and MUSIC: Jimmy Owens; based on Psalm 98:4

JOYFUL NOISE
12.8.12.8.10.8.10.8.

Clap Your Hands 24

O clap your hands, all ye people; shout unto God with the voice of triumph. Ps. 47:1

2 Part Canon

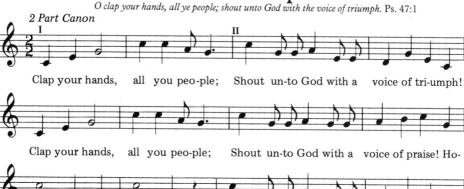

Clap your hands, all you peo-ple; Shout un-to God with a voice of tri-umph!

Clap your hands, all you peo-ple; Shout un-to God with a voice of praise! Ho-

san - na! Ho - san - na! Shout un-to God with a voice of tri-umph!

Praise Him! Praise Him! Shout un-to God with a voice of praise!

TEXT and MUSIC: Jimmy Owens; based on Psalm 47:1

CLAP YOUR HANDS
Irregular meter

25 Immortal, Invisible

Unto the King eternal, immortal, invisible, the only wise God, be honour. 1 Tim. 1:17

1. Im - mor - tal, in - vis - i - ble, God on - ly wise,
2. Un - rest - ing, un - hast - ing, and si - lent as light,
3. To all, life Thou giv - est— to both great and small,
4. Great Fa - ther of glo - ry, pure Fa - ther of light,

In light in - ac - ces - si - ble hid from our eyes,
Nor want - ing, nor wast - ing, Thou rul - est in might;
In all life Thou liv - est— the true life of all;
Thine an - gels a - dore Thee, all veil - ing their sight;

Most bless - ed, most glo - rious, the An - cient of Days,
Thy jus - tice, like moun - tains, high soar - ing a - bove
We blos - som and flour - ish as leaves on the tree,
All praise we would ren - der— O help us to see

Al - might - y, vic - to - rious—Thy great name we praise.
Thy clouds, which are foun - tains of good - ness and love.
And with - er and per - ish— but naught chang - eth Thee.
'Tis on - ly the splen - dor of light hid - eth Thee! A - men.

TEXT: Walter Chalmers Smith; based on 1 Timothy 1:17
MUSIC: Traditional Welsh Hymn melody
     from John Roberts' *Canaidau y Cyssegr*, 1839

ST. DENIO
11.11.11.11.

A Mighty Fortress Is Our God 26

The Lord of hosts is with us; the God of Jacob is our Refuge. Ps. 46:7

1. A might-y for-tress is our God, A bul-wark nev-er fail - ing;
2. Did we in our own strength con-fide, Our striv-ing would be los - ing,
3. And tho this world, with dev-ils filled, Should threat-en to un-do us,
4. That word a-bove all earth-ly pow'rs, No thanks to them, a-bid - eth;

Our help-er He a-mid the flood Of mor-tal ills pre-vail - ing.
Were not the right man on our side, The man of God's own choos - ing.
We will not fear, for God hath willed His truth to tri-umph thru us.
The Spir-it and the gifts are ours Thru Him who with us sid - eth.

For still our an-cient foe Doth seek to work us woe—His craft and pow'r are
Dost ask who that may be? Christ Je-sus, it is He— Lord Sab-a-oth His
The prince of dark-ness grim, We trem-ble not for him— His rage we can en-
Let goods and kin-dred go, This mor-tal life al-so— The bod-y they may

great, And, armed with cru-el hate, On earth is not his e - qual.
name, From age to age the same, And He must win the bat - tle.
dure, For lo, his doom is sure: One lit-tle word shall fell him.
kill; God's truth a-bid-eth still: His king-dom is for-ev - er. A-men.

TEXT: Martin Luther; translated by Frederick H. Hedge; based on Psalm 46
MUSIC: Martin Luther

EIN' FESTE BURG
8.7.8.7.6.6.6.6.7.

27 Tell Out, My Soul

He that is mighty hath done to me great things. Luke 1:49

Unison

1. Tell out, my soul, the great-ness of the Lord! Un-num-bered
2. Tell out, my soul, the great-ness of His Name! Make known His
3. Tell out, my soul, the great-ness of His might! Pow'rs and do-
4. Tell out, my soul, the glo-ries of His Word! Firm is His

bless-ings give my spir-it voice; Ten-der to me the
might, the deeds His arm has done; His mer-cy sure, from
min-ions lay their glo-ry by. Proud hearts and stub-born
prom-ise, and His mer-cy sure. Tell out, my soul, the

prom-ise of His Word; In God my Sav-ior shall my heart re-joice.
age to age the same; His ho-ly Name, the Lord, the Might-y One.
wills are put to flight, The hun-gry fed, the hum-ble lift-ed high.
great-ness of the Lord To chil-dren's chil-dren and for-ev-er-more!

TEXT: Timothy Dudley-Smith; based on Luke 1:46-55
MUSIC: Walter Greatorex

WOODLANDS
10.10.10.10.

HOW MAJESTIC IS YOUR NAME

A Brief Service in Recognition
of God's Majesty and Power

Suggested Hymn Stanzas

To facilitate an uninterrupted flow from stanza to stanza,
the suggested stanzas have been marked with an arrow: ▶

Glorify Thy Name, stanza 1
How Majestic Is Your Name, complete
Great Is the Lord, complete

WORSHIP LEADER and PEOPLE:

O Lord our Lord,
    how excellent is Thy name in all the earth!
Who hast set Thy glory
    above the heavens.
Out of the mouth of babes and sucklings
    hast Thou ordained strength
because of Thine enemies,
    that Thou mightest still the enemy
and the avenger.
When I consider Thy heavens,
    the work of Thy fingers,
the moon and the stars,
    which Thou hast ordained;
What is man, that Thou art mindful of him?
    and the son of man, that Thou visitest him:
For Thou hast made him a little lower than the angels,
    and hast crowned him with glory and honour.
Thou madest him to have dominion over the works of Thy hands;
    Thou hast put all things under his feet;
All sheep and oxen, yea,
    and the beasts of the field;
The fowl of the air, and the fish of the sea,
    and whatsoever passeth through the paths of the seas.
O Lord our Lord,
    how excellent is Thy name in all the earth!

Psalm 8.

Optional introduction to "Glorify Thy Name"

29 Glorify Thy Name

Father, glorify Thy name. John 12:28

1. Fa - ther, we love You, we wor - ship and a - dore You,
2. Je - sus, we love You, we wor - ship and a - dore You,
3. Spir - it, we love You, we wor - ship and a - dore You,

Glo - ri - fy Thy name in all the earth.

Glo - ri - fy Thy name, Glo - ri - fy Thy name,

Glo - ri - fy Thy name in all the earth.

TEXT and MUSIC: Donna Adkins

GLORIFY THY NAME
Irregular meter

Optional transition to "How Majestic Is Your Name"

Bright and Energetic

How Majestic Is Your Name 30

O Lord our Lord, how excellent is Thy name in all the earth! Ps. 8:1

O Lord, our Lord, how ma - jes - tic is Your name in all the earth. O earth. O Lord, we praise Your name. O Lord, we mag - ni - fy Your name: Prince of Peace, might - y God; O Lord God Al - might - y. O - y.

TEXT and MUSIC: Michael W. Smith

HOW MAJESTIC
Irregular meter

Optional transition to "Great Is the Lord"

New tempo
♩. = ca. 63

31 Great Is the Lord

Great is the Lord, and greatly to be praised. Ps. 145:3

Great is the Lord, He is ho-ly and just; By His pow-er we trust in His love. Great is the Lord, He is faith-ful and true; By His mer-cy He proves He is love.

1, 2. Great is the Lord and wor-thy of glo-ry!
(D.S.) Great are You, Lord, and wor-thy of glo-ry!

Great is the Lord and wor-thy of praise.
Great are You, Lord, and wor-thy of praise.

Great is the Lord; now lift up your voice, Now lift up your voice: Great is the
Great are You, Lord; I lift up my voice, I lift up my voice: Great are You,

TEXT and MUSIC: Michael W. Smith and Deborah D. Smith

GREAT IS THE LORD
Irregular meter

The end of "HOW MAJESTIC IS YOUR NAME—A Brief Service in Recognition of God's Majesty and Power"

Holy Lord 32

All the earth shall be filled with the glory of the Lord. Num. 14:21

TEXT: Gerald S. Henderson; based on Isaiah 6:3
MUSIC: Source unknown; adapted by Gerald S. Henderson

DONA NOBIS PACEM
Irregular meter

33 God the Omnipotent

He shall speak peace unto the heathen. Zech. 9:10

1. God the Om-nip-o-tent! King, who or-dain-est
2. God the All-mer-ci-ful! Earth hath for-sak-en
3. God the All-right-eous One! Man hath de-fied Thee;
4. So shall Thy peo-ple, with thank-ful de-vo-tion,

Thun-der Thy clar-ion, the light-ning Thy sword;
Meek-ness and mer-cy, and slight-ed Thy Word;
Yet to e-ter-ni-ty stand-eth Thy Word;
Praise Him who saved them from per-il and sword,

Show forth Thy pit-y on high where Thou reign-est;
Let not Thy wrath in its ter-rors a-wak-en;
False-hood and wrong shall not tar-ry be-side Thee;
Sing-ing in cho-rus from o-cean to o-cean,

Give to us peace in our time, O Lord.
Give to us peace in our time, O Lord.
Give to us peace in our time, O Lord.
Peace to the na-tions, and praise to the Lord. A-men.

TEXT: Henry F. Chorley, stanzas 1, 2; John Ellerton, stanzas 3, 4
MUSIC: Alexis F. Lvov

RUSSIAN HYMN
11.10.11.9.

The God of Abraham Praise 34

[Abraham] was strong in faith, giving glory to God. Rom. 4:20

1. The God of A-braham praise, Who reigns en-throned a-bove;
2. The God of A-braham praise, At whose su-preme com-mand
3. He by Him-self hath sworn, I on His oath de-pend,
4. The whole tri-um-phant host Give thanks to God on high;

An-cient of ev-er-last-ing days, And God of love.
From earth I rise, and seek the joys At His right hand.
I shall, on ea-gles wings up-borne, To heaven as-cend;
"Hail, Fa-ther, Son and Ho-ly Ghost!" They ev-er cry.

Je-ho-vah, great I AM, By earth and heaven con-fessed;
I all on earth for-sake, Its wis-dom, fame, and power;
I shall be-hold His face, I shall His power a-dore,
Hail, A-braham's God and mine! I join the heaven-ly lays;

I bow and bless the sa-cred name, For-ev-er blest.
And Him my on-ly por-tion make, My shield and tower.
And sing the won-ders of His grace For-ev-er-more.
All might and ma-jes-ty are Thine, And end-less praise. A-men.

TEXT: Thomas Olivers; based on Jewish *Doxology*
MUSIC: Traditional Hebrew melody; adapted by Meyer Lyon
A lower setting may be found at No. 472

LEONI
6.6.8.4.D.

35 The Majesty and Glory of Your Name

How excellent is Thy name in all the earth! Ps. 8:9

TEXT: Linda Lee Johnson; based on Psalm 8
MUSIC: Tom Fettke

SOLI DEO GLORIA
Irregular meter

lu - ia, Al - le - lu - ia, Al - le - lu - ia!

El Shaddai 36

I am the Almighty God; walk before Me, and be thou perfect. Gen. 17:1

Unison

*El Shad-dai, El Shad-dai, El El - yon na A - do-nai;

Age to age You're still the same By the pow-er of the name.

El Shad-dai, El Shad-dai, Er-kahm - ka na A - do-nai;

We will praise and lift You high, El Shad - dai.

*Translations of Hebrew terms:
El Shaddai: God Almighty   na Adonai: O Lord
El Elyon: The Most High God   Erkahmka: we will love You
TEXT and MUSIC: Michael Card and John Thompson

EL SHADDAI
Irregular meter

37 Hallelujah Chorus

Alleluia: for the Lord God omnipotent reigneth. Rev. 19:6

Hal-le-lu-jah! Hal-le-lu-jah! Hal-le-lu-jah! Hal-le-lu-jah! Hal-le-lu-jah!

Hal-le-lu-jah! Hal-le-lu-jah! Hal-le-lu-jah! Hal-le-lu-jah! Hal-le-lu-jah!

for the Lord God om-nip-o-tent reign-eth. Hal-le-lu-jah! Hal-le-lu-jah! Hal-le-

lu-jah! Hal-le-lu-jah! for the Lord God om-nip-o-tent reign-eth. Hal-le-

TEXT and MUSIC: George Frederick Handel

HALLELUJAH CHORUS
Irregular meter

This vocal score is complete and uniform with most editions.

GOD OUR FATHER

38 I Will Call upon the Lord

I will call upon the Lord, who is worthy to be praised. Ps. 18:3

TEXT and MUSIC: Michael O'Shields; based on Psalm 18:3; 2 Samuel 22:47

O'SHIELDS
Irregular meter

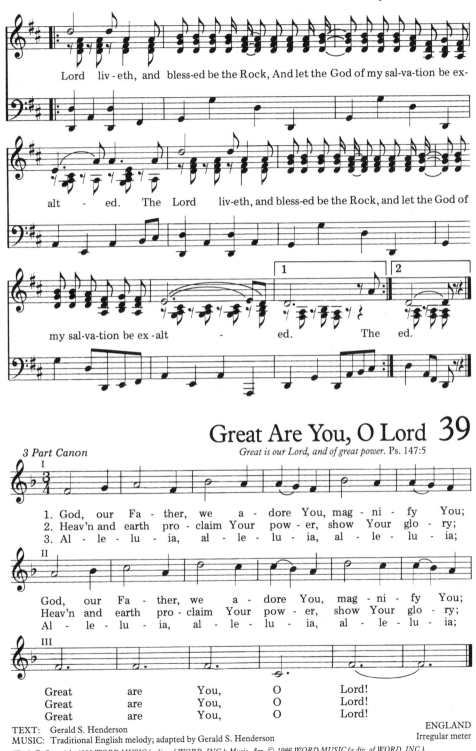

Lord liv-eth, and bless-ed be the Rock, And let the God of my sal-va-tion be ex-

alt - ed. The Lord liv-eth, and bless-ed be the Rock, and let the God of

my sal-va-tion be ex-alt - ed. The ed.

Great Are You, O Lord 39

Great is our Lord, and of great power. Ps. 147:5

3 Part Canon

1. God, our Fa - ther, we a - dore You, mag - ni - fy You;
2. Heav'n and earth pro - claim Your pow - er, show Your glo - ry;
3. Al - le - lu - ia, al - le - lu - ia, al - le - lu - ia;

God, our Fa - ther, we a - dore You, mag - ni - fy You;
Heav'n and earth pro - claim Your pow - er, show Your glo - ry;
Al - le - lu - ia, al - le - lu - ia, al - le - lu - ia;

Great are You, O Lord!
Great are You, O Lord!
Great are You, O Lord!

TEXT: Gerald S. Henderson
MUSIC: Traditional English melody; adapted by Gerald S. Henderson

ENGLAND
Irregular meter

40 A Perfect Heart

A new heart also will I give you, and a new spirit will I put within you. Ezek. 36:26

Bless the Lord (bless the Lord) who reigns in beau-ty; Bless the Lord (bless the Lord) who reigns in wis-dom and with pow'r. Bless the Lord (bless the Lord) who fills my life with so much love, He can make a per-fect heart.

TEXT and MUSIC: Dony McGuire and Reba Rambo

A PERFECT HEART
Irregular meter

41 God Is So Good

Give thanks unto the Lord; for He is good. 1 Chr. 16:34

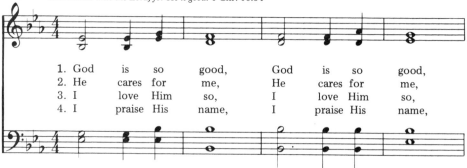

1. God is so good, God is so good,
2. He cares for me, He cares for me,
3. I love Him so, I love Him so,
4. I praise His name, I praise His name,

TEXT and MUSIC: Traditional

GOD IS SO GOOD
Irregular meter

God is so good, He's so good to me!
He cares for me, He's so good to me!
I love Him so, He's so good to me!
I praise His name, He's so good to me!

Seek Ye First 42

Seek ye first the kingdom of God, and His righteousness. Matt. 6:33

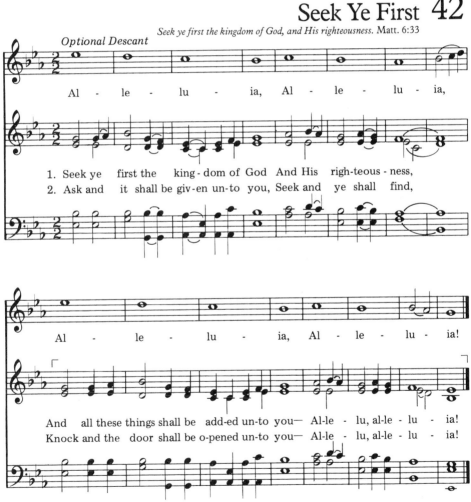

Optional Descant

Al - le - lu - ia, Al - le - lu - ia,

1. Seek ye first the king-dom of God And His righ-teous-ness,
2. Ask and it shall be giv-en un-to you, Seek and ye shall find,

Al - le - lu - ia, Al - le - lu - ia!

And all these things shall be add-ed un-to you— Al-le - lu, al-le - lu - ia!
Knock and the door shall be o-pened un-to you— Al-le - lu, al-le - lu - ia!

TEXT and MUSIC: Karen Lafferty; based on Matthew 6:33; 7:7

LAFFERTY
Irregular meter

43 Great Is Thy Faithfulness

The Lord's . . . compassions . . . are new every morning: great is Thy faithfulness. Lam. 3:22-23

1. Great is Thy faith-ful-ness, O God my Fa-ther, There is no
2. Sum-mer and win-ter, and spring-time and har-vest, Sun, moon and
3. Par-don for sin and a peace that en-dur-eth, Thy own dear

shad-ow of turn-ing with Thee; Thou chang-est not, Thy com-
stars in their cours-es a-bove Join with all na-ture in
pres-ence to cheer and to guide; Strength for to-day and bright

pas-sions they fail not; As Thou hast been Thou for-ev-er wilt be.
man-i-fold wit-ness To Thy great faith-ful-ness, mer-cy and love.
hope for to-mor-row, Bless-ings all mine, with ten thou-sand be-side!

Refrain

Great is Thy faith-ful-ness! Great is Thy faith-ful-ness! Morn-ing by

morn-ing new mer-cies I see; All I have need-ed Thy

TEXT: Thomas O. Chisholm
MUSIC: William M. Runyan

FAITHFULNESS
11.10.11.10 with Refrain

hand hath pro - vid - ed— Great is Thy faith - ful - ness, Lord, un - to me!

Optional choral ending
gradual cresc.   *rit.*   *Slowly* **ff**

Great is Thy faith-ful-ness, Great is Thy faith-ful-ness, Lord, un-to me!

Children of the Heavenly Father 44

What manner of love the Father hath bestowed upon us . . . the sons of God. 1 John 3:1

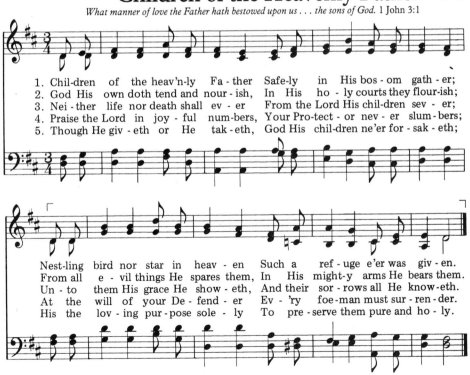

1. Chil-dren of the heav'n-ly Fa - ther   Safe-ly in His bos - om gath - er;
2. God His own doth tend and nour-ish,   In His ho - ly courts they flour-ish;
3. Nei - ther life nor death shall ev - er   From the Lord His chil-dren sev - er;
4. Praise the Lord in joy - ful num-bers,   Your Pro-tect - or nev - er slum-bers;
5. Though He giv - eth or He tak - eth,   God His chil-dren ne'er for - sak - eth;

Nest-ling bird nor star in heav - en   Such a ref - uge e'er was giv - en.
From all e - vil things He spares them,   In His might-y arms He bears them.
Un - to them His grace He show - eth,   And their sor - rows all He know-eth.
At the will of your De - fend - er   Ev - 'ry foe-man must sur - ren - der.
His the lov - ing pur-pose sole - ly   To pre - serve them pure and ho - ly.

TEXT: Carolina Sandell Berg; translated by Ernst W. Olson
MUSIC: Swedish Folk melody

TRYGGARE KAN INGEN VARA
L.M.

Text Copyright Board of Publication of the Lutheran Church in America. Reprinted by permission.

45 Surely Goodness and Mercy

Surely goodness and mercy shall follow me all the days of my life. Ps. 23:6

1. A pil-grim was I, and a-wand'ring— In the cold night of
2. He re-stor-eth my soul when I'm wea-ry, He giv-eth me
3. When I walk thru the dark lone-some val-ley, My Sav-ior will

sin I did roam When Je-sus the kind Shep-herd found me—
strength day by day; He leads me be-side the still wa-ters,
walk with me there; And safe-ly His great hand will lead me

And now I am on my way home.
He guards me each step of the way. *Refrain* Sure-ly good-ness
To the man-sions He's gone to pre-pare.

and mer-cy shall fol-low me All the days, all the

days of my life; Sure-ly good-ness and mer-cy shall

TEXT and MUSIC: John W. Peterson and Alfred B. Smith; based on Psalm 23

SURELY GOODNESS AND MERCY
Irregular meter

(optional D.C.)

fol - low me All the days, all the days of my life.

May be omitted until final Refrain

And I shall dwell in the house of the Lord for - ev - er, And I shall

feast at the ta - ble spread for me; Sure - ly good - ness

and mer - cy shall fol - low me All the days, all the days of

my life, All the days, all the days of my life.

46 God Leads Us Along

When thou passest through the waters, I will be with thee. Isa. 43:2

1. In shad-y, green pas-tures, so rich and so sweet, God leads His dear
2. Some-times on the mount where the sun shines so bright, God leads His dear
3. Though sor-rows be-fall us and Sa-tan op-pose, God leads His dear

chil-dren a - long; Where the wa - ter's cool flow bathes the wea-ry one's feet,
chil-dren a - long; Some - times in the val - ley, in dark-est of night,
chil-dren a - long; Through grace we can con-quer, de - feat all our foes,

Refrain

God leads His dear chil-dren a - long.
God leads His dear chil-dren a - long.
God leads His dear chil-dren a - long.

Some thro' the wa-ters, some thro' the

flood, Some thro' the fire, but all thro' the blood; Some thro' great sorrow, but

God gives a song, In the night sea - son and all the day long.

TEXT and MUSIC: G. A. Young

GOD LEADS US
11.8.11.8. with Refrain

God Will Take Care of You 47

He knoweth them that trust in Him. Nah. 1:7

1. Be not dis-mayed what-e'er be-tide, God will take care of you;
2. Thro' days of toil when heart doth fail, God will take care of you;
3. All you may need He will pro-vide, God will take care of you;
4. No mat-ter what may be the test, God will take care of you;

Be-neath His wings of love a-bide, God will take care of you.
When dan-gers fierce your path as-sail, God will take care of you.
Noth-ing you ask will be de-nied, God will take care of you.
Lean, wea-ry one, up-on His breast, God will take care of you.

Refrain

God will take care of you, Thro' ev-er-y day, o'er all the way;

He will take care of you, God will take care of you.

TEXT: Civilla D. Martin
MUSIC: W. Stillman Martin

GOD CARES
C.M. with Refrain

48

LEAD US, O GOD

A Brief Service of Prayer and Petition

Suggested Hymn Stanzas

To facilitate an uninterrupted flow from stanza to stanza,
the suggested stanzas have been marked with an arrow: ►

Lead Me, Lord, complete
The Lord's My Shepherd, I'll Not Want, stanzas 1, 2, 3
Guide Me, O Thou Great Jehovah, stanzas 1, 2
O God, Our Help in Ages Past, stanzas 1, 2, 3, 6

WORSHIP LEADER and PEOPLE:

In Thee, O Lord, do I put my trust; let me never be ashamed: deliver me in Thy righteousness. Bow down Thine ear to me; deliver me speedily: be Thou my strong rock, for an house of defence to save me. For Thou art my Rock and my Fortress; therefore for Thy name's sake lead me, and guide me.

Psalm 31:1-3.

49 Lead Me, Lord

Lead me, O Lord, in Thy righteousness. Ps. 5:8

TEXT: Based on Psalms 5:8 and 4:8
MUSIC: Samuel S. Wesley

LEAD ME, LORD
Irregular meter

"LEAD US, O GOD - A Brief Service of Prayer and Petition"

Optional transition to
"The Lord's My Shepherd, I'll Not Want"

The Lord's My Shepherd, I'll Not Want 50

He leadeth me in the paths of righteousness. Ps. 23:3

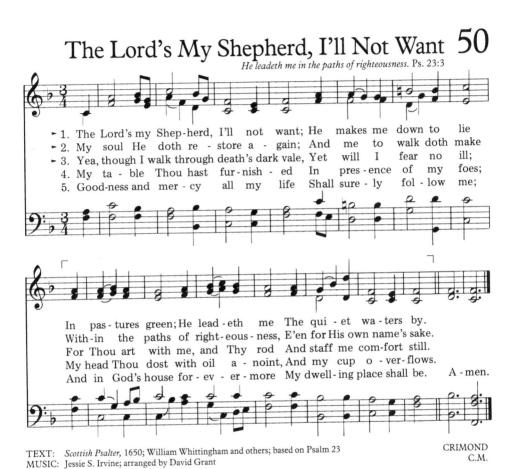

1. The Lord's my Shep-herd, I'll not want; He makes me down to lie
2. My soul He doth re - store a - gain; And me to walk doth make
3. Yea, though I walk through death's dark vale, Yet will I fear no ill;
4. My ta - ble Thou hast fur - nish - ed In pres - ence of my foes;
5. Good-ness and mer - cy all my life Shall sure - ly fol - low me;

In pas - tures green; He lead - eth me The qui - et wa - ters by.
With - in the paths of right - eous - ness, E'en for His own name's sake.
For Thou art with me, and Thy rod And staff me com-fort still.
My head Thou dost with oil a - noint, And my cup o - ver-flows.
And in God's house for - ev - er - more My dwell-ing place shall be. A - men.

TEXT: *Scottish Psalter*, 1650; William Whittingham and others; based on Psalm 23
MUSIC: Jessie S. Irvine; arranged by David Grant

CRIMOND
C.M.

Optional transition to
"Guide Me, O Thou Great Jehovah"

cresc. poco a poco

51 Guide Me, O Thou Great Jehovah

The Lord shall guide thee continually, and satisfy thy soul. Isa. 58:11

1. Guide me, O Thou great Je - ho - vah, Pil - grim through this bar - ren
2. O - pen now the crys - tal foun - tain, Whence the heal - ing stream doth
3. When I tread the verge of Jor - dan, Bid my anx - ious fears sub -

land; I am weak, but Thou art might - y; Hold me with Thy
flow; Let the fire and cloud - y pil - lar Lead me all my
side; Bear me thro' the swell - ing cur - rent, Land me safe on

pow'r - ful hand; Bread of heav - en, Bread of heav - en, Feed me
jour - ney through; Strong De - liv - er - er, strong De - liv - er - er, Be Thou
Ca - naan's side; Songs of prais - es, songs of prais - es I will

till I want no more, Feed me till I want no more.
still my strength and shield, Be Thou still my strength and shield.
ev - er give to Thee, I will ev - er give to Thee. A - men.

TEXT: William Williams; translated by Peter Williams and William Williams
MUSIC: John Hughes

CWM RHONDDA
8.7.8.7.8.7.7.

Optional transition to
"O God, Our Help in Ages Past"

mf

O God, Our Help in Ages Past 52

Lord, Thou hast been our dwelling place in all generations. Ps. 90:1

1. O God, our help in a - ges past, Our hope for years to come,
2. Un - der the shad - ow of Thy throne Thy saints have dwelt se - cure;
3. Be - fore the hills in or - der stood, Or earth re - ceived her frame,
4. A thou-sand a - ges in Thy sight Are like an eve - ning gone;
5. Time, like an ev - er - roll - ing stream, Bears all its sons a - way;
6. O God, our help in a - ges past, Our hope for years to come,

Our shel - ter from the storm - y blast, And our e - ter - nal home!
Suf - fi - cient is Thine arm a - lone, And our de - fense is sure.
From ev - er - last - ing Thou art God, To end - less years the same.
Short as the watch that ends the night Be - fore the ris - ing sun.
They fly, for - got - ten, as a dream Dies at the op - 'ning day.
Be Thou our guide while life shall last, And our e - ter - nal home. A - men.

TEXT: Isaac Watts; based on Psalm 90
MUSIC: William Croft

ST. ANNE
C.M.

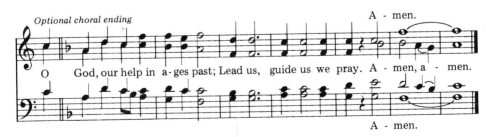

Optional choral ending

A - men.

O God, our help in a - ges past; Lead us, guide us we pray. A - men, a - men.

A - men.

The end of "LEAD US, O GOD—A Brief Service of Prayer and Petition"

53 The New 23rd

The Lord is my shepherd; I shall not want. Ps. 23:1

Be-cause the Lord is my Shep-herd, I have ev-'ry-thing that I need. He lets me rest in mead-ows green And leads me be-side the qui-et stream; He keeps on giv-ing life to me And helps me to do what hon-ors Him the most. E-ven when walk-ing thru the dark val-ley of death, val-ley of death, I will nev-er be a-fraid, For He is close be-side me,

TEXT and MUSIC: Ralph Carmichael; based on Psalm 23

THE NEW 23RD
Irregular meter

Guard-ing, guid-ing all the way; He spreads a feast be-fore me In the pres-ence

of my en-e-mies. He wel-comes me as His spe-cial guest. With bless-ing o-ver-

flow-ing, His good-ness and un-fail-ing kind-ness Shall be with me all of my
then Shall

life And af-ter-ward I will live with Him for-ev-er, for-ev-er
my life I live with Him

rit.

in His home, for-ev-er in His home, for-ev-er in His home.

54 His Way

So are my ways higher than your ways. Isa. 55:9

4 part canon

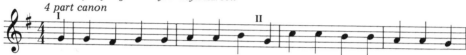

1. God moves in a mys-te-rious way His glo-rious won-ders to per-form;
2. You fear-ful saints, fresh cour-age take; the threat-'ning clouds you so much dread
3. God moves in a mys-te-rious way His glo-rious won-ders to per-form;

He plants His foot-steps in the sea, And rides up-on the rag-ing storm.
Are big with mer-cy, and shall break In count-less bless-ings on your head.
He plants His foot-steps in the sea, And rides up-on the rag-ing storm.

TEXT: William Cowper; altered and adapted by Gerald S. Henderson
MUSIC: Thomas Tallis

TALLIS' CANON
L.M.

Arr. © 1986 WORD MUSIC (a div. of WORD, INC.). All Rights Reserved. International Copyright Secured.

55 Day by Day—A Prayer

Love the Lord thy God, and keep His charge . . . always. Deut. 11:1

Optional Prelude to "Day by Day"*

Day by day, day by day, O, dear

Lord, three things I pray: To see Thee more clear-ly,

Love Thee more dear-ly, Fol-low Thee more near-ly, Day by day.

*May be sung by choir and/or congregation.

opt. segue to "Day by Day"

TEXT: St. Richard of Chichester
MUSIC: Ken Barker

FAYE
Irregular meter

Music © Copyright 1986 WORD MUSIC (a div. of WORD, INC.). All Rights Reserved. International Copyright Secured.

Day by Day 56

My grace is sufficient for thee: for My strength is made perfect in weakness. 2 Cor. 12:9

1. Day by day and with each pass-ing mo-ment, Strength I find to
2. Ev-'ry day the Lord Him-self is near me With a spe-cial
3. Help me then in ev-'ry trib-u-la-tion So to trust Your

meet my tri-als here; Trust-ing in my Fa-ther's wise be-stow-ment,
mer-cy for each hour; All my cares He fain would bear, and cheer me,
prom-is-es, O Lord, That I lose not faith's sweet con-so-la-tion

I've no cause for wor-ry or for fear. He whose heart is kind be-
He whose name is Coun-sel-or and Pow'r. The pro-tec-tion of His
Of-fered me with-in Your ho-ly Word. Help me, Lord, when toil and

yond all meas-ure Gives un-to each day what He deems best— Lov-ing-
child and treas-ure Is a charge that on Him-self He laid; "As your
trou-ble meet-ing, E'er to take, as from a fa-ther's hand, One by

ly, its part of pain and pleas-ure, Min-gling toil with peace and rest.
days, your strength shall be in meas-ure," This the pledge to me He made.
one, the days, the mo-ments fleet-ing, Till I reach the prom-ised land.

TEXT: Carolina Sandell Berg; translated by Andrew L. Skoog
MUSIC: Oscar Ahnfelt

BLOTT EN DAG
Irregular meter

57 He Careth for You

Cast thy burden upon the Lord, and He shall sustain thee. Ps. 55:22

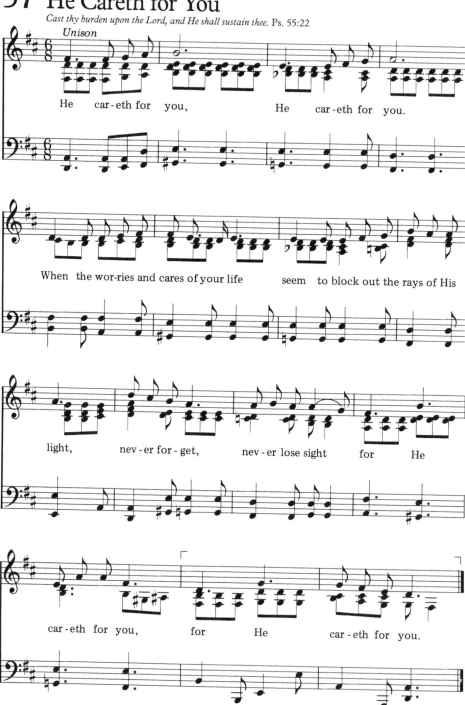

He car-eth for you, He car-eth for you.

When the wor-ries and cares of your life seem to block out the rays of His

light, nev-er for-get, nev-er lose sight for He

car-eth for you, for He car-eth for you.

TEXT and MUSIC: Kurt Kaiser

HE CARETH FOR YOU
Irregular meter

This Is My Father's World 58

The world is mine, and the fulness thereof. Ps. 50:12

1. This is my Fa-ther's world, And to my lis-tening ears
2. This is my Fa-ther's world, The birds their car-ols raise,
3. This is my Fa-ther's world, O let me ne'er for-get

All na-ture sings, and round me rings The mu-sic of the spheres.
The morn-ing light, the lil-y white, De-clare their Mak-er's praise.
That though the wrong seems oft so strong, God is the Rul-er yet.

This is my Fa-ther's world: I rest me in the thought
This is my Fa-ther's world: He shines in all that's fair;
This is my Fa-ther's world: The bat-tle is not done;

Of rocks and trees, of skies and seas—His hand the won-ders wrought.
In the rus-tling grass I hear Him pass, He speaks to me ev-ery-where.
Je-sus who died shall be sat-is-fied, And earth and heav'n be one.

TERRA BEATA
S.M.D.

TEXT: Maltbie D. Babcock
MUSIC: Franklin L. Sheppard

59 I Sing the Mighty Power of God

The Lord made heaven and earth, the sea, and all that in them is. Ex. 20:11

1. I sing the might-y pow'r of God, That made the moun-tains rise;
2. I sing the good-ness of the Lord, That filled the earth with food;
3. There's not a plant or flow'r be-low, But makes Thy glo-ries known;

That spread the flow-ing seas a-broad, And built the loft-y skies.
He formed the crea-tures with His word, And then pro-nounced them good.
And clouds a-rise, and tem-pests blow, By or-der from Thy throne;

I sing the wis-dom that or-dained The sun to rule the day;
Lord, how Thy won-ders are dis-played, Wher-e'er I turn my eye:
While all that bor-rows life from Thee Is ev-er in Thy care,

The moon shines full at His com-mand, And all the stars o-bey.
If I sur-vey the ground I tread, Or gaze up-on the sky!
And ev-'ry-where that man can be, Thou, God, art pres-ent there. A-men.

TEXT: Isaac Watts, altered
MUSIC: From *Gesangbuch der Herzogl,* Württemberg, 1784;
Last stanza harmonization and choral ending by Dick Bolks
A lower setting may be found at No. 174.

ELLACOMBE
C.M.D.

Optional last stanza harmonization
Broader - unison

rit.   3. There's not a plant or flow'r be - low, But makes Thy glo-ries

known; And clouds a - rise, and tem-pests blow, By or - der from Thy

throne; While all that bor-rows life from Thee Is ev - er in Thy care,

And ev - 'ry - where that man can be, Thou, God, art pres-ent there.

Optional choral ending
ff

Sing the pow - er, the might-y pow'r of God!

60 Morning Has Broken

I myself will awake early. I will praise Thee, O Lord. Ps. 57:8-9

Unison

1. Morn-ing has bro - ken Like the first morn - ing,
2. Sweet the rain's new fall Sun - lit from heav - en,
3. Mine is the sun - light! Mine is the morn - ing,

Black-bird has spo - ken Like the first bird.
Like the first dew - fall On the first grass.
Born of the one light E - den saw play!

Praise for the sing - ing! Praise for the morn - ing!
Praise for the sweet - ness Of the wet gar - den,
Praise with e - la - tion, Praise ev - 'ry morn - ing,

Praise for them spring - ing Fresh from the Word!
Sprung in com - plete - ness Where His feet pass.
God's re - cre - a - tion Of the new day!

TEXT: Eleanor Farjeon
MUSIC: Traditional Gaelic melody; arranged by Tom Fettke

BUNESSAN
5.5.5.4.D.

Lavish Love, Abundant Beauty 61

Great is His mercy toward them that fear Him. Ps. 103:11

1. Lav-ish love, a-bun-dant beau-ty, Gra-cious gifts for heart and hand,
2. Who am I that You should love me, Meet my ev-'ry need from birth?
3. I am Yours, E-ter-nal Fa-ther, All my bod-y, mind and heart.

Life that fills the soul and sen-ses— All burst forth at Your com-mand.
Why in-vest Your-self so ful-ly In a crea-ture made of earth?
Take and use me to Your glo-ry, Form Your-self in ev-'ry part.

Lord, our Lord, E-ter-nal Fa-ther, Great Cre-a-tor, God and Friend,
In Your lov-ing heart You planned me, Fash-ioned me with great-est care;
Lord, Your love brings joy and glad-ness Flow-ing forth with-in my soul.

Bound-less pow'r gave full ex-pres-sion To Your love which knows no end.
Through my soul You breathed Your Spir-it, Plant-ed Your own im-age there.
May my ver-y breath and be-ing Rise to You, their source and goal.

TEXT: Peter Ellis
MUSIC: Rowland H. Prichard; arranged by Robert Harkness
        Alternate tune: HYMN TO JOY, No. 1; Higher key, No. 124

HYFRYDOL
8.7.8.7.D.

62 The Spacious Firmament

The firmament sheweth His handiwork. Ps. 19:1

1. The spa - cious fir - ma - ment on high, With all the
2. Soon as the eve - ning shades pre - vail, The moon takes
3. What though in sol - emn si - lence all Move round the

blue e - the - real sky, And span - gled heav'ns, a
up the won - drous tale; And night - ly to the
dark ter - res - trial ball? What though no re - al

shin - ing frame, Their great O - rig - i - nal pro -
lis - tening earth Re - peats the sto - ry of her
voice nor sound A - mid their ra - diant orbs be

claim. Th'un - wear - ied sun, from day to day, Does
birth; While all the stars that round her burn, And
found? In rea - son's ear they all re - joice, And

his Cre - a - tor's pow'r dis - play; And pub - lish - es to
all the plan - ets in their turn, Con - firm the ti - dings
ut - ter forth a glo - rious voice, For - ev - er sing - ing

TEXT: Joseph Addison; based on Psalm 19
MUSIC: Franz Joseph Haydn

CREATION
L.M.D.

ev - ery land   The work   of   an   al - might - y   hand.
as   they roll,   And spread   the truth   from pole to   pole.
as   they shine, "The hand   that made   us   is   di - vine." A - men.

Psalm 136 63

Give thanks unto the Lord; for He is good. Ps. 136:1

Give   thanks to the   Lord   for   He   is   so   good, His   mer - cy en-

1,3,5   **2,4,6**

dures   for - ev - er. (for - ev - er.) Give   dures   for - ev - er. (for-

Last time fine

ev - er.)   1. To   Him   a - lone who   does   might - y   won - ders,
            2. He   made   the sun to   gov - ern the   day - time,

D.C.

Who   by   His un - der - stand-ing made the   hea   -   vens.
The   moon and stars to   gov - ern o'er the   night   -   time.

TEXT: Brenda Barker; a paraphrase of Psalm 136
MUSIC: Ken Barker and Debi Parker Ladd
© Copyright 1986 WORD MUSIC (a div. of WORD, INC). All Rights Reserved. International Copyright Secured.

CATHERINE
Irregular meter

64 All Creatures of Our God and King

Let them praise the name of the Lord: for His name alone is excellent. Ps. 148:13

1. All crea-tures of our God and King, Lift up your voice and with us sing
2. Thou rush-ing wind that art so strong, Ye clouds that sail in heav'n a - long,
3. Thou flow-ing wa-ter, pure and clear, Make mu-sic for thy Lord to hear,
4. And all ye men of ten-der heart, For - giv-ing oth-ers, take your part,
5. Let all things their Cre-a-tor bless, And wor-ship Him in hum-ble-ness,

Al-le - lu - ia, Al-le - lu - ia! Thou burn-ing sun with gold-en beam,
O praise Him, Al-le - lu - ia! Thou ris-ing morn in praise re - joice,
Al-le - lu - ia, Al-le - lu - ia! Thou fire so mas - ter-ful and bright,
O sing ye, Al-le - lu - ia! Ye who long pain and sor-row bear,
O praise Him, Al-le - lu - ia! Praise, praise the Fa-ther, praise the Son,

Thou sil - ver moon with soft-er gleam, O praise Him, O praise Him,
Ye lights of eve-ning, find a voice, O praise Him, O praise Him,
That giv - est man both warmth and light, O praise Him, O praise Him,
Praise God and on Him cast your care, O praise Him, O praise Him,
And praise the Spir-it, Three in One, O praise Him, O praise Him,

Al-le - lu - ia, al-le - lu - ia, al-le - lu - ia! A - men.

TEXT: St. Francis of Assisi; translated by William H. Draper
MUSIC: *Geistliche Kirchengesänge*, Cologne, 1623, Arranged by Ralph Vaughan Williams
From the *English Hymnal* by permission of Oxford University Press.

LASST UNS ERFREUEN
L.M. with Alleluias

The Wonder of It All 65

What is man, that Thou art mindful of him? Heb. 2:6

1. There's the won-der of sun-set at eve-ning, The won-der as
2. There's the won-der of spring-time and har-vest, The sky, the

sun-rise I see; But the won-der of won-ders that thrills my soul
stars, the sun; But the won-der of won-ders that thrills my soul

Refrain

Is the won-der that God loves me. O, the won-der of it all! The
Is a won-der that's on-ly be-gun.

won-der of it all! Just to think that God loves me. O, the won-der of it

all! The won-der of it all! Just to think that God loves me.

TEXT and MUSIC: George Beverly Shea

WONDER OF IT ALL
Irregular meter

66 To God Be the Glory

The Lord hath done great things for us; whereof we are glad. Ps. 126:3

1. To God be the glo-ry—great things He hath done! So loved He the
2. O per-fect re-demp-tion, the pur-chase of blood! To ev-'ry be-
3. Great things He hath taught us, great things He hath done, And great our re-

world that He gave us His Son, Who yield-ed His life an a-
liev-er the prom-ise of God; The vil-est of-fen-der who
joic-ing thru Je-sus the Son; But pur-er and high-er and

tone-ment for sin And o-pened the Life-gate that all may go in.
tru-ly be-lieves, That mo-ment from Je-sus a par-don re-ceives.
great-er will be Our won-der, our trans-port, when Je-sus we see.

Descant

Praise the Lord, hear His voice! Praise the

Refrain

Praise the Lord, Praise the Lord, Let the earth hear His voice! Praise the Lord,

TEXT: Fanny J. Crosby
MUSIC: William H. Doane;
Descant and choral ending by Doug Holck

TO GOD BE THE GLORY
11.11.11.11. with Refrain

Lord, Let the peo-ple re-joice! Come to the Fa-ther thru

Praise the Lord, Let the peo-ple re-joice! O come to the Fa-ther thru

Je - sus the Son, And give Him the glo - ry—great things He hath done!

Je - sus the Son, And give Him the glo - ry—great things He hath done!

Optional choral ending

cresc. poco a poco

mf

To God be the glo - ry, to God be the glo - ry; Oh, give Him the

rit.

glo - ry great things He hath done, great things He hath done! (He hath done!)

*sing cued notes if choral ending is not used.

67 The Love of God

I have loved thee with an everlasting love. Jer. 31:3

1. The love of God is great-er far Than tongue or pen can ev - er
2. When years of time shall pass a - way And earth-ly thrones and king-doms
3. Could we with ink the o - cean fill And were the skies of parch-ment

tell, It goes be - yond the high-est star And reach-es to the low - est
fall, When men, who here re - fuse to pray, On rocks and hills and mountains
made, Were ev-'ry stalk on earth a quill And ev - 'ry man a scribe by

hell; The guilt-y pair, bowed down with care, God gave His Son to
call, God's love so sure shall still en - dure, All mea-sure - less and
trade, To write the love of God a - bove Would drain the o - cean

win: His err - ing child He rec - on - ciled And par - doned from his sin.
strong: Re-deem-ing grace to Ad-am's race— The saints' and an - gels' song.
dry, Nor could the scroll con-tain the whole Tho stretched from sky to sky.

TEXT and MUSIC: Frederick M. Lehman

LOVE OF GOD
Irregular meter

Refrain

O love of God, how rich and pure! How mea-sure-less and strong!

It shall for-ev-er-more en-dure— The saints' and an-gels' song.

There's a Wideness in God's Mercy 68

Very great are His mercies. 1 Chr. 21:13

1. There's a wide-ness in God's mer-cy Like the wide-ness of the sea;
2. There is wel-come for the sin-ner And more grac-es for the good;
3. For the love of God is broad-er Than the meas-ure of man's mind;
4. If our love were but more sim-ple We should take Him at His word,

There's a kind-ness in His jus-tice Which is more than lib-er-ty.
There is mer-cy with the Sav-ior; There is heal-ing in His blood.
And the heart of the E-ter-nal Is most won-der-ful-ly kind.
And our lives would be all sun-shine In the sweet-ness of our Lord. A-men.

TEXT: Frederick W. Faber
MUSIC: Lizzie S. Tourjée

WELLESLEY
8.7.8.7.

69 Thy Loving Kindness

Because Thy lovingkindness is better than life, my lips shall praise Thee. Ps. 63:3

1. Thy lov-ing kind-ness is bet-ter than life. Thy lov-ing kind-ness is bet-ter than life. My lips shall praise Thee, thus will I bless Thee: I will lift up my hands un-to Thy name.
2. I lift my hands, Lord, un-to Thy name. I lift my hands, Lord, un-to Thy name. My lips shall praise Thee, thus will I bless Thee: I will lift up my hands un-to Thy name.

TEXT and MUSIC: Hugh Mitchell; based on Psalm 63:3, 4

THY LOVING KINDNESS
10.10.10.10.

70 Begin, My Tongue, Some Heavenly Theme

My tongue also shall talk of Thy righteousness all the day long. Ps. 71:24

1. Be - gin, my tongue, some heav'n-ly theme And speak some bound-less thing:
2. Tell of His won - drous faith-ful - ness And sound His pow'r a - broad;
3. His ver - y word of grace is strong As that which built the skies;
4. O might I hear Thy heav'n-ly tongue But whis - per, "Thou art mine!"

TEXT: Isaac Watts
MUSIC: From Henry W. Greatorex's *Collection of Church Music*, 1851
A lower setting may be found at No. 321

MANOAH
C.M.

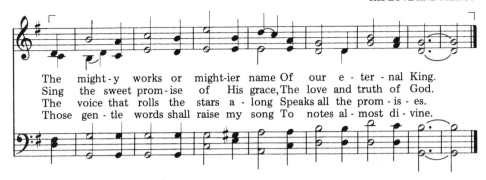

The might-y works or might-ier name Of our e - ter - nal King.
Sing the sweet prom-ise of His grace, The love and truth of God.
The voice that rolls the stars a - long Speaks all the prom - is - es.
Those gen - tle words shall raise my song To notes al - most di - vine.

Behold, What Manner of Love 71

Behold, what manner of love the Father hath bestowed upon us. 1 John 3:1

May be sung as a 2 part canon

I

Be - hold, what man-ner of love the Fa - ther has giv - en un - to

us, Be - hold what man-ner of love the Fa - ther has giv - en un - to

II

us, that we should be called the sons of

God, that we should be called the sons of God.

TEXT and MUSIC: Patricia Van Tine; based on 1 John 3:1;
arranged by Lee Herrington
© 1978 MARANATHA! MUSIC. All Rights Reserved. International Copyright Secured.

MANNER OF LOVE
Irregular meter

72 We Will Glorify

Honour and glory be unto Him that sitteth upon the throne and unto the Lamb. Rev. 5:13

1. We will glo-ri-fy the King of kings, we will glo-ri-fy the
2. Lord Je - ho-vah reigns in maj-es-ty, we will bow be-fore His
3. He is Lord of heav-en, Lord of earth, He is Lord of all who
4. Hal-le-lu-jah to the King of kings, hal-le-lu-jah to the

Lamb; We will glo-ri-fy the Lord of lords, who is the great I Am.
throne;We will wor-ship Him in right-eous-ness, we will wor-ship Him a - lone.
live; He is Lord a-bove the u - ni-verse, all praise to Him we give.
Lamb; Hal-le-lu-jah to the Lord of lords, who is the great I Am.

Optional last stanza setting
rit. *Broader*

give. 4. Hal-le- lu-jah to the King of kings, hal-le-

lu-jah to the Lamb; Hal-le-lu-jah to the

1 *mp* **2**

Lord of lords, who is the great I Am. Hal-le- Am.

TEXT and MUSIC: Twila Paris; arranged by David Allen

WE WILL GLORIFY
9.7.9.6.

Thou Art Worthy 73

Thou art worthy, O Lord, . . . for Thou hast created all things. Rev. 4:11

Thou art wor-thy, Thou art wor-thy, Thou art wor-thy, O Lord,

To re-ceive glo-ry, glo-ry and hon-or, Glo-ry and

hon-or and pow'r. For Thou hast cre-at-ed, hast all things cre-

at-ed; Thou hast cre-at-ed all things. And for Thy

plea-sure they are cre-at-ed; For Thou art wor-thy, O Lord.

TEXT and MUSIC: Pauline M. Mills; based on Revelation 4:11; 5:9

WORTHY
Irregular meter

74 Majesty

We see Jesus . . . crowned with glory and honour. Heb. 2:9

Maj - es - ty, wor-ship His maj - es - ty. Un - to

Je - sus be all glo - ry, hon - or, and praise. Maj - es - ty,

king-dom au - thor - i - ty flow from His throne un - to His own;

His an-them raise. So ex - alt, lift up on high the name of

Je - sus. Mag-ni - fy, come glo-ri - fy Christ Je-sus, the King.

TEXT and MUSIC: Jack Hayford; arranged by Eugene Thomas

MAJESTY
Irregular meter

Maj - es - ty, wor-ship His maj - es - ty;

Je - sus who died, now glo-ri - fied, King of all kings.

*cued notes optional for a few choir sopranos.

Praise the Savior 75

We should be to the praise of His glory. Eph. 1:12

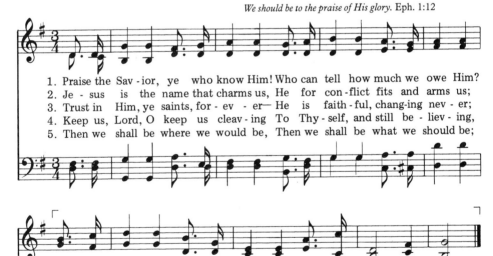

1. Praise the Sav-ior, ye who know Him! Who can tell how much we owe Him?
2. Je - sus is the name that charms us, He for con-flict fits and arms us;
3. Trust in Him, ye saints, for - ev - er— He is faith-ful, chang-ing nev - er;
4. Keep us, Lord, O keep us cleav-ing To Thy-self, and still be - liev-ing,
5. Then we shall be where we would be, Then we shall be what we should be;

Glad - ly let us ren - der to Him All we are and have.
Noth - ing moves and noth - ing harms us While we trust in Him.
Nei - ther force nor guile can sev - er Those He loves from Him.
Till the hour of our re - ceiv - ing Prom - ised joys with Thee.
Things that are not now, nor could be, Soon shall be our own.

TEXT: Thomas Kelly
MUSIC: Traditional German melody

ACCLAIM
8.8.8.5.

76 O for a Thousand Tongues

And my tongue shall speak . . . of Thy praise all the day long. Ps. 35:28

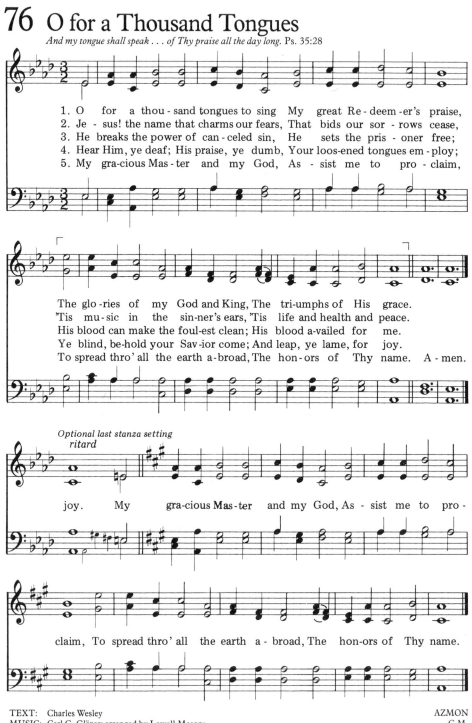

1. O for a thou-sand tongues to sing My great Re-deem-er's praise,
2. Je - sus! the name that charms our fears, That bids our sor - rows cease,
3. He breaks the power of can-celed sin, He sets the pris - oner free;
4. Hear Him, ye deaf; His praise, ye dumb, Your loos-ened tongues em-ploy;
5. My gra-cious Mas-ter and my God, As - sist me to pro - claim,

The glo-ries of my God and King, The tri-umphs of His grace.
'Tis mu-sic in the sin-ner's ears, 'Tis life and health and peace.
His blood can make the foul-est clean; His blood a-vailed for me.
Ye blind, be-hold your Sav-ior come; And leap, ye lame, for joy.
To spread thro' all the earth a-broad, The hon-ors of Thy name. A - men.

Optional last stanza setting
ritard

joy. My gra-cious Mas-ter and my God, As - sist me to pro -

claim, To spread thro' all the earth a - broad, The hon-ors of Thy name.

TEXT: Charles Wesley
MUSIC: Carl G. Gläzer; arranged by Lowell Mason;
Choral ending by Robert F. Douglas
A lower setting may be found at No. 440

AZMON
C.M.

Optional choral ending

The hon-ors of Thy name. A - men.

King of Kings 77

The King of kings, and Lord of lords. 1 Tim. 6:15

2 Part Canon (optional)

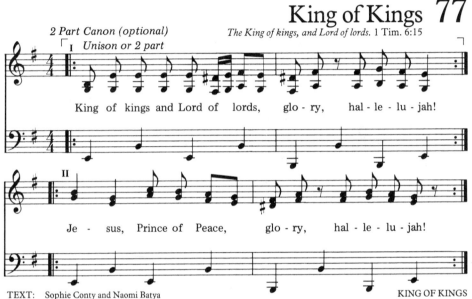

I Unison or 2 part

King of kings and Lord of lords, glo - ry, hal - le - lu - jah!

II

Je - sus, Prince of Peace, glo - ry, hal - le - lu - jah!

TEXT: Sophie Conty and Naomi Batya
MUSIC: Ancient Hebrew Folk song

KING OF KINGS
Irregular meter

Blessing and Honor 78

Blessing, and honour, and glory . . . be unto Him. Rev. 5:13

3 Part Canon

I

Bless - ing and hon - or and glo - ry be Thine;

II

Wor - thy are You, O Lord, to re - ceive end - less praise;

III

Bless - ing and hon - or and glo - ry be Thine.

TEXT: Gerald S. Henderson; based on Revelation 5:12, 13
MUSIC: German Folk song; adapted by Gerald S. Henderson

GERMAN FOLK
10.12.10.

79 Jesus, the Very Thought of Thee

Consider Him . . . lest ye be wearied and faint in your minds. Heb. 12:3

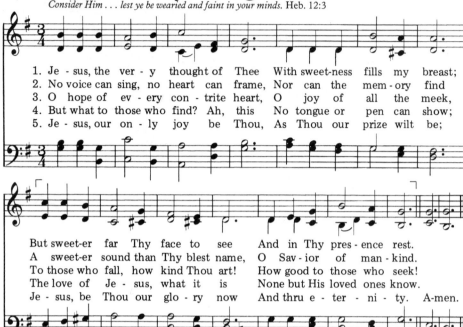

1. Je - sus, the ver - y thought of Thee With sweet-ness fills my breast;
2. No voice can sing, no heart can frame, Nor can the mem - ory find
3. O hope of ev - ery con - trite heart, O joy of all the meek,
4. But what to those who find? Ah, this No tongue or pen can show;
5. Je - sus, our on - ly joy be Thou, As Thou our prize wilt be;

But sweet-er far Thy face to see And in Thy pres - ence rest.
A sweet-er sound than Thy blest name, O Sav - ior of man - kind.
To those who fall, how kind Thou art! How good to those who seek!
The love of Je - sus, what it is None but His loved ones know.
Je - sus, be Thou our glo - ry now And thru e - ter - ni - ty. A-men.

TEXT: Attributed to Bernard of Clairvaux; translated by Edward Caswall
MUSIC: John B. Dykes
A lower setting may be found at No. 536

ST. AGNES
C.M.

80 I Love You, Lord

Love the Lord, all ye His saints. Ps. 31:23

I love You, Lord, and I lift my voice to wor - ship

You. O my soul, re - joice! Take joy, my King, in

TEXT and MUSIC: Laurie Klein; arranged by Eugene Thomas

I LOVE YOU LORD
Irregular meter

what You hear: may it be a sweet, sweet sound in Your ear.

What a Wonderful Savior! 81

We . . . know that this is indeed the Christ, the Saviour of the world. John 4:42

1. Christ has for sin a - tone - ment made—What a won-der-ful Sav-ior!
2. I praise Him for the cleans-ing blood—What a won-der-ful Sav-ior!
3. He cleansed my heart from all its sin— What a won-der-ful Sav-ior!
4. He gives me o - ver - com-ing pow'r— What a won-der-ful Sav-ior!

We are re-deemed, the price is paid—What a won-der-ful Sav-ior!
That rec-on-ciled my soul to God—What a won-der-ful Sav-ior!
And now He reigns and rules there-in— What a won-der-ful Sav-ior!
And tri-umph in each try-ing hour—What a won-der-ful Sav-ior!

Refrain

What a won-der-ful Sav - ior is Je - sus, my Je-sus!

What a won-der-ful Sav - ior is Je - sus, my Lord!

TEXT and MUSIC: Elisha A. Hoffman

BENTON HARBOR
8.7.8.7. with Refrain

82 O Come, Let Us Adore Him

We have . . . come to worship Him. Matt. 2:2

1. O come, let us a - dore Him, O come, let us a - dore
2. We'll praise His name for - ev - er, We'll praise His name for - ev -
3. We'll give Him all the glo - ry, We'll give Him all the glo -
4. For He a - lone is wor - thy, For He a - lone is wor -

Him, O come, let us a - dore Him, Christ the Lord.
er, We'll praise His name for - ev - er, Christ the Lord.
ry, We'll give Him all the glo - ry, Christ the Lord.
thy, For He a - lone is wor - thy, Christ the Lord.

TEXT: Traditional
MUSIC: Wade's *Cantus Diversi*, 1751

ADESTE FIDELES (Refrain only)
7.7.10.

83 Lord, We Praise You

Blessed be God, even the Father of our Lord Jesus Christ. 2 Cor. 1:3

1. Lord, we praise You. Lord, we praise You. Lord, we praise You. We
2. Lord, we love You. Lord, we love You. Lord, we love You. We
3. Lord, we thank You. Lord, we thank You. Lord, we thank You. We
4. Al - le - lu - ia! Al - le - lu - ia! Al - le - lu - ia! We

Optional choral ending

ff

praise You, Lord.
love You, Lord.
thank You, Lord.   Al - le - lu - ia! We give You praise.
give You praise.

TEXT and MUSIC: Otis Skillings
© 1972 by Lillenas Publishing Co. All Rights Reserved. Used by Permission.

LORD, WE PRAISE YOU
4.4.4.4.

Hallowed Be the Name 84

Call His name JESUS. He shall be great . . . He shall reign. Luke 1:31-33

1. Hal-low-ed be the name of Je - sus.
2. Wor - thy is the Lamb, Lord Je - sus.

Ho - ly is the name of Je - sus. Oth - er
Right-eous I can stand in Je - sus. We were

king - doms rise and fall, but He reign-eth o - ver all.
chained to death, but then You raised us up a - gain.

Hal-low-ed be the name of Je - sus.
Wor - thy is the Lamb, Lord Je - sus.

TEXT and MUSIC: Lilly Green; arranged by Robert F. Douglas

HALLOWED BE THE NAME
Irregular meter

85 Glorious Is Thy Name

Our God, we thank Thee, and praise Thy glorious name. 1 Chr. 29:13

1. Bless-ed Sav-ior, we a-dore Thee, We Thy love and grace pro-claim;
2. Great Re-deem-er, Lord and Mas-ter, Light of all e-ter-nal days;
3. From the throne of heav-en's glo-ry To the cross of sin and shame,
4. Come, O come, im-mor-tal Sav-ior, Come and take Thy roy-al throne;

Thou art might-y, Thou art ho-ly, Glo-rious is Thy match-less name!
Let the saints of ev-'ry na-tion Sing Thy just and end-less praise!
Thou didst come to die a ran-som, Guilt-y sin-ners to re-claim!
Come, and reign, and reign for-ev-er, Be the king-dom all Thine own!

Refrain

Glo - ri-ous, Glo - ri-ous,

Glo-rious is Thy name, O Lord! Glo-rious is Thy name, O Lord!

1. Glo-rious is Thy name, O Lord!

2. name, O Lord! A - men.

TEXT and MUSIC: B. B. McKinney

GLORIOUS NAME
8.7.8.7. with Refrain

GIVE HIM GLORY

A Brief Service
Exalting Our Lord, Jesus Christ

Suggested Hymn Stanzas

To facilitate an uninterrupted flow from stanza to stanza,
the suggested stanzas have been marked with an arrow: ▶

May Jesus Christ Be Praised, stanzas 1, 3, 4, 6
Fairest Lord Jesus, stanzas 1, 4
Our Great Savior, stanzas 1, 2, 4

WORSHIP LEADER:

[Christ] is the image of the invisible God, the firstborn of every crea-
ture: for by Him were all things created, that are in heaven, and that
are in earth, visible and invisible, whether they be thrones, or
dominions, or principalities, or powers: all things were created by
Him, and for Him: And He is the head of the body, the church: who
is the beginning, the firstborn from the dead; that in all things He
might have the preeminence. For it pleased the Father that in Him
should all fulness dwell; and, having made peace through the blood
of His cross, by Him to reconcile all things unto Himself; by Him, I
say, whether they be things in earth, or things in heaven. Looking
unto Jesus the author and finisher of our faith; who for the joy that
was set before Him endured the cross, despising the shame, and is set
down at the right hand of the throne of God.

WORSHIP LEADER AND PEOPLE:

Worthy is the Lamb that was slain to receive power, and riches, and
wisdom, and strength, and honour, and glory, and blessing. Bless-
ing, and honour, and glory, and power, be unto Him that sitteth
upon the throne, and unto the Lamb for ever and ever.

Col. 1:15-20; Heb. 12:2; Rev. 5:12,13.

Optional introduction to
"May Jesus Christ Be Praised"

mf

87 May Jesus Christ Be Praised

Christ . . . is over all, God blessed for ever. Rom. 9:5

1. When morn-ing gilds the skies, My heart a-wak-ing cries, May Je-sus Christ be praised! A-like at work and prayer To Je-sus I re-pair, May Je-sus Christ be praised!
2. Does sad-ness fill my mind? A sol-ace here I find, May Je-sus Christ be praised! Or fades my earth-ly bliss? My com-fort still is this, May Je-sus Christ be praised!
3. The night be-comes as day, When from the heart we say, May Je-sus Christ be praised! The pow'rs of dark-ness fear When this sweet chant they hear, May Je-sus Christ be praised!
4. Ye na-tions of man-kind, In this your con-cord find, May Je-sus Christ be praised! Let all the earth a-round Ring joy-ous with the sound, May Je-sus Christ be praised!
5. Sing, suns and stars of space, Sing, ye that see His face, May Je-sus Christ be praised! God's whole cre-a-tion o'er, For aye and ev-er-more May Je-sus Christ be praised!
6. Be this, while life is mine, My can-ti-cle di-vine, May Je-sus Christ be praised! Be this th'e-ter-nal song Thro' all the a-ges long, May Je-sus Christ be praised! A-men.

TEXT: *Katholisches Gesangbuch*, Würzburg, 1828;
translated by Edward Caswall
MUSIC: Joseph Barnby

LAUDES DOMINI
6.6.6.6.6.6.

Optional transition to
"Fairest Lord Jesus"

mp

Fairest Lord Jesus 88

Thine eyes shall see the King in His beauty. Isa. 33:17

1. Fair - est Lord Je - sus, Rul - er of all na - ture, O Thou of
2. Fair are the mead - ows, Fair - er still the wood - lands, Robed in the
3. Fair is the sun - shine, Fair - er still the moon - light, And all the
4. Beau - ti - ful Sav - ior! Lord of the na - tions! Son of

God and man the Son: Thee will I cher - ish, Thee will I
bloom-ing garb of spring: Je - sus is fair - er, Je - sus is
twin - kling star - ry host: Je - sus shines bright-er, Je - sus shines
God and Son of Man! Glo - ry and hon - or, Praise, ad - o -

hon - or, Thou my soul's glo - ry, joy, and crown.
pur - er, Who makes the woe - ful heart to sing.
pur - er Than all the an - gels heaven can boast.
ra - tion, Now and for - ev - er - more be Thine! A - men.

TEXT: Anonymous German Hymn, *Münster Gesangbuch*, 1677;
    translated, Source unknown, stanzas 1-3; Joseph A. Seiss, stanza 4
MUSIC: *Schlesische Volkslieder*, 1842; arranged by Richard S. Willis

CRUSADERS' HYMN
5.6.8.5.5.8.

Optional transition to "Our Great Savior"

cresc. poco a poco   *f*

89 Our Great Savior

The great God and our Saviour Jesus Christ . . . gave Himself for us. Titus 2:13-14

1. Je - sus! what a Friend for sin - ners! Je - sus! Lov - er of my soul;
2. Je - sus! what a Strength in weak - ness! Let me hide my - self in Him;
3. Je - sus! what a Help in sor - row! While the bil - lows o'er me roll,
4. Je - sus! what a Guide and Keep - er! While the tem - pest still is high,
5. Je - sus! I do now re - ceive Him, More than all in Him I find,

Friends may fail me, foes as - sail me, He, my Sav - ior, makes me whole.
Tempt - ed, tried, and some-times fail - ing, He, my Strength, my vic - t'ry wins.
E - ven when my heart is break - ing, He, my Com - fort, helps my soul.
Storms a - bout me, night o'er-takes me, He, my Pi - lot, hears my cry.
He hath grant - ed me for - give - ness, I am His, and He is mine.

Descant

Hal - le - lu - jah! what a Sav - ior! Hal - le -

Refrain

Hal - le - lu - jah! what a Sav - ior! Hal - le -

TEXT: J. Wilbur Chapman
MUSIC: Rowland H. Prichard; arranged by Robert Harkness;
Descant and choral ending by Tom Fettke
A higher setting may be found at No. 233

HYFRYDOL
8.7.8.7.D.

lu - jah! what a, what a Friend! Sav - ing, help - ing,

lu - jah! what a Friend! Sav - ing, help - ing,

keep - ing, lov - ing, He is with me to the end.

keep - ing, lov - ing, He is with me to the end.

Optional choral ending   *cresc.*   *rit.*   *Slowly*

He is with me to the end. A - men.

The end of "GIVE HIM GLORY—A Brief Service Exalting Our Lord, Jesus Christ"

90 In the Name of the Lord

Whatsoever ye shall ask in My name, that will I do. John 14:13

There is strength in the name of the Lord; There is pow'r in the name of the Lord;

There is hope in the name of the Lord! Bless-ed is He who comes in the

name of the Lord. There is strength in the name of the Lord;

There is pow'r in the name of the Lord; There is hope in the

name of the Lord! Bless-ed is He who comes in the name of the Lord.

Parts optional

2nd time fine

TEXT and MUSIC: Phill McHugh, Gloria Gaither and Sandi Patti Helvering;
arranged by Robert F. Douglas

NAME OF THE LORD
Irregular meter

Alleluia 91

Alleluia; Salvation, and glory, and honour, and power, unto the Lord. Rev. 19:1

1. Al - le - lu - ia, Al - le - lu - ia, Al - le - lu - ia, Al - le - lu - ia,
2. He's my Sav - ior, He's my Sav - ior, He's my Sav - ior, He's my Sav - ior,
3. He is wor - thy, He is wor - thy, He is wor - thy, He is wor - thy,
4. I will praise Him, I will praise Him, I will praise Him, I will praise Him,

Al - le - lu - ia, Al - le - lu - ia, Al - le - lu - ia, Al - le - lu - ia!
He's my Sav - ior, He's my Sav - ior, He's my Sav - ior, He's my Sav - ior!
He is wor - thy, He is wor - thy, He is wor - thy, He is wor - thy!
I will praise Him, I will praise Him, I will praise Him, I will praise Him!

Optional last stanza setting

wor - thy! 4. I will praise Him, I will praise Him, I will praise Him,

1 **2** *Optional choral ending*
rit. *pp*

I will praise Him, I will praise Him! Al - le - lu - ia, al - le - lu - ia!

TEXT and MUSIC: Jerry Sinclair

ALLELUIA
L.M.

92 Love Divine, All Loves Excelling

. . . the love of God toward us . . . God sent His only begotten Son. 1 John 4:9

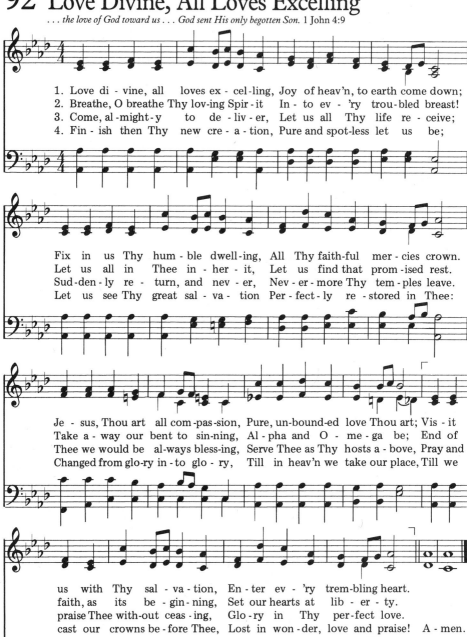

1. Love di - vine, all loves ex - cel - ling, Joy of heav'n, to earth come down;
2. Breathe, O breathe Thy lov-ing Spir - it In - to ev - 'ry trou-bled breast!
3. Come, al - might - y to de - liv - er, Let us all Thy life re - ceive;
4. Fin - ish then Thy new cre - a - tion, Pure and spot-less let us be;

Fix in us Thy hum - ble dwell-ing, All Thy faith-ful mer - cies crown.
Let us all in Thee in - her - it, Let us find that prom - ised rest.
Sud - den - ly re - turn, and nev - er, Nev - er - more Thy tem - ples leave.
Let us see Thy great sal - va - tion Per - fect - ly re - stored in Thee:

Je - sus, Thou art all com - pas - sion, Pure, un - bound - ed love Thou art; Vis - it
Take a - way our bent to sin - ning, Al - pha and O - me - ga be; End of
Thee we would be al - ways bless - ing, Serve Thee as Thy hosts a - bove, Pray and
Changed from glo - ry in - to glo - ry, Till in heav'n we take our place, Till we

us with Thy sal - va - tion, En - ter ev - 'ry trem - bling heart.
faith, as its be - gin - ning, Set our hearts at lib - er - ty.
praise Thee with - out ceas - ing, Glo - ry in Thy per - fect love.
cast our crowns be - fore Thee, Lost in won - der, love and praise! A - men.

TEXT: Charles Wesley
MUSIC: John Zundel; Choral ending arranged by David Allen
    A higher setting may be found at No. 268; Alternate tune: HYFRYDOL, No. 89

BEECHER
8.7.8.7.D.

Choral ending © 1986 WORD MUSIC (a div. of WORD, INC.). All Rights Reserved. International Copyright Secured.

Optional choral ending

Till we cast our crowns be - fore Thee, Lost in won - der,

love, and praise! A - men.

Praise the Name of Jesus 93

The Lord is my Rock, and my Fortress, and my Deliverer. Ps. 18:2

Praise the name of Je - sus, Praise the name of Je - sus.

He's my Rock, He's my For - tress, He's my De - liv - er - er, in

Him will I trust. Praise the name of Je - sus.

TEXT and MUSIC: Roy Hicks, Jr.; based on Psalm 18:1

HICKS
Irregular meter

94 How Sweet the Name of Jesus Sounds

Call upon the name of Jesus Christ our Lord. 1 Cor. 1:2

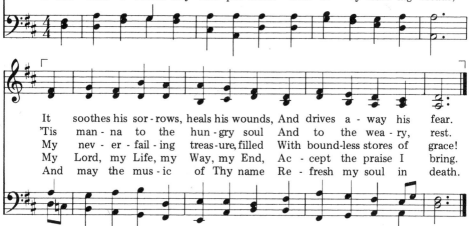

1. How sweet the name of Je - sus sounds In a be - liev - er's ear!
2. It makes the wound-ed spir - it whole And calms the trou-bled breast;
3. Dear name! the rock on which I build, My shield and hid - ing place;
4. Je - sus, my Shep - herd, Broth-er, Friend, My Proph-et, Priest and King,
5. Till then I would Thy love pro-claim With ev - 'ry fleet - ing breath;

It soothes his sor - rows, heals his wounds, And drives a - way his fear.
'Tis man - na to the hun - gry soul And to the wea - ry, rest.
My nev - er - fail - ing treas-ure, filled With bound-less stores of grace!
My Lord, my Life, my Way, my End, Ac - cept the praise I bring.
And may the mus - ic of Thy name Re - fresh my soul in death.

TEXT: John Newton
MUSIC: Alexander R. Reinagle

ST. PETER
C.M.

95 Jesus Is the Sweetest Name I Know

Jesus Christ the same yesterday, and today, and forever. Heb. 13:8

Je - sus is the sweet-est name I know, And He's just the same as His love-ly name,

And that's the rea-son why I love Him so; Oh, Je - sus is the sweet-est name I know.

TEXT and MUSIC: Lela Long

SWEETEST NAME
9.10.10.10.

All Hail the Power of Jesus' Name 96

God hath given Him a name which is above every name . . . Jesus Christ is Lord. Phil. 2:9-11

1. All hail the pow'r of Je - sus' name! Let an-gels pros-trate
2. Ye cho - sen seed of Is - rael's race, Ye ran-somed from the
3. Let ev - ery kin - dred, ev - 'ry tribe, On this ter-res-trial
4. O that with yon - der sa - cred throng We at His feet may

fall, Let an - gels pros-trate fall; Bring forth the roy - al di - a-
fall, Ye ran-somed from the fall; Hail Him who saves you by His
ball, On this ter - res-trial ball; To Him all maj - es - ty as-
fall, We at His feet may fall! We'll join the ev - er-last - ing

dem,
grace, And crown Him, crown Him,
cribe,
song, And crown Him, crown Him, crown Him, crown Him, crown Him,

crown

crown Him, crown Him, And crown Him Lord of all. A - men.

Him,

TEXT: Edward Perronet; adapted by John Rippon
MUSIC: James Ellor

DIADEM
C.M. with Refrain

97 All Hail the Power of Jesus' Name

God hath given Him a name which is above every name . . . Jesus Christ is Lord. Phil. 2:9-11

1. All hail the pow'r of Je - sus' name! Let an - gels pros - trate fall;
2. Ye cho - sen seed of Is - rael's race, Ye ran-somed from the fall,
3. Let ev - 'ry kin - dred, ev - 'ry tribe, On this ter - res - trial ball,
4. O that with yon - der sa - cred throng We at His feet may fall!

Bring forth the roy - al di - a - dem, And crown Him Lord of all;
Hail Him who saves you by His grace, And crown Him Lord of all;
To Him all maj - es - ty as - cribe, And crown Him Lord of all;
We'll join the ev - er - last - ing song, And crown Him Lord of all;

Bring forth the roy - al di - a - dem, And crown Him Lord of all!
Hail Him who saves you by His grace, And crown Him Lord of all!
To Him all maj - es - ty as - cribe, And crown Him Lord of all!
We'll join the ev - er - last - ing song, And crown Him Lord of all!

Optional choral ending f

Crown

all! Crown Him, crown Him, al - le - lu - ia! Crown Him, crown Him,

Crown

TEXT: Edward Perronet; adapted by John Rippon
MUSIC: Oliver Holden; Choral ending by Tom Fettke

CORONATION
C.M. with Repeats

Him, *cresc.* *rit.* *ff*

crown Him, And crown Him Lord of all. A - men.

Him,

Jesus, We Just Want to Thank You 98

Thanks be unto God for His unspeakable gift. 2 Cor. 9:15

1. Je - sus, we just want to thank You, Je - sus, we
2. Je - sus, we just want to praise You, Je - sus, we
3. Je - sus, we just want to tell You, Je - sus, we
4. Sav - ior, we just want to serve You, Sav - ior, we
5. Je - sus, we know You are com - ing, Je - sus, we

just want to thank You, Je - sus, we just want to
just want to praise You, Je - sus, we just want to
just want to tell You, Je - sus, we just want to
just want to serve You, Sav - ior, we just want to
know You are com - ing, Je - sus, we know You are

thank You, Thank You for be - ing so good.
praise You, Praise You for be - ing so good.
tell You, We love You for be - ing so good.
serve You, Serve You for be - ing so good.
com - ing, Take us to live in Your home.

TEXT: Gloria Gaither and William J. Gaither
MUSIC: William J. Gaither

THANK YOU
8.8.8.7.

99

THE NAME OF JESUS

A Brief Service of Worship and Praise

Suggested Hymn Stanzas

To facilitate an uninterrupted flow from stanza to stanza,
the suggested stanzas have been marked with an arrow: ▶

There Is No Name So Sweet on Earth, complete
His Name Is Wonderful, complete
There's Something About That Name, complete
Blessed Be the Name, complete

WORSHIP LEADER: Wherefore God also hath highly exalted Him, and given Him a name which is above every name: That at the name of Jesus every knee should bow, of things in heaven, and things in earth, and things under the earth; and that every tongue should confess that Jesus Christ is Lord, to the glory of God the Father.

Philippians 2:9-11.

100 There Is No Name So Sweet on Earth

Preach Jesus Christ. Acts 5:42

Optional introduction

mf

*Choir or congregation

We love to sing of Christ our King, And hail Him, bless-ed Je - sus; For

Optional transition to
"His Name Is Wonderful"

there's no word ear ev - er heard So dear, so sweet as "Je - sus."

*This song may be used as a choir introduction to the medley.

TEXT: George W. Bethune
MUSIC: William B. Bradbury

GOLDEN CHAIN (Refrain only)
8.7.8.7.

"THE NAME OF JESUS—A Brief Service of Worship and Praise"

His Name Is Wonderful 101

No man can say that Jesus is the Lord, but by the Holy Ghost. 1 Cor. 12:3

His name is Won-der-ful, His name is Won-der-ful, His name is Won-der-ful, Je-sus, my Lord; He is the might-y King, Mas-ter of ev-ery-thing, His name is Won-der-ful, Je-sus, my Lord. He's the great Shep-herd, the Rock of all a-ges, Al-might-y God is He; Bow down be-fore Him, Love and a-dore Him, His name is Won-der-ful, Je-sus, my Lord.

TEXT and MUSIC: Audrey Mieir

MIEIR
Irregular meter

102 There's Something About That Name

There is none other name . . . whereby we must be saved. Acts 4:12

Je-sus, Je-sus, Je - sus; There's just some-thing a - bout that name!

Mas-ter, Sav-ior, Je - sus, Like the fra-grance af-ter the

rain; Je-sus, Je-sus, Je - sus, Let all Heav-en and

earth pro - claim: Kings and king-doms will all pass a-

TEXT: Gloria Gaither and William J. Gaither

MUSIC: William J. Gaither

THAT NAME

Irregular meter

Optional transition to
"Blessed Be the Name"
accel.

way, But there's some-thing a-bout that name! name!

Blessed Be the Name 103

He hath by inheritance obtained a more excellent name. Heb. 1:4

1. All praise to Him who reigns a-bove In maj-es-ty su-preme,
2. His name a-bove all names shall stand, Ex-alt-ed more and more,
3. His name shall be the Coun-sel-lor, The might-y Prince of Peace,

Who gave His Son for man to die, That He might man re-deem!
At God the Fa-ther's own right hand, Where an-gel hosts a-dore.
Of all earth's king-doms Con-quer-or, Whose reign shall nev-er cease.

Refrain

Bless-ed be the name, bless-ed be the name, Bless-ed be the name of the Lord;

Bless-ed be the name, bless-ed be the name, Bless-ed be the name of the Lord.

TEXT: William H. Clark; Ralph E. Hudson, Refrain
MUSIC: Source unknown; arranged by Ralph E. Hudson
and William J. Kirkpatrick

Optional choral ending on the next page
BLESSED BE THE NAME
C.M. with Refrain

JESUS OUR SAVIOR

Optional choral ending to "Blessed Be the Name"

Bless-ed be the name, bless-ed be the name, Bless-ed be the name of the Lord.

The end of "THE NAME OF JESUS—A Brief Service of Worship and Praise"

104 King of Heaven, Lord Most High

. . . Who only hath immortality . . . whom no man hath seen, nor can see. 1 Tim. 6:16

1. Im - mor - tal, in - vis - i - ble King of Hea - ven, Lord Most High.
2. Im - mor - tal, in - vis - i - ble, Ev - er faith - ful, ev - er true.

Hon - or now we give to You, Au - thor of e - ter - nal life. Power, wisdom,
O - ver - come with love and awe, Lord of Hosts we wor - ship You. Now in hum - ble

strength and bless - ing; You are wor - thy to re - ceive our praise. Im - mor - tal, in -
ad - o - ra - tion, Plac - ing all be - fore Your roy - al throne. Im - mor - tal, in -

vis - i - ble Lord, to You all prais - es be!
vis - i - ble Sav - ior, we are Yours a - lone! A - men.

TEXT and MUSIC: Niles Borop and Dwight Liles

KING OF HEAVEN
Irregular meter

He Is Lord 105

Confess with thy mouth the Lord Jesus, . . . believe . . . that God raised Him. Rom. 10:9

1. Emp-tied of His glo - ry; God be-came a man, To walk on earth in
2. Hum-bled and re-ject-ed, beat-en, and de-spised. Up - on the cross the
3. Sa-tan's for - ces crum-bled like a might-y wall. The stone that held Him

rid - i - cule and shame. A Rul - er, yet a Ser - vant; a Shep-herd, yet a
Son of God was slain. Just like a lamb to slaugh-ter, a sin - less sac - ri -
in was rolled a - side. The Prince of Life in glo - ry was lift - ed o - ver

1, 2   **3**   *Refrain*

Lamb; A Man of Sor-rows, ag - o - ny and pain.
fice; But, by His death His loss be-came our gain. He is
all, Now earth and hea-ven ech-o with the cry.

Lord, He is Lord! He is ris-en from the dead and He is Lord!

1   **2**

Ev - 'ry knee shall bow, ev-'ry tongue con-fess that Je - sus Christ is Lord. Lord.

TEXT: Linda Lee Johnson, Claire Cloninger and Tom Fettke, stanzas;
        Traditional, Refrain; based on Isaiah 53 and Philippians 2:6-11
MUSIC: Tom Fettke, stanzas and arrangement; Traditional, Refrain

HE IS LORD
11.10.12.10. with Refrain

106 Praise Him! Praise Him!

Thou art worthy . . . for Thou . . . hast redeemed us to God by Thy blood. Rev. 5:9

1. Praise Him! praise Him! Je-sus, our bless-ed Re-deem-er! Sing, O Earth, His
2. Praise Him! praise Him! Je-sus, our bless-ed Re-deem-er! For our sins He
3. Praise Him! praise Him! Je-sus, our bless-ed Re-deem-er! Heav'n-ly por-tals

won-der-ful love pro-claim! Hail Him! hail Him! high-est arch-an-gels in glo-ry;
suf-fered, and bled and died; He our Rock, our hope of e-ter-nal sal-va-tion,
loud with ho-san-nas ring! Je-sus, Sav-ior, reign-eth for-ev-er and ev-er;

Strength and hon-or give to His ho-ly name! Like a shep-herd
Hail Him! hail Him! Je-sus the Cru-ci-fied. Sound His prais-es!
Crown Him! crown Him! Proph-et and Priest and King! Christ is com-ing!

Je-sus will guard His chil-dren, In His arms He car-ries them all day long:
Je-sus who bore our sor-rows; Love un-bound-ed, won-der-ful, deep and strong:
o-ver the world vic-to-rious, Pow'r and glo-ry un-to the Lord be-long:

Refrain

Praise Him! praise Him! tell of His ex-cel-lent great-ness;

TEXT: Fanny J. Crosby
MUSIC: Chester G. Allen

JOYFUL SONG
Irregular meter

Praise Him! praise Him! ev-er in joy-ful song!

Let's Just Praise the Lord 107

Lift up your hands . . . and bless the Lord. Ps. 134:2

Let's just praise the Lord! Praise the Lord! Let's just

lift our hearts* to heav-en and praise the Lord;

Let's just praise the Lord, Praise the Lord, Let's just

lift our hearts* to heav-en and praise the Lord!

*Alternate words "voice," "hands."

TEXT: Gloria Gaither and William J. Gaither
MUSIC: William J. Gaither

LET'S JUST PRAISE THE LORD
Irregular meter

108 Come, Christians, Join to Sing

. . . singing and making melody in your heart to the Lord; giving thanks always. Eph. 5:19-20

1. Come, Chris - tians, join to sing Al - le - lu - ia! A - men!
2. Come, lift your hearts on high, Al - le - lu - ia! A - men!
3. Praise yet our Christ a - gain, Al - le - lu - ia! A - men!

Loud praise to Christ our King; Al - le - lu - ia! A - men!
Let prais - es fill the sky; Al - le - lu - ia! A - men!
Life shall not end the strain; Al - le - lu - ia! A - men!

Let all, with heart and voice, Be - fore His throne re - joice;
He is our Guide and Friend; To us He'll con - de - scend;
On heav - en's bliss - ful shore His good - ness we'll a - dore,

Praise is His gra - cious choice: Al - le - lu - ia! A - men!
His love shall nev - er end: Al - le - lu - ia! A - men!
Sing - ing for - ev - er - more, "Al - le - lu - ia! A - men!"

TEXT: Christian H. Bateman
MUSIC: Traditional Spanish melody; arranged by David Evans;
       Choral ending arranged by Eugene Thomas

MADRID
6.6.6.6.D.

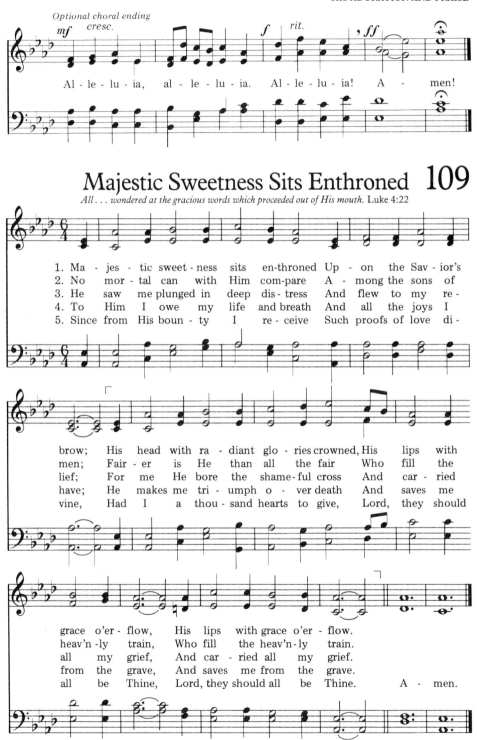

Majestic Sweetness Sits Enthroned 109

All . . . wondered at the gracious words which proceeded out of His mouth. Luke 4:22

1. Ma - jes - tic sweet - ness sits en - throned Up - on the Sav - ior's
2. No mor - tal can with Him com - pare A - mong the sons of
3. He saw me plunged in deep dis - tress And flew to my re -
4. To Him I owe my life and breath And all the joys I
5. Since from His boun - ty I re - ceive Such proofs of love di -

brow; His head with ra - diant glo - ries crowned, His lips with
men; Fair - er is He than all the fair Who fill the
lief; For me He bore the shame - ful cross And car - ried
have; He makes me tri - umph o - ver death And saves me
vine, Had I a thou - sand hearts to give, Lord, they should

grace o'er - flow, His lips with grace o'er - flow.
heav'n - ly train, Who fill the heav'n - ly train.
all my grief, And car - ried all my grief.
from the grave, And saves me from the grave.
all be Thine, Lord, they should all be Thine. A - men.

TEXT: Samuel Stennett
MUSIC: Thomas Hastings

ORTONVILLE
C.M. with Repeats

110 O Could I Speak the Matchless Worth

We beheld His glory . . . full of grace and truth. John 1:14

1. O could I speak the match-less worth, O
could I sound the glo-ries forth Which in my Sav-ior shine,
I'd sing His glo-rious right-eous-ness, And mag-ni-fy the
won-drous grace Which made sal-va-tion mine, Which made sal-va-tion mine.

2. I'd sing the char-ac-ters He bears, And
all the forms of love He wears, Ex-alt-ed on His throne:
In loft-iest songs of sweet-est praise, I would to ev-er-
last-ing days Make all His glo-ries known, Make all His glo-ries known.

3. Soon the de-light-ful day will come When
my dear Lord will bring me home, And I shall see His face;
Then with my Sav-ior, Broth-er, Friend, A blest e-ter-ni-
ty I'll spend, Tri-um-phant in His grace, Tri-um-phant in His grace.

TEXT: Samuel Medley
MUSIC: Source unknown; arranged by Lowell Mason

ARIEL
8.8.6.8.8.6.6.

Join All the Glorious Names 111

...far above ... every name that is named. Eph. 1:21

1. Join all the glo-rious names Of wis-dom, love, and pow'r,
2. Great Proph-et of my God, My tongue would bless Thy name:
3. Je - sus, my great High Priest, Of - fered His blood, and died;
4. Thou art my Coun - sel - or, My Pat - tern, and my Guide,
5. My Sav - ior and my Lord, My Con - qu'ror and my King,

That ev - er mor - tals knew, That an - gels
By Thee the joy - ful news Of our sal -
My guilt - y con - science seeks No sac - ri -
And Thou my Shep - herd art; O, keep me
Thy scep - tre and Thy sword, Thy reign - ing

ev - er bore: All are too poor to speak His worth,
va - tion came, The joy - ful news of sins for - giv'n,
fice be - side: His pow'r - ful blood did once a - tone
near Thy side; Nor let my feet e'er turn a - stray
grace, I sing: Thine is the pow'r; be - hold I sit

Too poor to set my Sav - ior forth.
Of hell sub - dued and peace with heav'n.
And now it pleads be - fore the throne.
To wan - der in the crook - ed way.
In will - ing bonds be - neath Thy feet. A - men.

TEXT: Isaac Watts
MUSIC: John Darwall
A lower setting may be found at No. 117

DARWALL
6.6.6.6.8.8.

112 Jesus, Name Above All Names

That the name of our Lord Jesus Christ may be glorified in you. 2 Thess. 1:12

Unison

Je - sus, name a - bove all names, beau-ti-ful Sav - ior,
glo - ri - ous Lord. Em - man - u - el, God is
with us, bless-ed Re - deem - er, Liv - ing Word.

TEXT and MUSIC: Naida Hearn

HEARN
7.8.8.8.

113 I Just Came to Praise the Lord

I will sing praises unto my God while I have any being. Ps. 146:2

1. I just came to praise the Lord, I just came to praise the Lord;
2. I just came to thank the Lord, I just came to thank the Lord;
3. I just came to love the Lord, I just came to love the Lord;

TEXT and MUSIC: Wayne Romero

ROMERO
7.7.9.7.

I just came to praise His ho-ly name, I just came to praise the Lord.
I just came to praise His ho-ly name, I just came to thank the Lord.
I just came to praise His ho-ly name, I just came to love the Lord.

His Name Is Life 114

I am ... the Life. John 14:6

His name is Mas-ter, Sav-ior, Li-on of Ju-dah, Bless-ed Prince of

Peace. Shep-herd, For-tress, Rock of Sal-va-tion, Lamb of God is

He. Son of Dav-id, King of the Ag-es, E-ter-nal

Life, Ho-ly Lord of Glo-ry, His name is Life.

TEXT and MUSIC: Carman, Gloria Gaither and William J. Gaither;
arranged by Eugene Thomas

HIS NAME IS LIFE
Irregular meter

115 Sometimes "Alleluia"

Blessed be the God and Father of our Lord Jesus Christ. 1 Pet. 1:3

Some-times "Al - le - lu - ia," Some-times "Praise the Lord,"

Last time: Fine

Some-times gent - ly sing - ing; Our hearts in one ac - cord.

1. O let us lift our voic - es, Look toward the sky and start to sing;
2. O let our joy be un-con-fined; Let us sing with free-dom un - re - strained;
3. O let us feel His pres - ence, Let the sound of prais-es fill the air.
4. O let the Spir -it o - ver-flow As we are filled from head to toe.

D.C.

O let us now re - turn His love, Just let our voic - es ring.
Let's take this feeling that we're feeling now Outside these walls and let it rain.
O let us sing the song of Je - sus' love To peo-ple ev - 'ry - where.
We love You, Father, Son, and Ho-ly Ghost; And we want this world to know.

TEXT and MUSIC: Chuck Girard

SOMETIMES ALLELUIA
Irregular meter

Take the Name of Jesus with You 116

Do all in the name of the Lord Jesus. Col. 3:17

1. Take the name of Je - sus with you, Child of sor - row and of woe;
2. Take the name of Je - sus ev - er, As a shield from ev - 'ry snare;
3. O the pre-cious name of Je - sus! How it thrills our souls with joy,
4. At the name of Je - sus bow - ing, Fall-ing pros-trate at His feet,

It will joy and com-fort give you—Take it, then, wher-e'er you go.
If temp - ta-tions round you gath - er, Breathe that ho - ly name in prayer.
When His lov - ing arms re - ceive us And His songs our tongues em-ploy!
King of kings in heav'n we'll crown Him When our jour - ney is com - plete.

Refrain

Pre - cious name, O how sweet! Hope of earth and joy of heav'n;

Pre - cious name, O how sweet! Hope of earth and joy of heav'n.

TEXT: Lydia Baxter
MUSIC: William H. Doane

PRECIOUS NAME
8.7.8.7. with Refrain

117 We Come, O Christ, to You

Lord, to whom shall we go? Thou hast the words of eternal life. John 6:68

1. We come, O Christ, to You, True Son of God and man, By Whom all things con - sist, In Whom all life be - gan: In You a - lone we live and move, And have our be - ing in Your love.

2. You are the Way to God, Your blood our ran - som paid; In You we face our Judge And Mak - er un - a - fraid. Be - fore the throne ab - solved we stand, Your love has met Your law's de - mand.

3. You are the liv - ing Truth! All wis - dom dwells in You, The Source of ev - ery skill, The One E - ter - nal True! O great I AM! In You we rest, Sure an - swer to our ev - ery quest.

4. You on - ly are true Life, To know You is to live The more a - bun - dant life That earth can nev - er give: O ris - en Lord! We live in You, in us each day Your life re - new!

5. We wor - ship You, Lord Christ, Our Sav - ior and our King, To You our youth and strength A - dor - ing - ly we bring: So fill our hearts, that all may view Your life in us, and turn to You! A - men.

TEXT: Margaret Clarkson
MUSIC: John Darwall
A higher setting may be found at No. 111

DARWALL
6.6.6.6.8.8.

Of the Father's Love Begotten 118

I am Alpha and Omega, the Beginning and the End. Rev. 22:13

Unison

1. Of the Fa-ther's love be-got-ten, Ere the worlds be-gan
2. O ye heights of heav'n a-dore Him; An-gel hosts, His prais-
3. Christ, to Thee with God the Fa-ther, And, O Ho-ly Ghost,

to be, He is Al-pha and O-me-ga, He the Source, the
es sing; Pow'rs, do-min-ions, bow be-fore Him, And ex-tol our
to Thee, Hymn and chant and high thanks-giv-ing And un-wea-ried

End-ing He, Of the things that are, that have been,
God and King; Let no tongue on earth be si-lent,
prais-es be: Hon-or, glo-ry, and do-min-ion,

And that fu-ture years shall see, Ev-er-more and ev-er-more!
Ev-'ry voice in con-cert ring, Ev-er-more and ev-er-more!
And e-ter-nal vic-to-ry, Ev-er-more and ev-er-more! A-men.

TEXT: Aurelius C. Prudentius, 4th century;
   translated by John M. Neale and Henry W. Baker
MUSIC: Plainsong, 13th century; arranged by C. Winfred Douglas

DIVINUM MYSTERIUM
8.7.8.7.8.7.7.

119 O Thou Joyful, O Thou Wonderful

We also joy in God through our Lord Jesus Christ. Rom. 5:11

1. O thou joy-ful, O thou won-der-ful Grace-re-veal-ing
2. O thou joy-ful, O thou won-der-ful Love-re-veal-ing
3. O thou joy-ful, O thou won-der-ful Peace-re-veal-ing

Christ-mas-tide! Je-sus came to win us From all sin with-
Christ-mas-tide! Loud ho-san-nas sing-ing And all prais-es
Christ-mas-tide! Dark-ness dis-ap-pear-eth, God's own light now

in us; Glo-ri-fy the ho-ly Child!
bring-ing: May Thy love with us a-bide!
near-eth: Peace and joy to all be-tide!

TEXT: Johannes D. Falk, stanza 1; Source unknown, stanza 3;
      translated by Henry Katterjohn
MUSIC: Tattersall's *Psalmody*, 1794
Words Used by permission of The United Church Press.

O SANCTISSIMA
4.5.7.6.6.7.

120 The Advent of Our God

Rejoice . . . for, lo, I come, and I will dwell in the midst of thee. Zech. 2:10

1. The Ad-vent of our God With ea-ger hearts we greet; And
2. All glo-ry to the Son, Who comes to set us free; With

TEXT: Charles Coffin; translated by John Chandler, altered
MUSIC: Aaron Williams
      A higher setting may be found at No. 21

ST. THOMAS
S.M.

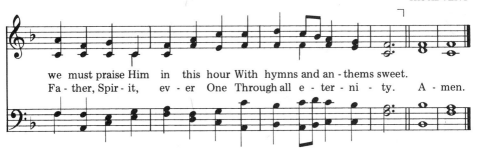

we must praise Him in this hour With hymns and an - thems sweet.
Fa - ther, Spir - it, ev - er One Through all e - ter - ni - ty. A - men.

The Word Made Flesh 121

Of His fulness have all we received, and grace for grace. John 1:16

1. The Word made flesh has dwelt a - mong us, full of grace and
2. The Word made flesh has dwelt a - mong us, from His full - ness

full of truth. We be - held His won - drous glo - ry of the on - ly
we re - ceived grace on grace and last - ing mer - cy, truth and wis - dom,

Refrain

Son of God. We have be - held His glo - ry, and we have seen the
hope and peace.

light. A - noint - ed Prince of glo - ry, we mar - vel at Thy sight.

TEXT and MUSIC: John Purifoy; based on John 1:14-17;
  arranged by Joseph Barlowe

VICKI
Irregular meter

122 THE ADVENT OF OUR LORD

A Brief Service of Joyful Expectation

Suggested Hymn Stanzas

To facilitate an uninterrupted flow from stanza to stanza,
the suggested stanzas have been marked with an arrow: ►

O Come, O Come, Emmanuel, stanzas 1, 2
Come, Thou Long-Expected Jesus, complete
Joy to the World!, stanzas 1, 4

WORSHIP LEADER: Who shall come in the fullness of time to
gladden the hearts of men?
Who shall bring new joy to the world
and the poor and lonely defend?
Who shall come on a cold winter's night,
when the world is hushed and still?
Only the silent stars keep watch as a
promise is fulfilled.

Just as a Child newly born He shall come
to a stable rough with sod.
'Tis gentle Jesus, Prince of Peace, the
blessed Son of God!

WORSHIP LEADER and PEOPLE:
We await Him with reverent hearts,
O come Lord Jesus, come!

"Who Shall Come" by Mary E. Caldwell

123 O Come, O Come, Emmanuel

A virgin shall . . . bear a Son, and shall call His name Immanuel. Isa. 7:14

1. O come, O come, Em - man - u - el, And
2. O come, Thou Day - spring, come and cheer Our
3. O come, Thou Wis - dom from on high, And
4. O come, De - sire of na - tions, bind All

optional introduction first verse only mp

TEXT: Latin Hymn, *Psalteriolum Cantionum Catholicarum,* 1710;
translated by John M. Neale, stanzas 1, 2, altered;
Henry S. Coffin, stanzas 3, 4, altered
MUSIC: Adapted from Plainsong by Thomas Helmore; arranged by Tom Fettke

VENI EMMANUEL
L.M. with Refrain

ran - som cap - tive Is - ra - el, That mourns in lone - ly ex - ile
spir - its by Thine ad - vent here; Dis - perse the gloom-y clouds of
or - der all things, far and nigh; To us the path of knowl - edge
peo - ples in one heart and mind; Bid en - vy, strife and quar - rels

here, Un - til the Son of God ap - pear.
night, And death's dark shad - ows put to flight.
show, And cause us in her ways to go.
cease, Fill all the world with heav - en's peace.

Refrain
parts optional

Re - joice! Re -

joice! Em - man - u - el Shall come to thee, O Is - ra - el!

Optional transition to
"Come, Thou Long-Expected Jesus"

accel. poco a poco   *cresc.*   *no rit.*

124 Come, Thou Long-Expected Jesus

He hath sent Me to bind up the brokenhearted, to proclaim liberty to the captives. Isa. 61:1

1. Come, Thou long - ex - pect - ed Je - sus, Born to set Thy peo - ple free;
2. Born Thy peo - ple to de - liv - er, Born a Child, and yet a King,

From our fears and sins re - lease us; Let us find our rest in Thee.
Born to reign in us for - ev - er, Now Thy gra - cious king-dom bring.

Is - rael's strength and con - so - la - tion, Hope of all the earth Thou art;
By Thine own e - ter - nal Spir - it Rule in all our hearts a - lone;

Dear De - sire of ev - 'ry na - tion, Joy of ev - 'ry long - ing heart.
By Thine all - suf - fi - cient mer - it, Raise us to Thy glo - rious throne.

TEXT: Charles Wesley
MUSIC: Rowland H. Prichard; arranged by Robert Harkness
     A lower setting may be found at No. 89

HYFRYDOL
8.7.8.7.D.

Optional transition to "Joy to the World"

accel. poco a poco   *accented*

Joy to the World! 125

Bethlehem . . . , out of thee shall He come forth unto Me that is to be ruler in Israel. Mic. 5:2

1. Joy to the world! the Lord is come; Let earth re-ceive her King;
2. Joy to the earth! the Sav-ior reigns; Let men their songs em-ploy;
3. No more let sins and sor-rows grow, Nor thorns in-fest the ground;
4. He rules the world with truth and grace, And makes the na-tions prove

Let ev-'ry heart pre-pare Him room,
While fields and floods, rocks, hills, and plains
He comes to make His bless-ings flow
The glo-ries of His righ-teous-ness,

And heav'n and na-ture sing, And heav'n and na-ture sing,
Re-peat the sound-ing joy, Re-peat the sound-ing joy,
Far as the curse is found, Far as the curse is found,
And won-ders of His love, And won-ders of His love,

1. And heav'n and na-ture sing,

1. And heav'n and na-ture sing, And heav'n and na-

And heav'n, and heav'n and na-ture sing.
Re-peat, re-peat the sound-ing joy.
Far as, far as the curse is found.
And won-ders, won-ders of His love.

ture sing,

Choral Ending on the following page.

TEXT: Isaac Watts
MUSIC: George Frederick Handel, arranged by Lowell Mason;
Choral ending arranged by Tom Fettke

ANTIOCH
C.M.

Optional choral ending - "Joy to the World"   cresc.

A - men, a - men, a -

world!   A - men!

rit.

men!   Joy   to   the   world!   A - men!

world!   A - men!

The end of "THE ADVENT OF OUR LORD—A Brief Service of Joyful Expectation"

126 A Nativity Prayer

Call His name JESUS: for He shall save His people from their sins. Matt. 1:21

O ho - ly Child of Beth - le - hem! De - scend to us, we pray;

Cast out our sin, and en - ter in; Be born in us to - day.   A - men.

TEXT: Phillips Brooks
MUSIC: William David Young

ELATA
C.M.

Thou Didst Leave Thy Throne 127

He came unto His own, and His own received Him not. John 1:11

1. Thou didst leave Thy throne and Thy king - ly crown When Thou
2. Heav - en's arch - es rang when the an - gels sang, Pro -
3. The fox - es found rest, and the birds their nest In the
4. Thou cam - est, O Lord, with the liv - ing word That should
5. When the heav'ns shall ring and the an - gels sing At Thy

cam - est to earth for me; But in Beth - le-hem's home was there
claim - ing Thy roy - al de - cree; But of low - ly birth didst Thou
shade of the for - est tree; But Thy couch was the sod, O Thou
set Thy peo - ple free; But with mock - ing scorn and with
com - ing to vic - to - ry, Let Thy voice call me home, say - ing,

found no room For Thy ho - ly na - tiv - i - ty. O
come to earth, And in great hu - mil - i - ty. O
Son of God, In the des - erts of Gal - i - lee. O
crown of thorn They bore Thee to Cal - va - ry. O
"Yet there is room— There is room at My side for thee." My

come to my heart, Lord Je - sus—There is room in my heart for Thee!
come to my heart, Lord Je - sus—There is room in my heart for Thee!
come to my heart, Lord Je - sus—There is room in my heart for Thee!
come to my heart, Lord Je - sus—There is room in my heart for Thee!
heart shall re-joice, Lord Je - sus, When Thou com - est and call- est for me!

TEXT: Emily E. S. Elliott
MUSIC: Timothy R. Matthews

MARGARET
Irregular meter

128 It Came upon the Midnight Clear

The angel of the Lord came upon them, and the glory of the Lord shone . . . about them. Luke 2:9

1. It came up-on the mid-night clear, That glo-rious song of old,
2. Still thru the clo-ven skies they come With peace-ful wings un-furled,
3. And ye, be-neath life's crush-ing load, Whose forms are bend-ing low,
4. For lo, the days are hast'ning on, By proph-ets seen of old,

From an-gels bend-ing near the earth To touch their harps of gold:
And still their heav'n-ly mu-sic floats O'er all the wea-ry world:
Who toil a-long the climb-ing way With pain-ful steps and slow,
When with the ev-er-cir-cling years Shall come the time fore-told,

"Peace on the earth, good-will to men, From heav'n's all-gra-cious King!"
A-bove its sad and low-ly plains They bend on hov-'ring wing,
Look now! for glad and gold-en hours Come swift-ly on the wing:
When the new heav'n and earth shall own The Prince of Peace their King,

The world in sol-emn still-ness lay To hear the an-gels sing.
And ev-er o'er its Ba-bel sounds The bless-ed an-gels sing.
O rest be-side the wea-ry road And hear the an-gels sing.
And the whole world send back the song Which now the an-gels sing.

TEXT: Edmund H. Sears
MUSIC: Richard S. Willis

CAROL
C.M.D.

Break Forth, O Beauteous Heavenly Light 129

... A light to lighten the Gentiles, and the glory of Thy people. Luke 2:32

1. Break forth, O beau-teous heav'n-ly light, And ush-er in the
2. He comes, a Child, from realms on high, He comes the heav'ns a-

morn - ing; Ye shep-herds, shrink not with af-fright, But
dor - ing; He comes to earth to live and die, A

hear the an-gel's warn - ing. This Child, now weak in in-fan-cy,
bro-ken race re-stor - ing. Al-though the King of kings is He,

Our con-fi-dence and joy shall be. The pow'r of Sa-tan
He comes in deep hu-mil-i-ty; His peo-ple to de-

break - ing, Our peace e-ter-nal mak - ing.
liv - er, And reign in us for-ev - er.

TEXT: Johann Rist, stanza 1; translated by John Troutbeck;
Joseph Barlowe, stanza 2
MUSIC: Johann Schop; harmonized by J. S. Bach

ERMUNTRE DICH
8.7.8.7.8.8.7.7.

130

GLORIA IN EXCELSIS DEO

A Brief Service of
Proclamation and Praise

Suggested Hymn Stanzas

To facilitate an uninterrupted flow from stanza to stanza,
the suggested stanzas have been marked with an arrow: ►
Angels from the Realms of Glory, stanzas 1, 2
Angels We Have Heard on High, stanzas 1,3
Hark! the Herald Angels Sing, complete

WORSHIP LEADER:
And there were in the same country shepherds abiding in the field,
keeping watch over their flock by night. And, lo, the angel of the
Lord came upon them, and the glory of the Lord shone round about
them: and they were sore afraid. And the angel said unto them, Fear
not: for, behold, I bring you good tidings of great joy, which shall be
to all people. For unto you is born this day in the city of David a
Saviour, which is Christ the Lord. And this shall be a sign unto you;
Ye shall find the Babe wrapped in swaddling clothes, lying in a man-
ger. And suddenly there was with the angel a multitude of the heavenly host praising God, and saying,

WORSHIP LEADER and PEOPLE:
Glory to God in the highest, and on earth peace, good will toward
men.

Luke 2:8-14.

Optional introduction to
"Angels, from the Realms of Glory"

Angels, from the Realms of Glory 131

Bethlehem, . . . out of thee shall come a Governor, that shall rule. Matt. 2:6

1. An-gels, from the realms of glo-ry, Wing your flight o'er all the earth;
2. Shep-herds, in the fields a-bid-ing, Watch-ing o'er your flocks by night,
3. Sag-es, leave your con-tem-pla-tions, Bright-er vi-sions beam a-far;
4. Saints be-fore the al-tar bend-ing, Watch-ing long in hope and fear,

Ye who sang cre-a-tion's sto-ry, Now pro-claim Mes-si-ah's birth:
God with man is now re-sid-ing, Yon-der shines the in-fant Light:
Seek the great De-sire of na-tions, Ye have seen His na-tal star:
Sud-den-ly the Lord, de-scend-ing, In His tem-ple shall ap-pear:

Come and wor-ship, come and wor-ship, Wor-ship Christ, the new-born King.

TEXT: James Montgomery
MUSIC: Henry T. Smart
    A lower setting may be found at No. 241

REGENT SQUARE
8.7.8.7.8.7.

Optional transition to
"Angels We Have Heard On High"

8va opt.   *loco*

132 Angels We Have Heard on High

There was with the angel a multitude of the heavenly host praising God. Luke 2:13

1. An - gels we have heard on high, Sweet - ly sing - ing o'er the plains,
2. Shep-herds, why this ju - bi - lee? Why your joy - ous strains pro-long?
3. Come to Beth - le - hem, and see Him whose birth the an - gels sing;
4. See with - in a man - ger laid Je - sus, Lord of heav'n and earth!

And the moun-tains in re - ply Ech - o back their joy - ous strains.
Say what may the ti - dings be, Which in -spire your heav'n - ly song?
Come, a - dore on bend - ed knee Christ the Lord, the new - born King.
Ma - ry, Jo - seph, lend your aid, With us sing our Sav - ior's birth.

Refrain

Glo - - - ri - a in ex-cel-sis De - o,

Glo - - - ri - a in ex-cel-sis De - o.

Segue to "Hark! the Herald Angels Sing"

TEXT: Traditional French carol
MUSIC: Traditional French melody

GLORIA
7.7.7.7. with Refrain

Hark! the Herald Angels Sing 133

Glory to God in the highest, and on earth peace. Luke 2:14

1. Hark! the her-ald an-gels sing, "Glo-ry to the new-born King;
2. Christ, by high-est heav'n a-dored; Christ, the ev-er-last-ing Lord!
3. Hail the heav'n-born Prince of Peace! Hail the Sun of Right-eous-ness!

Peace on earth, and mer-cy mild, God and sin-ners rec-on-ciled!"
Late in time be-hold Him come, Off-spring of the Vir-gin's womb:
Light and life to all He brings, Ris'n with heal-ing in His wings.

Joy-ful, all ye na-tions, rise, Join the tri-umph of the skies;
Veiled in flesh the God-head see; Hail th'in-car-nate De-i-ty,
Mild He lays His glo-ry by, Born that man no more may die,

With th'an-gel-ic host pro-claim, "Christ is born in Beth-le-hem!"
Pleased as man with men to dwell, Je-sus, our Em-man-u-el.
Born to raise the sons of earth, Born to give them sec-ond birth.

Hark! the her-ald an-gels sing, "Glo-ry to the new-born King."

Optional choral ending on the next page

TEXT: Charles Wesley, altered
MUSIC: Felix Mendelssohn; arranged by William H. Cummings

MENDELSSOHN
7.7.7.7.D. with Refrain

Optional choral ending to
"Hark! the Herald Angels Sing"

Glo-ri-a Glo-ri-a
Glo-ri-a Glo-ri-a in ex-cel-sis, in ex-cel-sis

De-o. Glo-ri-a!
Glo-ri-a!

The end of "GLORIA IN EXCELSIS DEO—A Brief Service of Proclamation and Praise"

134 Emmanuel

They shall call His name Emmanuel, which being interpreted is, God with us. Matt. 1:23

Unison

Em-man-u-el, Em-man-u-el,

His name is called Em-man-u-el;

God with us, re-vealed in us;

TEXT and MUSIC: Bob McGee

EMMANUEL
Irregular meter

His name is called Em - man - u - el.

While Shepherds Watched Their Flocks 135

Unto you is born this day in the city of David a Saviour. Luke 2:11

1. While shep - herds watched their flocks by night, All seat - ed on
2. "Fear not!" said he; for might - y dread Had seized their trou -
3. "To you, in Da - vid's town this day, Is born of Da -
4. "The heav'n - ly Babe you there shall find To hu - man view
5. "All glo - ry be to God on high, And to the earth

the ground, The an - gel of the Lord came down,
bled mind, "Glad ti - dings of great joy I bring
vid's line, The Sav - ior who is Christ the Lord,
dis - played, All mean - ly wrapped in swath - ing bands,
be peace: Good will hence - forth from heav'n to men,

And glo - ry shone a - round, And glo - ry shone a - round.
To you and all man - kind, To you and all man - kind.
And this shall be the sign: And this shall be the sign:
And in a man - ger laid; And in a man - ger laid.
Be - gin and nev - er cease, Be - gin and nev - er cease."

TEXT: Nahum Tate
MUSIC: George Frederick Handel; from Weyman's, *Melodia Sacra,* 1815

CHRISTMAS
C.M. with Repeats

JESUS OUR SAVIOR

136 The First Noel

There were . . . shepherds abiding in the field, keeping watch over their flock. Luke 2:8

1. The first No - el, the an - gel did say, Was to cer-tain poor shep-herds in
2. They look - ed up and saw a star Shin-ing in the east, be -
3. And by the light of that same star Three wise men came from
4. This star drew nigh to the north-west, O'er Beth - le - hem it
5. Then en - tered in those wise men three, Full rev - 'rent - ly up -
6. Then let us all with one ac - cord Sing prais - es to our

fields as they lay; In fields where they lay keep-ing their sheep, On a
yond them far, And to the earth it gave great light, And
coun - try far; To seek for a king was their in - tent, And to
took its rest, And there it did both stop and stay, Right
on their knee, And of - fered there in His pres - ence Their
heav'n - ly Lord, That hath made heav'n and earth of naught, And

Refrain

cold win - ter's night that was so deep.
so it con - tin -ued both day and night.
fol - low the star wher - ev - er it went. No - el, No - el, No -
o - ver the place where Je - sus lay.
gold, and myrrh, and frank - in - cense.
with His blood man - kind hath bought.

el, No - el, Born is the King of Is - ra - el.

TEXT: Traditional English carol
MUSIC: W. Sandys' *Christmas Carols*, 1833; arranged by John Stainer

THE FIRST NOEL
Irregular meter

What Child Is This? 137

They made known abroad the saying which was told them concerning this Child. Luke 2:17

1. What Child is this, who, laid to rest, On Mary's lap is sleeping?
2. Why lies He in such mean estate Where ox and ass are feeding?
3. So bring Him incense, gold and myrrh, Come, peasant, king, to own Him;

Whom angels greet with anthems sweet, While shepherds watch are keeping?
Good Christian, fear; for sinners here The silent Word is pleading.
The King of kings salvation brings, Let loving hearts enthrone Him.

Refrain

This, this is Christ the King, Whom shepherds guard and angels sing:

Haste, haste to bring Him laud, The Babe, the Son of Mary.

TEXT: William C. Dix
MUSIC: Traditional English melody, 16th century

GREENSLEEVES
8.7.8.7. with Refrain

138 Go, Tell It on the Mountain

Let them shout from the top of the mountains. Let them give glory unto the Lord. Isa. 42:11-12

Refrain: Go tell it on the moun-tain, O-ver the hills and ev-'ry-where;

Go tell it on the moun-tain That Je-sus Christ is born.

1. While shep-herds kept their watch-ing O'er si-lent flocks by night, Be-
2. The shep-herds feared and trem-bled When, lo! a-bove the earth Rang
3. Down in a low-ly man-ger The hum-ble Christ was born And

hold, through-out the heav-ens There shone a ho-ly light.
out the an-gel cho-rus That hailed our Sav-ior's birth.
God sent us sal-va-tion That bless-ed Christ-mas morn.

TEXT: Traditional Spiritual, stanzas written by John W. Work II
MUSIC: Traditional Spiritual; arranged by Bill Wolaver

GO TELL IT
Irregular meter

I Wonder as I Wander 139

All they that heard it wondered at those things which were told them. Luke 2:18

Unison

1. I won-der as I wan-der, out un-der the sky, How
2. When Ma-ry birthed Je-sus, 'twas in a cow's stall, With
3. If Je-sus had want-ed for an-y wee thing, A
4. I won-der as I wan-der, out un-der the sky, How

Je-sus the Sav-ior did come for to die For
wise men and farm-ers and shep-herds and all. But
star in the sky or a bird on the wing, Or
Je-sus the Sav-ior did come for to die For

poor, orn-'ry peo-ple like you and like I; I
high from God's heav-en a star's light did fall, The
all of God's an-gels in heav'n for to sing, He
poor, orn-'ry peo-ple like you and like I; I

Optional Coda

won-der as I wan-der, out un-der the sky.
prom-ise of a-ges it then did re-call.
sure-ly could have it, 'cause He was the King.
won-der as I wan-der, out un-der the sky. Out un-der the sky.

TEXT: Appalachian carol; adapted by John Jacob Niles
MUSIC: John Jacob Niles; arranged by Donald P. Hustad

I WONDER AS I WANDER
Irregular meter

140 A Communion Hymn for Christmas

Shew the Lord's death till He come. 1 Cor. 11:26

Unison

1. Gath-ered round Your ta - ble on this ho - ly eve,
2. Prince of Glo - ry, gra - cing Heav'n ere time be - gan,
3. Beth-lehem's In - car - na - tion, Cal - vary's bit - ter cross,
4. With pro-found - est won - der we Your bo - dy take—
5. Christ-mas Babe so ten - der, Lamb who bore our blame,

View - ing Beth - lehem's sta - ble we re - joice and grieve;
Now for us em - brac - ing death as Son of Man;
Wrought for us sal - va - tion by Your pain and loss;
Laid in man - ger yon - der, bro - ken for our sake;
How shall sin - ners ren - der prais - es due Your name?

Joy to see You ly - ing in Your man - ger bed,
By Your birth so low - ly, by Your love so true,
Now we fall be - fore You in this ho - ly place,
Hushed in ad - o - ra - tion we ap - proach the cup—
Do Your own good plea - sure in the lives we bring;

Weep to see You dy - ing in our sin - ful stead.
By Your cross most ho - ly, Lord, we wor-ship You!
Pros - trate we a - dore You, for Your gift of grace.
Beth-lehem's pure ob - la - tion free - ly of - fered up.
In Your ran - somed trea - sure reign for-ev - er King! A - men.

TEXT: Margaret Clarkson
MUSIC: Tom Fettke

GREENRIDGE
11.11.11.11.

O Little Town of Bethlehem 141

Bethlehem . . . , out of thee shall He come forth unto Me that is to be ruler in Israel. Mic. 5:2

1. O lit - tle town of Beth - le - hem, How still we see thee lie!
2. For Christ is born of Ma - ry, And gath - ered all a - bove,
3. How si - lent - ly, how si - lent - ly The won-drous gift is giv'n!
4. O ho - ly Child of Beth - le - hem! De - scend to us, we pray;

A - bove thy deep and dream-less sleep The si - lent stars go by.
While mor - tals sleep, the an - gels keep Their watch of won-d'ring love.
So God im - parts to hu - man hearts The bless - ings of His heav'n.
Cast out our sin, and en - ter in; Be born in us to - day.

Yet in thy dark streets shin - eth The ev - er - last - ing Light;
O morn - ing stars, to - geth - er Pro - claim the ho - ly birth!
No ear may hear His com - ing, But in this world of sin,
We hear the Christ - mas an - gels The great glad ti - dings tell;

The hopes and fears of all the years Are met in thee to - night.
And prais - es sing to God the King, And peace to men on earth.
Where meek souls will re - ceive Him still The dear Christ en - ters in.
O come to us, a - bide with us, Our Lord Em - man - u - el. A - men.

TEXT: Phillips Brooks
MUSIC: Lewis H. Redner

ST. LOUIS
8.6.8.6.7.6.8.6.

142

FOR UNTO US A CHILD IS BORN

A Brief Service in Celebration of Our Lord's Birth

Suggested Hymn Stanzas

To facilitate an uninterrupted flow from stanza to stanza,
the suggested stanzas have been marked with an arrow: ►

Infant Holy, Infant Lowly, complete
How Great Our Joy!, stanzas 1, 2
O Come, All Ye Faithful, stanzas 1, 2
For Unto Us a Child Is Born, complete

WORSHIP LEADER:
Now the birth of Jesus Christ was on this wise: When as His mother Mary was espoused to Joseph, before they came together, she was found with Child of the Holy Ghost. Then Joseph her husband, being a just man, and not willing to make her a publick example, was minded to put her away privily. But while he thought on these things, behold, the angel of the Lord appeared unto him in a dream, saying, Joseph, thou son of David, fear not to take unto thee Mary thy wife: for that which is conceived in her is of the Holy Ghost. And she shall bring forth a Son, and thou shalt call His name JESUS: for He shall save His people from their sins. Now all this was done, that it might be fulfilled which was spoken of the Lord by the prophet, saying, Behold, a virgin shall be with Child, and shall bring forth a Son, and they shall call His name Emmanuel, which being interpreted is,

WORSHIP LEADER and PEOPLE:
God with us.

Matthew 1:18-23.

Optional introduction to "Infant Holy, Infant Lowly"

lightly

Infant Holy, Infant Lowly 143

He hath . . . a name written, KING OF KINGS, AND LORD OF LORDS. Rev. 19:16

1. In-fant ho-ly, In-fant low-ly, for His bed a cat-tle stall;
2. Flocks were sleep-ing, shep-herds keep-ing vig-il till the morn-ing new

Ox-en low-ing, lit-tle know-ing Christ the Babe is Lord of all.
Saw the glo-ry, heard the sto-ry, tid-ings of a gos-pel true.

Swift are wing-ing an-gels sing-ing, no-els ring-ing, tid-ings bring-ing:
Thus re-joic-ing, free from sor-row, prais-es voic-ing, greet the mor-row:

Christ the Babe is Lord of all, Christ the Babe is Lord of all.
Christ the Babe was born for you. Christ the Babe was born for you.

TEXT: Polish carol; paraphrase by Edith E. M. Reed
MUSIC: Traditional Polish carol; arranged by Joseph Barlowe

W ZLOBIE LEZY
8.7.8.7.8.8.7.7.

Arr. © 1986 WORD MUSIC (a div. of WORD, INC.) All Rights Reserved. International Copyright Secured.

Optional transition to "How Great Our Joy"

accel.   *brightly*

144 How Great Our Joy!

I bring you good tidings of great joy. Luke 2:10

1. While by the sheep we watched at night, Glad tid-ings brought an
2. There shall be born, so he did say, In Beth-le - hem a
3. There shall the Child lie in a stall, This Child who shall re -
4. This gift of God we'll cher - ish well, That ev - er joy our

an - gel bright.
Child to - day. How great our joy! Great our joy!
deem us all.
hearts shall fill.

Joy, joy, joy, Joy, joy, joy! Praise we the Lord in

heav'n on high! Praise we the Lord in heav'n on high!

TEXT: Traditional German carol
MUSIC: Traditional German melody; arranged by Hugo Jüngst

JÜNGST
Irregular meter

Optional transition to "O Come, All Ye Faithful"

O Come, All Ye Faithful **145**

Let us now go even unto Bethlehem, and see this thing which is come to pass. Luke 2:15

1. O come, all ye faith-ful, joy-ful and tri-um-phant, O come ye, O come ye to Beth-le-hem! Come and be-hold Him, born the King of an-gels!

2. Sing choirs of an-gels, sing in ex-ul-ta-tion, O sing, all ye bright hosts of heav'n a-bove! Glo-ry to God, all glo-ry in the high-est!

3. Yea, Lord, we greet Thee, born this hap-py morn-ing, Je-sus, to Thee be all glo-ry giv'n; Word of the Fa-ther, now in flesh ap-pear-ing!

Refrain

O come, let us a-dore Him, O come, let us a-dore Him, O come, let us a-dore Him, Christ the Lord! Lord!

(slight rit. last time) Optional transition to "For Unto Us"

TEXT: Latin Hymn; ascribed to John Francis Wade;
translated by Frederick Oakeley
MUSIC: John Francis Wade

ADESTE FIDELES
Irregular meter

146 For Unto Us a Child Is Born

For unto us a Child is born, unto us a Son is given. Isa. 9:6

*Optional choral ending

**For un-to us a Child is born, un-to us a Son is giv-en, un-to us a Son is giv-en: and His name shall be call-ed Won-der-ful, Coun-se-lor, The Might-y God, The Ev-er-last-ing Fa-ther, The Prince of Peace, The

*Congregation may join if desired.
**Harmonies and vocal parts conform to Handel's original score.
TEXT and MUSIC: George Frederick Handel; based on Isaiah 9:6, 7;
arranged by Tom Fettke

FOR UNTO US
Irregular meter

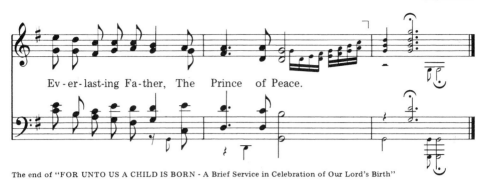

Ev - er - last-ing Fa - ther, The Prince of Peace.

The end of "FOR UNTO US A CHILD IS BORN - A Brief Service in Celebration of Our Lord's Birth"

Silent Night! Holy Night! 147

They . . . found Mary, and Joseph, and the Babe. Luke 2:16

1. Si - lent night, ho - ly night, All is calm, all is bright
2. Si - lent night, ho - ly night, Shep-herds quake at the sight.
3. Si - lent night, ho - ly night, Son of God, love's pure light

Round yon vir - gin moth-er and Child. Ho - ly In-fant so ten-der and mild,
Glo - ries stream from heav - en a - far, Heaven-ly hosts sing al - le - lu - ia;
Ra - diant beams from Thy ho - ly face, With the dawn of re - deem - ing grace,

Sleep in heav-en-ly peace, Sleep in heav - en - ly peace.
Christ the Sav - ior is born! Christ the Sav - ior is born!
Je - sus, Lord, at Thy birth, Je - sus, Lord, at Thy birth.

TEXT: Joseph Mohr; translated by John F. Young
MUSIC: Franz Grüber

STILLE NACHT
Irregular meter

148 O Holy Night!

That Holy Thing which shall be born of thee shall be called the Son of God. Luke 1:35

Introduction (use arpeggiated chords
in a triplet feeling throughout)

1. O ho-ly night! the stars are bright-ly
2. Led by the light of faith se-rene-ly
3. Tru-ly He taught us to love one an-

use accompaniment
figure from 1st 2 bars

shin-ing, It is the night of the dear Sav-ior's birth; Long lay the
beam-ing, With glow-ing hearts by His cra-dle we stand; So led by
oth-er; His law is love and His gos-pel is peace; Chains shall He

world in sin and er-ror pin-ing, Till He ap-peared and the soul felt its
light of a star sweet-ly gleam-ing, Here came the wise men from O-ri-ent
break, for the slave is our broth-er, And in His name all op-pres-sion shall

worth. A thrill of hope the wea-ry world re-joic-es, For yon-der breaks a
land. The King of kings lay thus in low-ly man-ger, In all our tri-als
cease. Sweet hymns of joy in grate-ful chor-us raise we, Let all with-in us

TEXT: John S. Dwight
MUSIC: Adolphe Adam

CANTIQUE DE NOËL
11.10.11.10.11.10.11.10.10.

new and glo-rious morn; Fall   on your knees, Oh,   hear   the an-gel
born to be our Friend;   He   knows our need, To our weak - ness is   no
praise His ho-ly name;   Christ is the Lord, Oh,   praise   His name for-

voic - es! O   night   di - vine,   O   night   when Christ was born!
strang-er. Be-hold   your King,   be - fore   Him low-ly   bend!
ev - er! His   pow'r and   glo - ry   ev - er-more pro-claim!

cued notes opt. on last refrain

O   night, O   ho - ly   night, O   night di - vine!
Be-hold   your King,   be - fore   Him   low-ly   bend!
His   pow'r and   glo - ry   ev - er-more pro-claim.

Jesus Is Born 149

4 Part Canon

There is but . . . one Lord Jesus Christ. 1 Cor. 8:6

I   II

Al - le - lu - ia!   Born   is   the   King   of kings,

III   IV

Born   is   the   Lord   of   lords. Je - sus   is   born!

TEXT and MUSIC: Gerald S. Henderson

NATIVITY CANON
4.6.6.4.

150 O Hearken Ye

My soul doth magnify the Lord. Luke 1:46

1. O heark-en ye who would be-lieve, The gra-cious ti-dings now re-ceive: Glo-ri-a, glo-ri-a, In ex-cel-sis De - o. For The might-y Lord of heav'n and earth, To - day is come to hu - man birth.

2. O heark-en ye who long for peace, Your trou-bled search-ing now may cease. Glo-ri-a, glo-ri-a, In ex-cel-sis De - o. The at this cra - dle you shall find God's heal-ing grace for all man-kind.

3. O heark-en ye who long for love, And turn your hearts to God a - bove. The an - gel's song the won - der tells: Now Love In - car - nate with us dwells!

Glo - ri - a, glo - ri - a, In ex - cel - sis De - o.

TEXT: Wihla Hutson
MUSIC: Alfred Burt

O HEARKEN YE
8.8.6.6.D.

Good Christian Men, Rejoice 151

My spirit hath rejoiced in God my Saviour. Luke 1:47

1. Good Chris-tian men, re-joice With heart and soul and voice;
2. Good Chris-tian men, re-joice With heart and soul and voice;
3. Good Chris-tian men, re-joice With heart and soul and voice;

Give ye heed to what we say: News! news! Je-sus Christ is born to-day!
Now ye hear of end-less bliss: Joy! joy! Je-sus Christ was born for this!
Now ye need not fear the grave:Peace! peace! Je-sus Christ was born to save!

Ox and ass be-fore Him bow, And He is in the man-ger now:
He has o-pened heav-en's door, And man is bless-ed ev-er-more:
Calls you one and calls you all To gain His ev-er-last-ing hall:

Christ is born to-day! Christ is born to-day!
Christ was born for this! Christ was born for this!
Christ was born to save! Christ was born to save!

TEXT: Latin carol, 14th century; translated by John M. Neale
MUSIC: German melody, 14th century; harmonized by John Stainer

IN DULCI JUBILO
Irregular meter

152 I Heard the Bells on Christmas Day

This Man shall be the peace. Mic. 5:5

1. I heard the bells on Christ - mas day Their old fa - mil - iar
2. I thought how, as the day had come, The bel - fries of all
3. And in de - spair I bowed my head: "There is no peace on
4. Yet pealed the bells more loud and deep: "God is not dead, nor
5. Then ring - ing, sing - ing on its way, The world re - volved from

car - ols play, And wild and sweet the words re - peat Of
Chris - ten - dom Had rolled a - long th'un - bro - ken song Of
earth," I said, "For hate is strong, and mocks the song Of
doth He sleep; The wrong shall fail, the right pre - vail, With
night to day— A voice, a chime, a chant sub - lime Of

Optional transition to "Come On, Ring Those Bells"

peace on earth, good will to men.
peace on earth, good will to men.
peace on earth, good will to men."
peace on earth, good will to men."
peace on earth, good will to men! will to men!

faster

TEXT: Henry W. Longfellow
MUSIC: Jean Baptiste Calkin

WALTHAM
L.M.

153 Come On, Ring Those Bells

Thy King cometh unto thee. Zech. 9:9

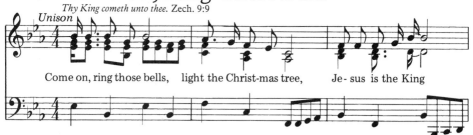

Unison

Come on, ring those bells, light the Christ-mas tree, Je - sus is the King

TEXT and MUSIC: Andrew Culverwell

RING THOSE BELLS
Irregular meter

born for you and me. Come on, ring those bells, ev-'ry-bod-y say, "Je-sus, we remember this Your birth - day." birth - day."

What Can I Give Him? 154

They . . . first gave their own selves to the Lord. 2 Cor. 8:5

What can I give Him, poor as I am? If I were a shep-herd I would bring a lamb; If I were a wise-man I would do my part; Yet what can I give Him? Give Him my heart.

TEXT: Christina Rossetti
MUSIC: Don Cason

CASTLE
9.11.11.10.

155 Once in Royal David's City

Of His government . . . there shall be no end, upon the throne of David. Isa. 9:7

1. Once in roy - al Da - vid's cit - y Stood a low - ly cat - tle shed, Where a moth - er laid her Ba - by In a man - ger for His bed: Ma - ry was that moth - er mild, Je - sus Christ her lit - tle Child.

2. He came down to earth from heav - en Who is God and Lord of all, And His shel - ter was a sta - ble, And His cra - dle was a stall: With the poor, and mean, and low - ly Lived on earth, our Sav - ior ho - ly.

3. Je - sus is our child-hood's pat - tern, Day by day like us He grew; He was lit - tle, weak, and help - less, Tears and smiles like us He knew: And He feel - eth for our sad - ness, And He shar - eth in our glad - ness.

4. And our eyes at last shall see Him Thro' His own re - deem - ing love; For that Child so dear and gen - tle Is our Lord in heav'n a - bove, And He leads His chil - dren on To the place where He is gone.

TEXT: Cecil F. Alexander
MUSIC: Henry J. Gauntlett

IRBY
8.7.8.7.7.7.

Child of Love 156

...preaching peace by Jesus Christ: (He is Lord of all). Acts 10:36

TEXT and MUSIC: Tina English
DESCANT: Traditional French melody

CHILD OF LOVE
Irregular meter

157 Away in a Manger

She brought forth her firstborn Son . . . and laid Him in a manger. Luke 2:7

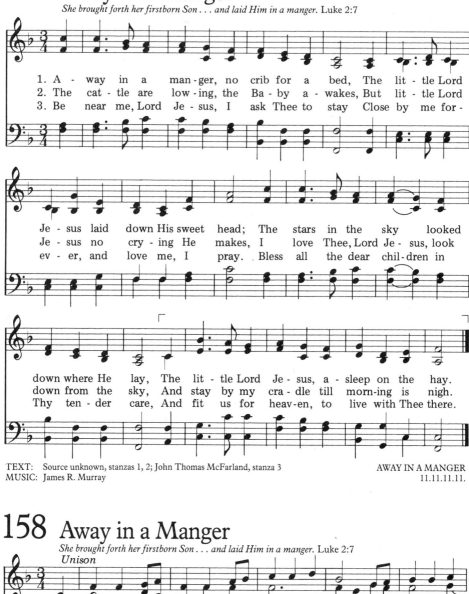

1. A - way in a man-ger, no crib for a bed, The lit - tle Lord
2. The cat - tle are low - ing, the Ba - by a - wakes, But lit - tle Lord
3. Be near me, Lord Je - sus, I ask Thee to stay Close by me for -

Je - sus laid down His sweet head; The stars in the sky looked
Je - sus no cry - ing He makes, I love Thee, Lord Je - sus, look
ev - er, and love me, I pray. Bless all the dear chil - dren in

down where He lay, The lit - tle Lord Je - sus, a - sleep on the hay.
down from the sky, And stay by my cra - dle till morn-ing is nigh.
Thy ten - der care, And fit us for heav-en, to live with Thee there.

TEXT: Source unknown, stanzas 1, 2; John Thomas McFarland, stanza 3
MUSIC: James R. Murray

AWAY IN A MANGER
11.11.11.11.

158 Away in a Manger

She brought forth her firstborn Son . . . and laid Him in a manger. Luke 2:7

Unison

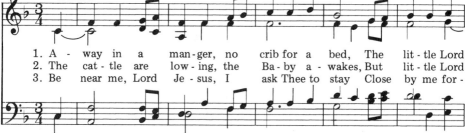

1. A - way in a man - ger, no crib for a bed, The lit - tle Lord
2. The cat - tle are low - ing, the Ba - by a - wakes, But lit - tle Lord
3. Be near me, Lord Je - sus, I ask Thee to stay Close by me for -

TEXT: Source unknown, stanzas 1, 2; John Thomas McFarland, stanza 3
MUSIC: William J. Kirkpatrick

CRADLE SONG
11.11.11.11.

Je - sus laid down His sweet head; The stars in the bright sky looked
Je - sus, no cry - ing He makes. I love Thee, Lord Je - sus, look
ev - er, and love me, I pray. Bless all the dear chil - dren in

down where He lay, The lit - tle Lord Je - sus a - sleep on the hay.
down from the sky, And stay by my cra - dle till morn - ing is nigh.
Thy ten - der care, And fit us for heav - en, to live with Thee there.

A Thousand Candles 159

I am come a light into the world. John 12:46

1. We light a thou - sand can - dles bright a - round the earth to - day,
2. Yes o - ver land and sea to - night the joy - ful mes - sage brings
3. Dear bright-est star o'er Beth - le - hem, O let your pre - cious light
4. In all our house so cold and dark please send your warmth sub - lime,

And all the beams will shine a - cross the heav - en's grand dis - play.
The birth of Him, our Lord and Christ, our Sav - ior and our King.
Shine in with hope and peace toward men in ev - 'ry home to - night.
The warmth that comes from Je - sus' love this bless - ed Christ-mas time.

TEXT: Swedish carol; translated by Evie Karlsson
MUSIC: Emmy Kohler; arranged by Eugene Thomas

THOUSAND CANDLES
8.7.8.6.

160 Lo! How a Rose E'er Blooming

There shall come forth a rod out of the stem of Jesse. Isa. 11:1

1. Lo, how a Rose e'er bloom-ing From ten-der stem hath sprung!
2. I - sa - iah 'twas fore - told it, The Rose I have in mind;
3. This Flower, whose fra-grance ten - der With sweet-ness fills the air,

Of Jes-se's lin-eage com - ing As men of old have sung.
With Mar - y we be-hold it, The vir - gin moth - er kind.
Dis - pels with glo - rious splen-dor The dark-ness ev - ery - where.

It came, a Flow-er bright, A - mid the cold of
To show God's love a - right She bore to men a
True man, yet ver - y God, From sin and death He

win - ter, When half - gone was the night.
Sav - ior, When half - gone was the night.
saves us And light - ens ev - ery load.

TEXT: German carol, 16th century; translated by Theodore
Baker, stanzas 1, 2 and Harriet Krauth Spaeth, stanza 3
MUSIC: *Geistliche Kirchengesäng*, Cologne, 1599;
harmonized by Michael Praetorius

ES IST EIN' ROS'
7.6.7.6.6.7.6.

Our Day of Joy Is Here Again 161

The shepherds returned, glorifying and praising God. Luke 2:20

1. Our day of joy is here a-gain, With love and peace and song;
2. When dark-ness lay up-on this earth, A glo-rious light did shine;
3. Now to the man-ger let us go To wor-ship and a-dore
4. How won-der-ful that God's own Son Should so Him-self a-base!

Come, let us join th'an-gel-ic strain With voic-es clear and strong.
God sent a Gift of price-less worth And showed His love di-vine.
The ten-der Babe up-on the straw, Our Sav-ior ev-er-more.
He thrust the might-y from their throne, And gave the low-ly grace.

Refrain

Glo-ry to our God, we sing, Glo-ry to our Lord and King;

Peace, good-will with all a-bide This ho-ly Christ-mas tide.

TEXT and MUSIC: Andrew L. Skoog

NU GLÄDJENS TIMME
C.M. with Refrain

162 The Birthday of a King

I will raise unto David a righteous Branch, and a King shall reign and prosper. Jer. 23:5

1. In the lit-tle vil-lage of Beth - le - hem, there lay a Child one day, And the sky was bright with a ho - ly light o'er the place where Je - sus lay. Al - le - lu - ia! O how the an - gels sang. Al - le - lu - ia! How it rang! And the sky was bright with a ho - ly light, 'twas the birth-day of a King.

2. 'Twas a hum-ble birth-place, but oh, how much God gave to us that day, From the man - ger bed what a path has led, what a per - fect ho - ly way.

TEXT and MUSIC: William Harold Neidlinger;
arranged by Robert F. Douglas

NEIDLINGER
10.6.10.7. with Refrain

As with Gladness Men of Old 163

When they saw the star; they rejoiced . . . and worshipped Him. Matt. 2:10-11

1. As with glad - ness men of old Did the guid - ing
2. As with joy - ful steps they sped To that low - ly
3. As they of - fered gifts most rare At that man - ger
4. Ho - ly Je - sus, ev - ery day Keep us in the

star be - hold; As with joy they hailed its light,
man - ger bed, There to bend the knee be - fore
rude and bare, So may we with ho - ly joy,
nar - row way; And when earth - ly things are past,

Lead - ing on - ward, beam - ing bright, So, most gra - cious
Him Whom heav'n and earth a - dore, So, may we with
Pure and free from sin's al - loy, All our cost - liest
Bring our ran - somed souls at last Where they need no

Lord, may we Ev - er - more be led to Thee.
will - ing feet Ev - er seek the mer - cy seat.
treas - ures bring, Christ, to Thee our heav'n-ly King.
star to guide, Where no clouds Thy glo - ry hide. A - men.

TEXT: William C. Dix
MUSIC: Conrad Kocher

DIX
7.7.7.7.7.7.

164 One Small Child

She brought forth a man Child, who was to rule all nations. Rev. 12:5

Unison

1. One small Child in a land of a thou-sand, One small dream of a
2. One king bring-ing his gold and rich - es, One King rul - ing an
3. One small light from the flame of a can - dle, One small light from a
4. One small Child in a land of a thou-sand, One small dream in a

Sav - ior to - night, One small hand reach-ing out to the star - light,
ar - my of might, One king kneel-ing with in - cense and can-dle light,
cit - y of might, One small light from the stars in the end-less night,
peo - ple of might, One small hand reach-ing out to the star - light,

1, 4 *Fine*

One small cit - y of life. Oh
One King bring - ing us life. Oh
One small light from a face. Oh
One small Sav - ior of life. Oh

2, 3

2. See Him ly - ing, a cra-dle be-neath Him, See Him smil-ing in the
3. See the shep-herds kneel-ing be-fore Him, See the kings on bend - ed

TEXT and MUSIC: David Meece

ONE SMALL CHILD
Irregular meter

D.S. al Fine

stall. See His moth-er prais-ing His Fa-ther, See His tin - y eye - lids fall.
knee. See His moth-er prais-ing His Fa-ther, See the Bless-ed In - fant sleep.

Adoration 165

Worship the Lord in the beauty of holiness. Ps. 96:9

1. Wor - ship the Lord in the beau - ty of ho - li - ness!
2. Fear not to en - ter His pres - ence in pov - er - ty,

Bow down be - fore Him, His glo - ry pro - claim; With
Bear - ing no gifts to pre - sent as your own. Bring

gold of o - be - dience and in - cense of low - li - ness,
truth in its beau - ty and love in its pur - i - ty—

kneel and a - dore Him: the Lord is His name!
these are the off - 'rings to lay at His throne. A - men.

TEXT: John S. B. Monsell, stanza 1; David Steele, stanza 2
MUSIC: Tom Fettke

JANICE
12.10.13.10.

166 We Three Kings

When Jesus was born in Bethlehem . . . there came wise men from the east. Matt. 2:1

1. We three kings of O - ri - ent are: Bear - ing gifts we trav - erse a - far—
2. Born a King on Beth - le - hem's plain: Gold I bring to crown Him a - gain,
3. Frank - in - cense to of - fer have I: In - cense owns a De - i - ty nigh;
4. Myrrh is mine: its bit - ter per - fume Breathes a life of gath - er - ing gloom—
5. Glo - rious now be - hold Him a - rise: King and God and Sac - ri - fice;

Field and foun - tain, moor and moun - tain— Fol - low - ing yon - der star.
King for - ev - er, ceas - ing nev - er O - ver us all to reign.
Prayer and prais - ing, all men rais - ing, Wor - ship Him, God on high.
Sor - r'wing, sigh - ing, bleed - ing, dy - ing, Sealed in the stone - cold tomb.
Al - le - lu - ia, Al - le - lu - ia! Earth to heav'n re - plies.

Refrain

O star of won - der, star of night, Star with roy - al beau - ty bright,

West - ward lead - ing, still pro - ceed - ing, Guide us to thy per - fect light.

TEXT and MUSIC: John H. Hopkins, Jr.

KINGS OF ORIENT
8.8.4.4.6. with Refrain

O Sing a Song of Bethlehem 167

God was manifest . . . justified . . . believed on . . . received up. 1 Tim. 3:16

1. O sing a song of Beth-le-hem, Of shep-herds watch-ing there,
And of the news that came to them From an-gels in the air:
The light that shone on Beth-le-hem Fills all the world to-day;
Of Je-sus' birth and peace on earth The an-gels sing al-way.

2. O sing a song of Naz-a-reth, Of sun-ny days of joy,
O sing of fra-grant flow-ers' breath, And of the sin-less Boy:
For now the flowers on Naz-a-reth In ev-ery heart may grow;
Now spreads the fame of His dear name On all the winds that blow.

3. O sing a song of Gal-i-lee, Of lake and woods and hill,
Of Him who walked up-on the sea And bade the waves be still:
For though like waves on Gal-i-lee, Dark seas of trou-ble roll,
When faith has heard the Mas-ter's word, Falls peace up-on the soul.

4. O sing a song of Cal-va-ry, Its glo-ry and dis-may;
Of Him who hung up-on the tree, And took our sins a-way:
For He who died on Cal-va-ry Is ris-en from the grave,
And Christ, our Lord, by heav'n a-dored, Is might-y now to save.

TEXT: Louis F. Benson
MUSIC: Melody collected by Lucy Broadwood; adapted & arranged by
Ralph Vaughan Williams

KINGSFOLD
C.M.D.

From "The English Hymnal" by permission of Oxford University Press, London.

168 Who Is He in Yonder Stall?

The Lamb . . . is Lord of lords, and King of kings. Rev. 17:14

1. Who is He in yon-der stall, At whose feet the shep-herds fall?
2. Who is He the peo-ple bless For His words of gen-tle-ness?
3. Who is He that stands and weeps At the grave where Laz-arus sleeps?
4. Lo! at mid-night, who is He Prays in dark Geth-sem-a-ne?
5. Who is He that from the grave Comes to heal and help and save?

Who is He in deep dis-tress, Fast-ing in the wil-der-ness?
Who is He to whom they bring All the sick and sor-row-ing?
Who is He the gath-'ring throng Greet with loud tri-um-phant song?
Who is He on yon-der tree Dies in grief and ag-o-ny?
Who is He that from His throne Rules through all the world a-lone?

Refrain

'Tis the Lord! O won-drous sto-ry! 'Tis the Lord! the King of glo-ry! At His feet we hum-bly fall, Crown Him! crown Him, Lord of all!

TEXT and MUSIC: Benjamin R. Hanby

LOWLINESS
7.7.7.7. with Refrain

The Unveiled Christ 169

. . . a new and living way . . . consecrated for us, through the veil . . . His flesh. Heb. 10:20

1. Once our bless-ed Christ of beau - ty   Was   veiled off from hu - man view;
2. Now He is with God the Fa - ther,   In - ter - ced - ing there for you;
3. Ho - ly an - gels bow be - fore   Him,   Men   of earth give prais-es due;
4. Thro'-out time and end-less a - ges,   Heights and depths of love so true;

But thro' suf-f'ring, death and sor - row   He   has rent the veil in   two.
For   He is the might-y   con - qu'ror   Since He rent the veil in   two.
For   He is the well - be - lov - ed   Since He rent the veil in   two.
He   a - lone can be the   giv - er   Since He rent the veil in   two.

Refrain

O   be-hold the Man of Sor - rows,   O   be-hold Him in plain view;

Lo! He is the might-y con - qu'ror, Since He rent the veil in   two.

Lo! He is the might-y con - qu'ror, Since He rent the veil in   two.

TEXT and MUSIC: N.B. Herrell

THE UNVEILED CHRIST
8.7.8.7. with Refrain

Copyright 1916. Renewed 1943 by Nazarene Publishing House. Used by Permission.

170 One Day

When we were yet without strength, in due time Christ died for the ungodly. Rom. 5:6

1. One day when heav - en was filled with His prais - es, One day when sin was as black as could be, Je - sus came forth to be born of a vir - gin, Dwelt a - mong men— my ex - am - ple is He!
2. One day they led Him up Cal - va - ry's moun - tain, One day they nailed Him to die on the tree; Suf - fer - ing an - guish, de - spised and re - ject - ed, Bear - ing our sins, my Re - deem - er is He!
3. One day they left Him a - lone in the gar - den, One day He rest - ed, from suf - fer - ing free; An - gels came down o'er His tomb to keep vig - il— Hope of the hope - less, my Sav - ior is He!
4. One day the grave could con - ceal Him no long - er, One day the stone rolled a - way from the door; Then He a - rose, o - ver death He had con - quered, Now is as - cend - ed, my Lord ev - er - more!
5. One day the trum - pet will sound for His com - ing, One day the skies with His glo - ry will shine; Won - der - ful day, my be - lov - ed ones bring - ing! Glo - ri - ous Sav - ior, this Je - sus is mine!

Refrain

Liv - ing—He loved me, dy - ing—He saved me, Bur - ied—He

TEXT: J. Wilbur Chapman
MUSIC: Charles H. Marsh

ONE DAY
11.10.11.10. with Refrain

car - ried my sins far a - way; Ris - ing—He jus - ti - fied

free - ly, for - ev - er: One day He's com - ing— O glo - ri - ous day!

Come and Praise the Lord Our King 171

Offer the sacrifice of praise to God continually. Heb. 13:15

1. Come and praise the Lord our King, Al - le - lu, al - le - lu - ia!
2. Christ was born in Beth - le - hem, Al - le - lu, al - le - lu - ia!
3. He grew up an earth - ly child, Al - le - lu, al - le - lu - ia!
4. Je - sus died at Cal - va - ry, Al - le - lu, al - le - lu - ia!
5. He has con-quered death and sin, Al - le - lu, al - le - lu - ia!
6. Now He rules from heav'n a - bove, Al - le - lu, al - le - lu - ia!
7. We will live with Him some-day, Al - le - lu, al - le - lu - ia!

Lift your voice and with us sing, Al - le - lu, al - le - lu - ia!
Son of God and Son of Man, Al - le - lu, al - le - lu - ia!
In the world, but un - de - filed, Al - le - lu, al - le - lu - ia!
Rose a - gain tri - um - phant - ly, Al - le - lu, al - le - lu - ia!
Great His tri - umph— glo - rious win, Al - le - lu, al - le - lu - ia!
King of mer - cy, King of love, Al - le - lu, al - le - lu - ia!
And for - ev - er with Him stay, Al - le - lu, al - le - lu - ia!

TEXT: William David Young, stanzas 1b, 5, 6;
Traditional sources, stanzas 1a, 2, 3, 4, 7, altered
MUSIC: William David Young

CULL CANYON
7.7.7.7.

172 Tell Me the Story of Jesus

Philip . . . began at the same scripture, and preached unto him Jesus. Acts 8:35

1. Tell me the sto - ry of Je - sus, Write on my heart ev - ery word;
2. Fast - ing a - lone in the des - ert, Tell of the days that are past,
3. Tell of the cross where they nailed Him, Writh-ing in an - guish and pain;

Refrain: Tell me the sto - ry of Je - sus, Write on my heart ev - ery word;

Fine

Tell me the sto - ry most pre - cious, Sweet-est that ev - er was heard.
How for our sins He was tempt - ed, Yet was tri - um-phant at last.
Tell of the grave where they laid Him, Tell how He liv - eth a - gain.
Tell me the sto - ry most pre - cious, Sweet-est that ev - er was heard.

Tell how the an - gels in cho - rus Sang as they wel-comed His birth,
Tell of the years of His la - bor, Tell of the sor - row He bore,
Love in that sto - ry so ten - der, Clear - er than ev - er I see:

D.C. for Refrain

"Glo - ry to God in the high - est! Peace and good ti - dings to earth."
He was de-spised and af - flict - ed, Home-less, re - ject - ed and poor.
Stay, let me weep while you whis - per, Love paid the ran - som for me.

TEXT: Fanny J. Crosby
MUSIC: John R. Sweney

STORY OF JESUS
8.7.8.7.D. with Refrain

All Glory, Laud and Honor 173

Blessed is the King of Israel that cometh in the name of the Lord. John 12:13

1. All glo-ry, laud and hon-or To Thee, Re-deem-er, King,
2. The com-pa-ny of an-gels Are prais-ing Thee on high,
3. To Thee, be-fore Thy pas-sion, They sang their hymns of praise;

To whom the lips of chil-dren Made sweet ho-san-nas ring: Thou
And mor-tal men and all things Cre-at-ed make re-ply: The
To Thee, now high ex-alt-ed, Our mel-o-dy we raise: Thou

art the King of Is-rael, Thou Da-vid's roy-al Son, Who
peo-ple of the He-brews With palms be-fore Thee went: Our
didst ac-cept their prais-es— Ac-cept the praise we bring, Who

in the Lord's name com-est, The King and bless-ed One!
praise and prayer and an-thems Be-fore Thee we pre-sent.
in all good de-light-est, Thou good and gra-cious King! A-men.

TEXT: Theodulph of Orleans; translated by John M. Neale
MUSIC: Melchior Teschner

ST. THEODULPH
7.6.7.6.D.

174 Hosanna, Loud Hosanna

Hosanna to the Son of David . . . Hosanna in the highest. Matt. 21:9

1. Ho - san - na, loud ho - san - na The lit - tle chil - dren sang;
2. From Ol - i - vet they fol - lowed 'Mid an ex - ult - ant crowd,
3. "Ho - san - na in the high - est!" That an - cient song we sing,

Optional Children's Choir (1st and 3rd stanzas)

Ho - san - na, ho - san - na, ho - san - na to the King;

Through pil - lared court and tem - ple The love - ly an - them rang;
The vic - tor palm branch wav - ing, And chant - ing clear and loud;
For Christ is our Re - deem - er, The Lord of heav'n, our King;

Ho - san - na, praise ye the Lord, Sing in one ac - cord!

To Je - sus, who had blessed them Close fold - ed to His breast,
The Lord of men and an - gels Rode on in low - ly state,
O may we ev - er praise Him With heart and life and voice,

TEXT: Jenette Threlfall; based on Matthew 21:15, 16
MUSIC: *Gesangbuch der Herzogl*, Württemburg, 1784;
Descant, final ending and handbell parts by Bruce Greer
A higher setting may be found at No. 59

ELLACOMBE
7.6.7.6.D.

Ho - san - na, ho - san - na, ho - san - na to the King!

The chil - dren sang their prais - es, The sim - plest and the best.
Nor scorned that lit - tle chil - dren Should on His bid - ding wait.
And in His bliss - ful pres - ence E - ter - nal - ly re - joice!

Optional final ending
Children alone   *ritard*

King! Ho - san - na, ho - san - na, ho - san - na to the King!

joice! *Keyboard only*   *ritard*

Optional 2 Octave Handbells (2nd and 3rd stanzas)

175 Hallelujah, What a Savior!

. . . a Man of Sorrows, and acquainted with grief. Isa. 53:3

1. "Man of Sor-rows!" what a name For the Son of God, who came
2. Bear-ing shame and scoff-ing rude, In my place con-demned He stood—
3. Guilt-y, vile and help-less we, Spot-less Lamb of God was He;
4. Lift-ed up was He to die, "It is fin-ished!" was His cry;
5. When He comes, our glo-rious King, All His ran-somed home to bring,

Ru-ined sin-ners to re-claim! Hal-le-lu-jah, what a Sav-ior!
Sealed my par-don with His blood: Hal-le-lu-jah, what a Sav-ior!
Full a-tone-ment! can it be? Hal-le-lu-jah, what a Sav-ior!
Now in heav'n ex-alt-ed high: Hal-le-lu-jah, what a Sav-ior!
Then a-new this song we'll sing: Hal-le-lu-jah, what a Sav-ior!

Optional last stanza setting
Broader

rit.

5. When He comes, our glo-rious King, All His ran-somed home to

rit.

bring, Then a-new this song we'll sing: Hal-le-lu-jah, what a Sav-ior!

TEXT and MUSIC: Philip P. Bliss

MAN OF SORROWS
7.7.7.8.

Lead Me to Calvary 176

I determined not to know any thing . . . save Jesus Christ, and Him crucified. 1 Cor. 2:2

1. King of my life, I crown Thee now, Thine shall the glo - ry be;
2. Show me the tomb where Thou wast laid, Ten - der-ly mourned and wept;
3. Let me like Ma - ry, through the gloom, Come with a gift to Thee;
4. May I be will - ing, Lord, to bear Dai - ly my cross for Thee;

Lest I for-get Thy thorn-crowned brow, Lead me to Cal - va - ry.
An - gels in robes of light ar - rayed Guard-ed Thee whilst Thou slept.
Show to me now the emp - ty tomb, Lead me to Cal - va - ry.
E - ven Thy cup of grief to share, Thou hast borne all for me.

Refrain

Lest I for-get Geth - sem - a - ne; Lest I for-get Thine ag - o - ny;

Lest I for-get Thy love for me, Lead me to Cal - va - ry.

TEXT: Jennie Evelyn Hussey
MUSIC: William J. Kirkpatrick

DUNCANNON
C.M. with Refrain

177 What Wondrous Love Is This

He that is hanged is accursed of God. Deut. 21:23

Unison

1. What won-drous love is this, O my soul, O my soul! What won-drous love is this, O my soul! What won-drous love is this That caused the Lord of bliss To bear the dread-ful curse for my soul, for my soul, To bear the dread-ful curse for my soul.

2. When I was sink-ing down, sink-ing down, sink-ing down, When I was sink-ing down, sink-ing down, When I was sink-ing down Be - neath God's right - eous frown, Christ laid a - side His crown for my soul, for my soul, Christ laid a - side His crown for my soul.

3. To God and to the Lamb I will sing, I will sing, To God and to the Lamb I will sing, To God and to the Lamb Who is the great "I Am," While mil-lions join the theme, I will sing, I will sing, While mil-lions join the theme, I will sing.

4. And when from death I'm free, I'll sing on, I'll sing on, And when from death I'm free, I'll sing on, And when from death I'm free, I'll sing and joy - ful be, And thro' e - ter - ni - ty I'll sing on, I'll sing on, And thro' e - ter - ni - ty I'll sing on.

TEXT: American Folk Hymn
MUSIC: William Walker's *Southern Harmony,* 1835

WONDROUS LOVE
12.9.6.6.12.9.

O Sacred Head, Now Wounded 178

They . . . platted a crown of thorns, and put it about His head. Mark 15:17

1. O sa - cred Head, now wound - ed, With grief and shame weighed down,
2. What Thou, my Lord, hast suf - fered Was all for sin - ners' gain;
3. What lan - guage shall I bor - row To thank Thee, dear-est Friend,

Now scorn-ful-ly sur - round - ed With thorns Thine on - ly crown:
Mine, mine was the trans - gres - sion, But Thine the dead-ly pain.
For this, Thy dy - ing sor - row, Thy pit - y with - out end?

How pale Thou art with an - guish, With sore a - buse and scorn, How
Lo, here I fall, my Sav - ior; 'Tis I de - serve Thy place; Look
O make me Thine for - ev - er, And should I faint - ing be, Lord,

does that vis - age lan - guish, Which once was bright as morn!
on me with Thy fa - vor, As - sist me with Thy grace.
let me nev - er, nev - er Out - live my love to Thee. A - men.

TEXT: Paul Gerhardt; based on Medieval Latin poem ascribed to Bernard
of Clairvaux; translated from the German by James W. Alexander
MUSIC: Hans Leo Hassler; harmonized by J. S. Bach

PASSION CHORALE
7.6.7.6.D.

179 Behold the Lamb

... the Lamb slain from the foundation of the world. Rev. 13:8

Be - hold the Lamb, be - hold the Lamb, slain from the foun-

da-tion of the world. For sin-ners cru-ci-fied, O ho-ly

Fine

sac-ri-fice, be-hold the Lamb of God, be-hold the Lamb.

play cued notes first time only

More movement

Crown Him, crown Him, wor-thy is the Lamb.

D.S. al Fine

Praise Him, praise Him. Heav'n and earth re-sound. Be-

TEXT and MUSIC: Dottie Rambo; arranged by Lee Herrington

BEHOLD THE LAMB
Irregular meter

Worthy Is the Lamb 180

Worthy is the Lamb that was slain. Rev. 5:12

Wor-thy is the Lamb that was slain, Wor-thy is the Lamb that was slain, Wor-thy is the Lamb that was slain, to re - ceive:

Pow-er and rich-es and wis-dom and strength, Hon-or and glo-ry and bless-ing! Wor-thy is the Lamb, Wor-thy is the Lamb, Wor-thy is the Lamb that was slain, Wor - thy is the Lamb!

TEXT: Revelation 5:12; adapted by Don Wyrtzen
MUSIC: Don Wyrtzen

WORTHY IS THE LAMB
Irregular meter

181 Were You There?

It was the third hour, and they crucified Him. Mark 15:25

1. Were you there when they cru-ci-fied my Lord? Were you
2. Were you there when they nailed Him to the tree? Were you
3. Were you there when they laid Him in the tomb? Were you
†opt. 4. Were you there when He rose up from the dead? Were you

†May be omitted, especially for Holy Week services.

there when they cru-ci-fied my Lord?
there when they nailed Him to the tree? O!_____
there when they laid Him in the tomb?
there when He rose up from the dead?

Some-times it caus-es me to trem-ble, trem-ble, trem-ble!
(4. Some-times I feel like shout-ing glo-ry, glo-ry, glo-ry!)

Were you there when they cru-ci-fied my Lord?
Were you there when they nailed Him to the tree?
Were you there when they laid Him in the tomb?
Were you there when He rose up from the dead?

TEXT and MUSIC: Traditional Spiritual

WERE YOU THERE?
Irregular meter

GLORY IN THE CROSS

A Brief Service of
Reflection and Praise

Suggested Hymn Stanzas

To facilitate an uninterrupted flow from stanza to stanza,
the suggested stanzas have been marked with an arrow: ▶
Beneath the Cross of Jesus, stanzas 1, 2
In the Cross of Christ I Glory, stanzas 1, 2
When I Survey the Wondrous Cross, complete

WORSHIP LEADER:

And Jesus answered them, saying, The hour is come, that the Son of Man should be glorified. Father, glorify Thy name. Then came there a voice from heaven, saying, I have both glorified it, and will glorify it again. The people therefore, that stood by, and heard it, said that it thundered: others said, An angel spake to Him. Jesus answered and said, This voice came not because of Me, but for your sakes. Now is the judgment of this world: now shall the prince of this world be cast out. And I, if I be lifted up from the earth, will draw all men unto Me. This He said, signifying what death He should die.

PEOPLE:

And being found in fashion as a man, He humbled Himself, and became obedient unto death, even the death of the cross. Wherefore God also hath highly exalted Him, and given Him a name which is above every name.

WORSHIP LEADER:

Looking unto Jesus the author and finisher of our faith; who for the joy that was set before Him endured the cross, despising the shame, and is set down at the right hand of the throne of God.

ALL:

But God forbid that I should glory, save in the cross of our Lord Jesus Christ, by whom the world is crucified unto Me, and I unto the world.

John 12:23,28-33; Phil.2:8-9;
Heb. 12:2; Gal. 6:14.

Optional introduction to
"Beneath the Cross of Jesus"

mp

183 Beneath the Cross of Jesus

Now there stood by the cross of Jesus His mother . . . John 19:25

1. Be-neath the cross of Je - sus I fain would take my stand—
2. Up-on that cross of Je - sus Mine eye at times can see
3. I take, O cross, thy shad-ow For my a - bid - ing place;

The shad-ow of a might-y Rock With-in a wea-ry land;
The ver-y dy-ing form of One Who suf-fered there for me;
I ask no oth-er sun-shine than The sun-shine of His face;

A home with-in the wil-der-ness, A rest up-on the way,
And from my smit-ten heart with tears Two won-ders I con-fess—
Con-tent to let the world go by, To know no gain nor loss,

From the burn-ing of the noon-tide heat, And the bur-den of the day.
The won-ders of re-deem-ing love And my un-wor-thi-ness.
My sin-ful self my on-ly shame, My glo-ry all the cross.

TEXT: Elizabeth C. Clephane
MUSIC: Frederick C. Maker

ST. CHRISTOPHER
7.6.8.6.8.6.8.6.

Optional transition to
"In the Cross of Christ I Glory"

In the Cross of Christ I Glory 184

Jesus . . . for the joy . . . set before Him endured the cross, despising the shame. Heb. 12:2

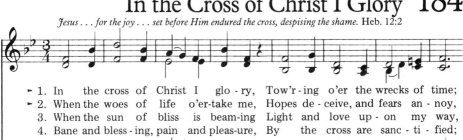

1. In the cross of Christ I glo - ry, Tow'r-ing o'er the wrecks of time;
2. When the woes of life o'er-take me, Hopes de - ceive, and fears an - noy,
3. When the sun of bliss is beam-ing Light and love up - on my way,
4. Bane and bless - ing, pain and pleas-ure, By the cross are sanc - ti - fied;

All the light of sa - cred sto - ry Gath-ers round its head sub-lime.
Nev - er shall the cross for - sake me: Lo! it glows with peace and joy.
From the cross the ra - diance stream-ing Adds more lus-ter to the day.
Peace is there that knows no meas-ure, Joys that thro' all time a - bide. A - men.

TEXT: John Bowring
MUSIC: Ithamar Conkey

RATHBUN
8.7.8.7.

Optional transition to
"When I Survey the Wondrous Cross"

decresc. poco a poco

185 When I Survey the Wondrous Cross

They shall look on Him whom they pierced. John 19:37

1. When I sur-vey the won-drous cross On which the Prince of glo-ry died, My rich-est gain I count but loss, And pour con-tempt on all my pride.
2. For-bid it, Lord, that I should boast, Save in the death of Christ, my God; All the vain things that charm me most— I sac-ri-fice them to His blood.
3. See, from His head, His hands, His feet, Sor-row and love flow min-gled down; Did e'er such love and sor-row meet, Or thorns com-pose so rich a crown?
4. Were the whole realm of na-ture mine, That were a pres-ent far too small: Love so a-maz-ing, so di-vine, De-mands my soul, my life, my all.

Optional last stanza harmonization **Broader** Unison

crown? *rit.* 4. Were the whole realm of na-ture

TEXT: Isaac Watts
MUSIC: Based on a Gregorian chant; arranged by Lowell Mason;
Last stanza harmonization by Robert F. Douglas; Alternate tune: APPALACHIA at No. 401

HAMBURG
L.M.

mine,   That   were   a   pres - ent   far   too   small:

Love   so   a - maz - ing,   so   di -   vine,

Play cued notes if opt.
choral ending is used

De - mands my   soul,   my   life,   my   all.

Optional choral ending   **Great rit.**

De - mands my   soul,   my   life,   my   all.

The end of "GLORY IN THE CROSS—A Brief Service of Reflection and Praise"

186 The Old Rugged Cross

He humbled Himself, and became obedient unto . . . the death of the cross. Phil. 2:8

1. On a hill far a - way stood an old rug-ged cross, The
2. O that old rug-ged cross, so de - spised by the world, Has a
3. In the old rug-ged cross, stained with blood so di - vine, A
4. To the old rug-ged cross I will ev - er be true, Its

em - blem of suf-f'ring and shame; And I love that old cross where the
won-drous at - trac - tion for me; For the dear Lamb of God left His
won - drous beau - ty I see; For 'twas on that old cross Je - sus
shame and re - proach glad-ly bear; Then He'll call me some day to my

dear - est and best For a world of lost sin - ners was slain.
glo - ry a - bove To bear it to dark Cal - va - ry.
suf - fered and died To par - don and sanc - ti - fy me.
home far a - way, Where His glo - ry for - ev - er I'll share.

Refrain

So I'll cher - ish the old rug - ged cross, Till my
cross, the old rug - ged cross,

TEXT and MUSIC: George Bennard

OLD RUGGED CROSS
Irregular meter

tro-phies at last I lay down; I will cling to the old rug-ged cross, the

cross, And ex-change it some day for a crown.
old rug-ged cross,

In His Cross I Glory 187

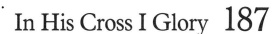

. . . justified freely by His grace through the redemption that is in Christ. Rom. 3:24

2 part Canon

1. In the cross of Christ I glo - ry, There for all was
2. In the cross of Christ I glo - ry, Not in pow - er,

grace made free. None de - serv - ing, yet re - ceiv - ing
wealth or fame. In the cross sin's curse is bro - ken

Coda (optional) - to be sung after part II has completed verse 2. Parts divide.

Life thru death at Cal - va - ry.
For the sake of Je - sus' name. For the sake of Je - sus' name.

TEXT and MUSIC: Tricia Walker

WALKER
8.7.8.7.

188 At the Cross

The preaching of the cross . . . is the power of God. 1 Cor. 1:18

1. A - las! and did my Sav - ior bleed? And did my Sov - 'reign die?
2. Was it for crimes that I have done He groaned up - on the tree?
3. Well might the sun in dark-ness hide And shut His glo - ries in,
4. But drops of grief can ne'er re - pay The debt of love I owe:

Would He de-vote that sa-cred head For sin - ners such as I!
A - maz-ing pit - y! grace un-known! And love be - yond de - gree!
When Christ, the might - y Mak - er, died For man the crea - ture's sin.
Here, Lord, I give my - self a - way— 'Tis all that I can do!

Refrain

At the cross, at the cross where I first saw the light And the

bur-den of my heart rolled a - way— It was there by faith

I re - ceived my sight, And now I am hap-py all the day!

TEXT: Isaac Watts; Ralph E. Hudson, Refrain
MUSIC: Ralph E. Hudson

HUDSON
C.M. with Refrain

Calvary Covers It All 189

Having forgiven you all trespasses. Col. 2:13

1. Far dear-er than all that the world can im-part Was the mes-sage that
2. The stripes that He bore and the thorns that He wore Told His mer-cy and
3. How match-less the grace, when I looked on the face Of this Je-sus, my
4. How bless-ed the thought, that my soul by Him bought, Shall be His in the

came to my heart; How that Je-sus a-lone for my sin did a-tone,
love ev-er-more; And my heart bowed in shame as I called on His name,
cru-ci-fied Lord; My re-demp-tion com-plete I then found at His feet,
glo-ry on high; Where with glad-ness and song I'll be one of the throng,

Refrain

And Cal-va-ry cov-ers it all. Cal-va-ry cov-ers it

all, My past with its sin and stain; My guilt and de-spair Je-sus

took on Him there, And Cal-va-ry cov-ers it all.

TEXT and MUSIC: Mrs. Walter G. Taylor

CALVARY COVERS IT
Irregular meter

190 Are You Washed in the Blood?

They . . . have washed their robes, and made them white in the blood of the Lamb. Rev. 7:14

1. Have you been to Je-sus for the cleans-ing power? Are you washed in the
2. Are you walk-ing dai-ly by the Sav-ior's side? Are you washed in the
3. When the Bride-groom com-eth will your robes be white? Are you washed in the
4. Lay a - side the gar-ments that are stained with sin, And be washed in the

blood of the Lamb? Are you ful - ly trust-ing in His grace this hour? Are you
blood of the Lamb? Do you rest each mo-ment in the Cru - ci - fied? Are you
blood of the Lamb? Will your soul be read - y for the man-sions bright, And be
blood of the Lamb? There's a foun-tain flow-ing for the soul un - clean, O be

Refrain

washed in the blood of the Lamb? Are you washed in the blood,
Are you washed in the blood,

In the soul - cleans-ing blood of the Lamb? Are your gar - ments
of the Lamb?

spot-less? Are they white as snow? Are you washed in the blood of the Lamb?

TEXT and MUSIC: Elisha A. Hoffmann

WASHED IN THE BLOOD
11.9.11.9. with Refrain

There Is Power in the Blood 191

They overcame him by the blood of the Lamb. Rev. 12:11

1. Would you be free from the bur - den of sin? There's pow'r in the blood,
2. Would you be free from your pas - sion and pride? There's pow'r in the blood,
3. Would you be whit - er, much whit - er than snow? There's pow'r in the blood,
4. Would you do serv - ice for Je - sus your King? There's pow'r in the blood,

pow'r in the blood; Would you o'er e - vil a vic - to - ry win? There's
pow'r in the blood; Come for a cleans - ing to Cal - va - ry's tide? There's
pow'r in the blood; Sin - stains are lost in its life - giv - ing flow; There's
pow'r in the blood; Would you live dai - ly His prais - es to sing? There's

Refrain

won - der - ful pow'r in the blood. There is pow'r, pow'r, won-der-work-ing pow'r
there is

In the blood of the Lamb; There is pow'r, pow'r,
In the blood of the Lamb; there is

won - der - work - ing pow'r In the pre - cious blood of the Lamb.

TEXT and MUSIC: Lewis E. Jones

POWER IN THE BLOOD
10.9.10.8. with Refrain

192 The Blood Will Never Lose Its Power

. . . the blood of the everlasting covenant. Heb. 13:20

1. The blood that Je - sus shed for me, 'Way back on
2. It soothes my doubts and calms my fears, And it dries

Cal - va - ry; The blood that gives me strength from day to
all my tears; The blood that gives me strength from day to

day, It will nev - er lose its power.
day, It will nev - er lose its power.

Refrain

It reach-es to the high - est moun - tain. It flows to the

low - est val - ley. The blood that gives me strength from

TEXT and MUSIC: Andraé Crouch

THE BLOOD
Irregular meter

day to day, It will nev - er lose its power.

Jesus, Thy Blood and Righteousness 193

. . . whom God hath set forth to be a propitiation through faith in His blood. Rom. 3:25

1. Je - sus, Thy blood and right - eous - ness My beau - ty
2. Bold shall I stand in Thy great day, For who aught
3. Lord, I be - lieve Thy pre - cious blood, Which at the
4. Lord, I be - lieve were sin - ners more Than sands up -

are, my glo - rious dress; 'Midst flam - ing worlds, in
to my charge shall lay? Ful - ly ab - solved through
mer - cy seat of God For - ev - er doth for
on the o - cean shore, Thou hast for all a

these ar - rayed, With joy shall I lift up my head.
these I am, From sin and fear, from guilt and shame.
sin - ners plead, For me, e'en for my soul, was shed.
ran - som paid, For all a full a - tone - ment made.

TEXT: Nicolaus L. von Zinzendorf; translated by John Wesley
MUSIC: William Gardiner's *Sacred Melodies,* 1815

GERMANY
L.M.

194

I KNOW A FOUNT
A Medley

WORSHIP LEADER:

Forasmuch as ye know that ye were not redeemed with corruptible things, as silver and gold, from your vain conversation received by tradition from your fathers; but with the precious blood of Christ, as of a lamb without blemish and without spot. Who by Him do believe in God, that raised Him up from the dead, and gave Him glory; that your faith and hope might be in God.

1 Pet. 1:18-19,21.

I know a fount where sins are washed a - way,

I know a place where night is turned to day;

Bur - dens are lift - ed, blind eyes made to see; There's a

won - der work - ing pow'r in the blood of Cal - va - ry.

*Cued notes
for transition
to "Nothing
But the Blood"*

TEXT and MUSIC: Oliver Cooke

I KNOW A FOUNT
10.10.10.15.

Nothing But the Blood 195

The blood of Jesus Christ His Son cleanseth us from all sin. 1 John 1:7

1. What can wash a - way my sin? Noth-ing but the blood of Je - sus;
2. For my par - don this I see, Noth-ing but the blood of Je - sus;
3. Noth - ing can for sin a - tone, Noth-ing but the blood of Je - sus;
4. This is all my hope and peace, Noth-ing but the blood of Je - sus;

What can make me whole a - gain? Noth-ing but the blood of Je - sus.
For my cleans-ing, this my plea, Noth-ing but the blood of Je - sus.
Naught of good that I have done, Noth-ing but the blood of Je - sus.
This is all my right-eous - ness, Noth-ing but the blood of Je - sus.

Refrain

Oh! pre - cious is the flow That makes me white as snow;

No oth - er fount I know, Noth-ing but the blood of Je - sus.

The end of "I KNOW A FOUNT - a medley"

TEXT and MUSIC: Robert Lowry

PLAINFIELD
7.8.7.8. with Refrain

196 There Is a Fountain

There shall be a fountain opened . . . for sin. Zech. 13:1

1. There is a foun-tain filled with blood Drawn from Im-man-uel's veins,
2. The dy-ing thief re-joiced to see That foun-tain in his day,
3. Dear dy-ing Lamb, Thy pre-cious blood Shall nev-er lose its pow'r,
4. E'er since by faith I saw the stream Thy flow-ing wounds sup-ply,
5. When this poor lisp-ing, stam-m'ring tongue Lies si-lent in the grave,

And sin-ners plunged be-neath that flood Lose all their guilt-y stains:
And there may I, though vile as he, Wash all my sins a-way:
Till all the ran-somed Church of God Be saved to sin no more:
Re-deem-ing love has been my theme And shall be till I die:
Then in a no-bler, sweet-er song I'll sing Thy pow'r to save:

Lose all their guilt-y stains, Lose all their guilt-y stains;
Wash all my sins a-way, Wash all my sins a-way;
Be saved to sin no more, Be saved to sin no more;
And shall be till I die, And shall be till I die;
I'll sing Thy pow'r to save, I'll sing Thy pow'r to save;

And sin-ners plunged be-neath that flood Lose all their guilt-y stains.
And there may I, though vile as he, Wash all my sins a-way.
Till all the ran-somed Church of God Be saved to sin no more.
Re-deem-ing love has been my theme And shall be till I die.
Then in a no-bler, sweet-er song I'll sing Thy pow'r to save.

TEXT: William Cowper
MUSIC: Traditional American melody; arranged by Lowell Mason

CLEANSING FOUNTAIN
C.M.D.

Lamb of Glory 197

Behold the Lamb of God, which taketh away the sin of the world. John 1:29

1. Hear the sto-ry from God's Word That kings and priests and
2. On the cross God loved the world While all the pow'rs of

pro-phets heard; There would be a sac-ri-fice And
hell were hurled; No one there could un-der-stand The

rit. *Refrain* *a tempo*

blood would flow to pay sin's price. Pre-cious Lamb of
One they saw was Christ the Lamb.

glo-ry, Love's most won-drous sto-ry.

Heart of God's re-demp-tion of man; Wor-ship the Lamb of glo-ry.

TEXT and MUSIC: Greg Nelson and Phill McHugh;
arranged by Eugene Thomas

LAMB OF GLORY
7.8.7.8. with Refrain

198 Wonderful Grace of Jesus

Ye know the grace of our Lord Jesus Christ. 2 Cor. 8:9

1. Won - der - ful grace of Je - sus, Great - er than all my sin;
2. Won - der - ful grace of Je - sus, Reach - ing to all the lost,
3. Won - der - ful grace of Je - sus, Reach - ing the most de - filed,

How shall my tongue de - scribe it, Where shall its praise be - gin?
By it I have been par - doned, Saved to the ut - ter - most;
By its trans-form - ing pow - er Mak - ing him God's dear child,

Tak - ing a - way my bur - den, Set - ting my spir - it free,
Chains have been torn a - sun - der, Giv - ing me lib - er - ty,
Pur - chas - ing peace and heav - en For all e - ter - ni - ty;

For the won - der - ful grace of Je - sus reach - es me.
For the won - der - ful grace of Je - sus reach - es me.
For the won - der - ful grace of Je - sus reach - es me.

Refrain

the match-less grace of Je - sus,
Won-der-ful the match-less grace of Je - sus, Deep - er

TEXT and MUSIC: Haldor Lillenas

WONDERFUL GRACE
Irregular meter

than the might-y roll-ing sea; the roll-ing sea; Won - Higher than the

der - ful grace, all - suf - fi - cient for
moun-tain, spar-kling like a foun - tain, All - suf - fi - cient grace for e - ven

me, for e - ven me; Broad - er than the scope of my trans-
me; trans-

gres - sions, Great -er far than all my sin and shame;
gres-sions, sing it! my sin and shame;

O mag - ni - fy the pre - cious name of Je - sus, Praise His name!

199 Arise, My Soul, Arise

He ever liveth to make intercession for them. Heb. 7:25

1. A - rise, my soul, a - rise. Shake off thy guilt - y fears.
2. He ev - er lives a - bove For me to in - ter - cede,
3. Five bleed-ing wounds He bears, Re - ceived on Cal - va - ry.
4. The Fa - ther hears Him pray, His dear A - noint-ed One;
5. My God is rec - on - ciled; His par - d'ning voice I hear.

The bleed-ing Sac - ri - fice In my be - half ap - pears.
His all - re - deem-ing love, His pre - cious blood to plead.
They pour ef - fec - tual prayers; They strong-ly plead for me.
He can - not turn a - way The pres - ence of His Son.
He owns me for His child; I can no lon - ger fear.

Be - fore the throne my Sure - ty stands, Be - fore the throne my
His blood a - toned for all our race, His blood a - toned for
"For - give him, oh, for - give," they cry, "For - give him, oh, for -
His Spir - it an - swers to the blood, His Spir - it an - swers
With con - fi - dence I now draw nigh, With con - fi - dence I

Sure - ty stands; My name is writ - ten on His hands.
all our race, And sprin-kles now the throne of grace.
give," they cry, "Nor let that ran-somed sin - ner die."
to the blood, And tells me I am born of God.
now draw nigh, And, "Fa - ther, Ab - ba, Fa - ther," cry. A - men.

TEXT: Charles Wesley
MUSIC: Lewis Edson

LENOX
6.6.6.6.8.8. with Repeat

GOD'S AMAZING GRACE

A Brief Service in
Recognition of His Love and Provision

Suggested Hymn Stanzas

To facilitate an uninterrupted flow from stanza to stanza,
the suggested stanzas have been marked with an arrow: ▶

Grace Greater Than Our Sin, stanzas 1, 4
Amazing Grace, stanzas 1, 2, 4
And Can It Be?, stanzas 1, 2, 4

PEOPLE:
And of His fulness have all we received, and grace for grace. For the law was given by Moses, but grace and truth came by Jesus Christ.

WORSHIP LEADER:
Having loved His own which were in the world, He loved them unto the end.

PEOPLE:
But God commendeth His love toward us, in that, while we were yet sinners, Christ died for us.

WORSHIP LEADER:
For ye know the grace of our Lord Jesus Christ, that, though He was rich, yet for your sakes He became poor, that ye through His poverty might be rich.

PEOPLE:
But God, who is rich in mercy, for His great love wherewith He loved us, even when we were dead in sins, hath quickened us together with Christ, (by grace ye are saved).

WORSHIP LEADER:
In this was manifested the love of God toward us, because that God sent His only begotten Son into the world, that we might live through Him. Herein is love, not that we loved God, but that He loved us, and sent His Son to be the propitiation for our sins.

John 1:16-17; John 13:1; Rom. 5:8;
2 Cor. 8:9; Eph. 2:4-5; 1 John 4:9-10.

Optional introduction to
"Grace Greater Than Our Sin"

mp

201 Grace Greater Than Our Sin

Where sin abounded, grace did much more abound. Rom. 5:20

1. Mar - vel - ous grace of our lov - ing Lord, Grace that ex - ceeds our
2. Sin and de - spair, like the sea - waves cold, Threat-en the soul with
3. Dark is the stain that we can - not hide— What can a - vail to
4. Mar - vel - ous, in - fi - nite, match - less grace, Free - ly be - stowed on

sin and our guilt! Yon - der on Cal - va - ry's mount out - poured—
in - fi - nite loss; Grace that is great - er—yes, grace un - told—
wash it a - way? Look! there is flow - ing a crim - son tide—
all who be - lieve! You that are long - ing to see His face,

Refrain

There where the blood of the Lamb was spilt.
Points to the ref - uge, the might - y cross. Grace, grace,
Whit - er than snow you may be to - day. Mar - vel - ous grace,
Will you this mo - ment His grace re - ceive?

God's grace, Grace that will par-don and cleanse with - in, Grace,
in - fi - nite grace, Mar-vel-ous

TEXT: Julia H. Johnston
MUSIC: Daniel B. Towner

MOODY
9.9.9.9. with Refrain

*Optional transition
to "Amazing Grace"*

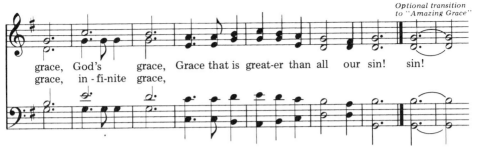

grace, God's grace, Grace that is great-er than all our sin! sin!
grace, in - fi-nite grace,

Amazing Grace 202

One thing I know, that, whereas I was blind, now I see. John 9:25

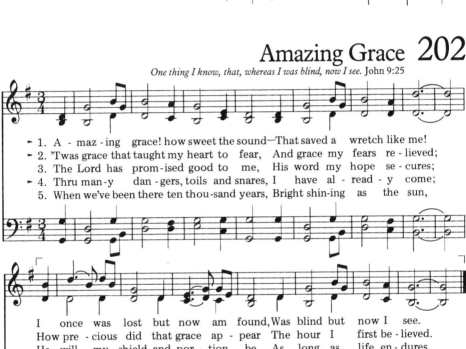

1. A - maz - ing grace! how sweet the sound—That saved a wretch like me!
2. 'Twas grace that taught my heart to fear, And grace my fears re - lieved;
3. The Lord has prom-ised good to me, His word my hope se - cures;
4. Thru man-y dan-gers, toils and snares, I have al - read - y come;
5. When we've been there ten thou-sand years, Bright shin-ing as the sun,

I once was lost but now am found, Was blind but now I see.
How pre - cious did that grace ap - pear The hour I first be - lieved.
He will my shield and por - tion be As long as life en - dures.
'Tis grace hath brought me safe thus far, And grace will lead me home.
We've no less days to sing God's praise Than when we'd first be - gun.

TEXT: John Newton; John P. Rees, stanza 5
MUSIC: Traditional American melody from Carrell and Clayton's
    Virginia Harmony, 1831; arranged by Edwin O. Excell

AMAZING GRACE
C.M.

*Optional transition to
"And Can It Be?"*

cresc. poco a poco

203 And Can It Be?

...the exceeding riches of His grace in His kindness toward us through Christ. Eph. 2:7

1. And can it be that I should gain An in-t'rest in
2. He left His Fa-ther's throne a-bove, So free, so in-
3. Long my im-pris-oned spir-it lay Fast bound in sin
4. No con-dem-na-tion now I dread: Je-sus, and all

the Sav-ior's blood? Died He for me, who caused His pain?
fi-nite His grace! Emp-tied Him-self of all but love,
and na-ture's night. Thine eye dif-fused a quick-'ning ray:
in Him, is mine! A-live in Him, my liv-ing Head,

For me, who Him to death pur-sued? A-maz-ing love!
And bled for Ad-am's help-less race! 'Tis mer-cy all,
I woke— the dun-geon flamed with light! My chains fell off,
And clothed in right-eous-ness di-vine, Bold I ap-proach

how can it be That Thou, my God shouldst
im-mense and free, For, O my God, it
my heart was free, I rose, went forth, and
th'e-ter-nal throne, And claim the crown, thru

TEXT: Charles Wesley
MUSIC: Thomas Campbell; Choral ending by Joseph Linn

SAGINA
8.8.8.8.8.8. with Refrain

Refrain

die for me?
found out me.
fol - lowed Thee.
Christ my own.

A - maz - ing love! how can it

A - maz-ing love! how

be That Thou, my God, shouldst die for me!

can it be

Optional choral ending

sop. A - men, a - men,

A - men, a -

me! A - men, a -

A - men, a -

a - men, a - men. A - men.

men, a - men. A - men.

men, a - men.

The End of "GOD'S AMAZING GRACE—A Brief Service in Recognition of His Love and Provision"

204 Rock of Ages

They drank of that spiritual Rock that followed them: and that Rock was Christ. 1 Cor. 10:4

1. Rock of A - ges, cleft for me, Let me hide my - self in Thee;
2. Not the la - bors of my hands Can ful - fill Thy law's de - mands;
3. Noth-ing in my hand I bring, Sim - ply to Thy cross I cling;
4. While I draw this fleet - ing breath, When my eyes shall close in death,

Let the wa - ter and the blood, From Thy riv - en side which flowed,
Could my zeal no res - pite know, Could my tears for - ev - er flow,
Na - ked, come to Thee for dress, Help - less, look to Thee for grace;
When I soar to worlds un - known, See Thee on Thy judg-ment throne,

Be of sin the dou - ble cure, Cleanse me from its guilt and pow'r.
All for sin could not a - tone; Thou must save and Thou a - lone.
Foul, I to the foun-tain fly, Wash me, Sav - ior, or I die!
Rock of A - ges, cleft for me, Let me hide my-self in Thee. A-men.

TEXT: Augustus M. Toplady
MUSIC: Thomas Hastings

TOPLADY
7.7.7.7.7.7.

205 For God So Loved

That whosoever believeth in Him should . . . have eternal life. John 3:15

4 Part Canon

For God so loved the world That He gave His Son to die;

TEXT: John 3:16; adapted by Gerald S. Henderson
MUSIC: Gerald S. Henderson; based on an English Folk song

GIFT OF LIFE
6.7.8.6.

Text adaptation and Arr. © 1986 WORD MUSIC (a div. of WORD, INC.). All Rights Reserved. International Copyright Secured.

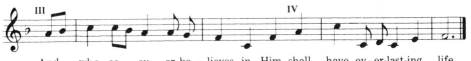

And who-so-ev-er be-lieves in Him shall have ev-er-last-ing life.

There Is a Redeemer 206

Christ Jesus . . . is made unto us . . . righteousness, and sanctification, and redemption. 1 Cor. 1:30

1. There is a Re-deem-er, Je-sus, God's own Son;
2. Je-sus, my Re-deem-er, name a-bove all names;
3. When I stand in Glo-ry, I will see His face,

Pre-cious Lamb of God, Mes-si-ah, Ho - ly One.
Pre-cious Lamb of God, Mes-si-ah, O for sin-ners slain.
There I'll serve my King for-ev-er In that ho-ly place.

Refrain

Thank You, oh, my Fa-ther, for giv-ing us Your Son, and

leav-ing Your Spir-it 'til the work on earth is done.

TEXT and MUSIC: Melody Green; arranged by Keith Phillips

GREEN
Irregular meter

207 God So Loved the World

For God so loved the world, that He gave His only begotten Son. John 3:16

God so loved the world, God so loved the world,

that He gave His on-ly be-got-ten Son, that who-so be-

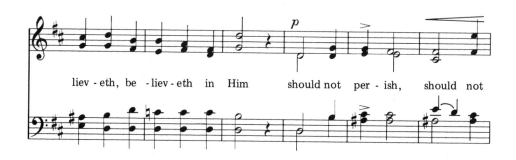

liev-eth, be-liev-eth in Him should not per-ish, should not

per-ish but have ev-er-last-ing life. For God sent not His

TEXT: John 3:16, 17
MUSIC: John Stainer

STAINER
Irregular meter

208 Alas! and Did My Savior Bleed?

The preaching of the cross . . . is the power of God. 1 Cor. 1:18

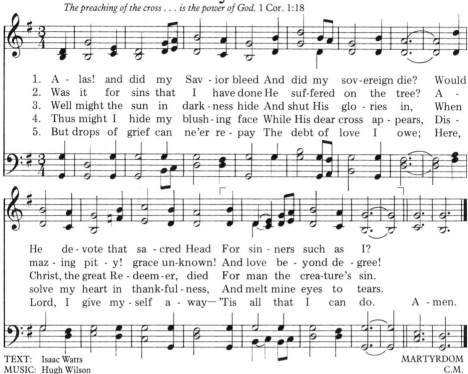

1. A - las! and did my Sav - ior bleed And did my sov-ereign die? Would
2. Was it for sins that I have done He suf-fered on the tree? A -
3. Well might the sun in dark-ness hide And shut His glo - ries in, When
4. Thus might I hide my blush-ing face While His dear cross ap - pears, Dis-
5. But drops of grief can ne'er re - pay The debt of love I owe; Here,

He de - vote that sa - cred Head For sin - ners such as I?
maz - ing pit - y! grace un-known! And love be - yond de - gree!
Christ, the great Re - deem-er, died For man the crea-ture's sin.
solve my heart in thank-ful - ness, And melt mine eyes to tears.
Lord, I give my - self a - way—'Tis all that I can do. A - men.

TEXT: Isaac Watts
MUSIC: Hugh Wilson
    Alternate tune with Refrain: HUDSON, No. 188

MARTYRDOM
C.M.

209 We Are the Reason

While we were yet sinners, Christ died for us. Rom. 5:8

Unison

We are the rea - son that He gave His life, We are the rea - son that He

suf-fered and died. To a world that was lost He gave all He could give,

TEXT and MUSIC: David Meece

MEECE
Irregular meter

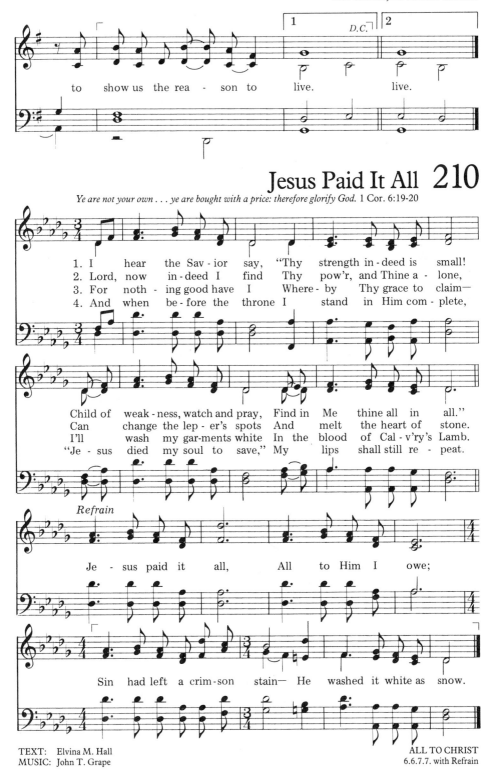

Jesus Paid It All 210

Ye are not your own . . . ye are bought with a price: therefore glorify God. 1 Cor. 6:19-20

1. I hear the Sav-ior say, "Thy strength in-deed is small!
2. Lord, now in-deed I find Thy pow'r, and Thine a-lone,
3. For noth-ing good have I Where-by Thy grace to claim—
4. And when be-fore the throne I stand in Him com-plete,

Child of weak-ness, watch and pray, Find in Me thine all in all."
Can change the lep-er's spots And melt the heart of stone.
I'll wash my gar-ments white In the blood of Cal-v'ry's Lamb.
"Je-sus died my soul to save," My lips shall still re-peat.

Refrain

Je-sus paid it all, All to Him I owe;

Sin had left a crim-son stain— He washed it white as snow.

TEXT: Elvina M. Hall
MUSIC: John T. Grape

ALL TO CHRIST
6.6.7.7. with Refrain

211 O the Deep, Deep Love of Jesus

. . . to comprehend . . . what is the . . . depth . . . and to know the love of Christ. Eph. 3:18-19

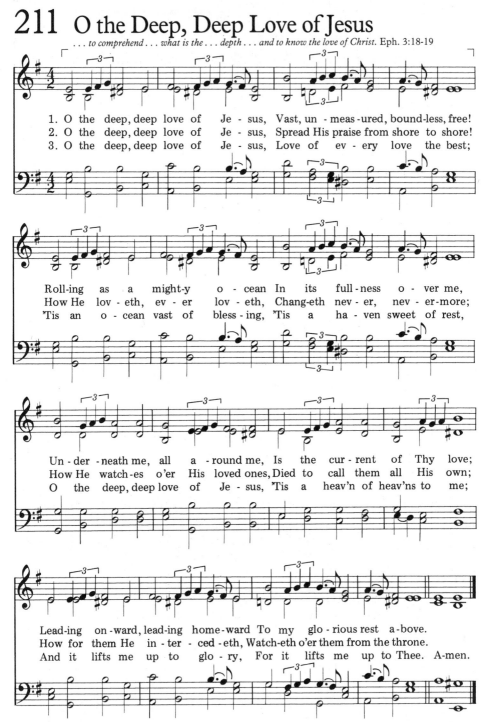

1. O the deep, deep love of Jesus, Vast, un-meas-ured, bound-less, free!
2. O the deep, deep love of Jesus, Spread His praise from shore to shore!
3. O the deep, deep love of Jesus, Love of ev-ery love the best;

Roll-ing as a might-y o-cean In its full-ness o-ver me,
How He lov-eth, ev-er lov-eth, Chang-eth nev-er, nev-er-more;
'Tis an o-cean vast of bless-ing, 'Tis a ha-ven sweet of rest,

Un-der-neath me, all a-round me, Is the cur-rent of Thy love;
How He watch-es o'er His loved ones, Died to call them all His own;
O the deep, deep love of Je-sus, 'Tis a heav'n of heav'ns to me;

Lead-ing on-ward, lead-ing home-ward To my glo-rious rest a-bove.
How for them He in-ter-ced-eth, Watch-eth o'er them from the throne.
And it lifts me up to glo-ry, For it lifts me up to Thee. A-men.

TEXT: Samuel Trevor Francis
MUSIC: Thomas J. Williams
    A higher setting may be found at No. 475

EBENEZER
8.7.8.7.D.

Music used by permission of Eluned Crump and Dilys Evans.

O the Deep, Deep Love of Jesus 212

. . . to comprehend . . . what is the . . . depth . . . and to know the love of Christ. Eph. 3:18-19

1. O the deep, deep love of Je - sus,
2. Un - der-neath me, all a - round me
3. O the deep, deep love of Je - sus,
4. O the deep, deep love of Je - sus,
5. O the deep, deep love of Je - sus,

Vast, un - mea - sured, bound - less free!
Is the cur - rent of His love;
Love of ev - 'ry love the best;
'Tis a heav'n of heav'ns to me;
Spread His praise from shore to shore;

Roll - ing as a might - y o - cean
Lead - ing on - ward, lead - ing home - ward
'Tis an o - cean vast of bless - ing,
And it lifts me up to glo - ry,
Sing of His great - ness, sing of His good - ness,

In its full - ness o - ver me.
To my glo - rious rest a - bove.
'Tis the source of peace and rest.
For it lifts me up to Thee.
Sing of His love for - ev - er - more.

TEXT: Samuel Trevor Francis, altered; adapted by Tom Fettke
MUSIC: Traditional Gaelic melody; arranged by Tom Fettke

BUNESSAN
5.5.5.4.D.

213 Because He Lives

Because I live, ye shall live also. John 14:19

1. God sent His Son, they called Him Je - sus, He came to love,
2. How sweet to hold a new-born ba - by, And feel the pride,
3. And then one day I'll cross the riv - er, I'll fight life's fi -

heal, and for - give; He lived and died to buy my
and joy he gives; But great - er still the calm as -
- nal war with pain; And then as death gives way to

par - don, An emp-ty grave is there to prove my Sav - ior lives.
sur - ance, This child can face un-cer - tain days be-cause He lives.
vic - tory, I'll see the lights of glo - ry and I'll know He lives.

Refrain

Be - cause He lives I can face to - mor - row, Be-cause He

lives all fear is gone; Be - cause I know

TEXT: Gloria Gaither and William J. Gaither
MUSIC: William J. Gaither

RESURRECTION
Irregular meter

HE IS RISEN! ALLELUIA!

A Brief Service in
Celebration of Our Lord's Resurrection

Suggested Hymn Stanzas

To facilitate an uninterrupted flow from stanza to stanza,
the suggested stanzas have been marked with an arrow: ►

Alleluia! Alleluia!, complete
Christ Arose, stanzas 1, 2
Christ the Lord Is Risen Today, complete

WORSHIP LEADER:

In the end of the Sabbath, as it began to dawn toward the first day of the week, came Mary Magdalene and the other Mary to see the sepulchre.

PEOPLE:

And, behold, there was a great earthquake: for the angel of the Lord descended from heaven, and came and rolled back the stone from the door, and sat upon it.

WORSHIP LEADER:

His countenance was like lightning, and his raiment white as snow; and for fear of him the keepers did shake, and became as dead men.

PEOPLE:

And the angel answered and said unto the women, Fear not ye: for I know that ye seek Jesus, which was crucified.

WORSHIP LEADER:

He is not here: for He is risen, as He said.

PEOPLE:

He is not here: He has risen! Alleluia!

Matthew 28:1-6.

Optional introduction to "Alleluia! Alleluia!"

f

Alleluia! Alleluia! 215

He shewed Himself alive after His passion by many infallible proofs. Acts 1:3

1. Al - le - lu - ia! Al - le - lu - ia! Hearts to heav'n and voic - es raise;
2. Now the i - ron bars are bro - ken, Christ from death to life is born,

Sing to God a hymn of glad - ness, Sing to God a hymn of praise.
Glo - rious life, and life im - mor - tal, On this res - ur - rec - tion morn;

He who on the cross as Sav - ior For the world's sal - va - tion bled,
Christ has tri - umphed, and we con - quer By His might - y en - ter - prise,

Je - sus Christ, the King of Glo - ry, Now is ris - en from the dead.
We with Him to life e - ter - nal By His res - ur - rec - tion rise.

TEXT: Christopher Wordsworth, altered
MUSIC: Ludwig van Beethoven; adapted by Edward Hodges

HYMN TO JOY
8.7.8.7.D.

Optional transition to
"Christ Arose"

decresc.

mp

216 Christ Arose

It was not possible that He should be holden of [death]. Acts 2:24

1. Low in the grave He lay, Je - sus my Sav - ior! Wait - ing the com-ing day,
2. Vain - ly they watch His bed, Je - sus my Sav - ior! Vain - ly they seal the dead,
3. Death can-not keep his prey, Je - sus my Sav - ior! He tore the bars a - way,

Je - sus my Lord! Up from the grave He a - rose, With a
He a-rose,

might - y tri - umph o'er His foes; He a - rose a Vic-tor from the
He a-rose!

dark do - main, And He lives for - ev - er with His saints to reign, He a -

rose! He a - rose! Hal - le - lu - jah! Christ a - rose!
He a-rose! He a-rose!

Segue to "Christ the Lord Is Risen Today"

TEXT and MUSIC: Robert Lowry

CHRIST AROSE
6.5.6.4. with Refrain

Christ the Lord Is Risen Today 217

O death, where is thy sting? O grave, where is thy victory? 1 Cor. 15:55

1. Christ the Lord is ris'n to - day, Al - le - lu - ia!
2. Lives a - gain our glo - rious King, Al - le - lu - ia!
3. Love's re - deem - ing work is done, Al - le - lu - ia!
4. Soar we now where Christ has led, Al - le - lu - ia!

Sons of men and an - gels say: Al - le - lu - ia!
Where, O death, is now thy sting? Al - le - lu - ia!
Fought the fight, the bat - tle won, Al - le - lu - ia!
Fol - l'wing our ex - alt - ed Head, Al - le - lu - ia!

Raise your joys and tri - umphs high, Al - le - lu - ia!
Dy - ing once He all doth save, Al - le - lu - ia!
Death in vain for - bids Him rise, Al - le - lu - ia!
Made like Him, like Him we rise, Al - le - lu - ia!

Sing, ye heav'ns, and earth re - ply: Al - le - lu - ia!
Where thy vic - to - ry, O grave? Al - le - lu - ia!
Christ has o - pened Par - a - dise, Al - le - lu - ia!
Ours the cross, the grave, the skies, Al - le - lu - ia!

Optional choral ending on the next page

TEXT: Charles Wesley
MUSIC: from *Lyra Davidica*, London, 1708

EASTER HYMN
7.7.7.7. with Alleluias

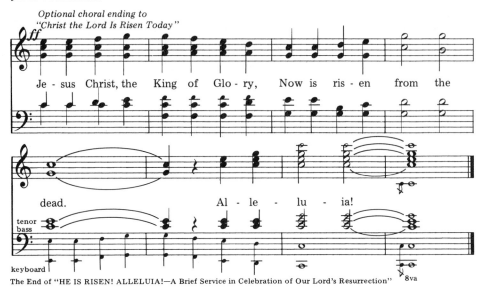

Optional choral ending to "Christ the Lord Is Risen Today"

Je - sus Christ, the King of Glo - ry, Now is ris - en from the

dead. Al - le - lu - ia!

tenor
bass

keyboard

The End of "HE IS RISEN! ALLELUIA!—A Brief Service in Celebration of Our Lord's Resurrection" 8va

218 I Know That My Redeemer Liveth

I am the Resurrection, and the Life. John 11:25

Optional introduction

I know, I know

that Je - sus liv - eth, And on the earth a - gain shall stand. I know, I

know that life He giv - eth, That grace and pow'r are in His hand. hand.

TEXT: Jessie B. Pounds
MUSIC: James H. Fillmore and George Frederick Handel (introduction);
arranged by Keith Phillips

HANNAH (Refrain only)
9.8.9.8.

He Rose Triumphantly 219

Jesus died and rose again. 1 Thess. 4:14

Slowly

1. Our bless-ed Lord was slain, (was slain), The Christ who came to
2. They sor-rowed when He died, (He died), Nor sought their tears to
3. The stone was rolled a - way, (a - way), For Christ was raised that

accel.

reign, And in a grave He lay, To wait the com - ing
hide; But soon their bit - ter pain Was turned to joy a -
day; And now He lives a - bove To man - i - fest His

Refrain
Brightly

day.
gain.
love.

He rose tri - um-phant-ly, In pow'r and maj - es - ty,

The Sav-ior rose no more to die; O let us now pro-claim

The glo - ry of His name, And tell to all, He lives to - day.

TEXT: Oswald J. Smith
MUSIC: Bentley D. Ackley

HE ROSE TRIUMPHANTLY
6.6.6.6. with Refrain

220 He Lives

I am He that liveth, and was dead; and, behold, I am alive for evermore. Rev. 1:18

1. I serve a ris - en Sav - ior, He's in the world to - day;
2. In all the world a - round me I see His lov - ing care,
3. Re - joice, re -joice, O Chris - tian, lift up your voice and sing

And And E - And The None

I know that He is liv - ing, what - ev - er men may say;
And tho' my heart grows wea - ry, I nev - er will de - spair;
E - ter - nal hal - le - lu - jahs to Je - sus Christ the King!

I see His hand of mer - cy, I hear His voice of cheer,
I know that He is lead - ing thro' all the storm - y blast,
The Hope of all who seek Him, the Help of all who find,

And just the time I need Him He's al - ways near.
The day of His ap - pear-ing will come at last.
None oth - er is so lov - ing, so good and kind.

Refrain

He lives, He lives, Christ Je -sus lives to - day! He walks with me and
He lives, He lives,

TEXT and MUSIC: Alfred H. Ackley

ACKLEY
Irregular meter

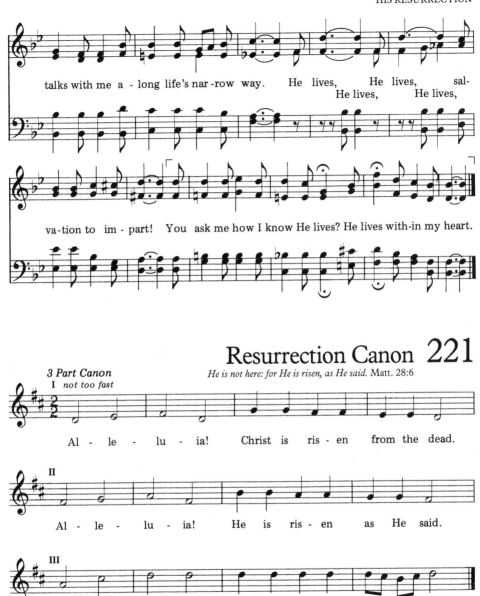

talks with me a - long life's nar - row way. He lives, He lives, sal -
He lives, He lives,

va - tion to im - part! You ask me how I know He lives? He lives with-in my heart.

Resurrection Canon 221

3 Part Canon

He is not here: for He is risen, as He said. Matt. 28:6

I *not too fast*

Al - le - lu - ia! Christ is ris - en from the dead.

II

Al - le - lu - ia! He is ris - en as He said.

III

Al - le - lu - ia! Christ is ris - en from the dead.

Optional choral ending - to be sung after part 3 completes canon.

Al - le - lu - ia! He is ris - en!

TEXT: Gerald S. Henderson; based on Matthew 28:6, 7
MUSIC: German Folk song; arranged by Gerald S. Henderson

RESURRECTION CANON
11.11.11.

222 Easter Song

He is risen; He is not here . . . go your way, tell His disciples. Mark 16:6-7

1. Hear the bells ring - ing, they're sing-ing that we can be born a-
2. Hear the bells ring - ing, they're sing-ing "Christ is ris - en from the

gain!
dead!''

The

an - gel up - on the tomb-stone said, "He is

ris - en just as He said. Quick - ly now, go

tell His dis - ci - ples that Je - sus Christ is no long - er

TEXT and MUSIC: Anne Herring

EASTER SONG
Irregular meter

dead!" Joy to the world, He is ris - en, al - le - lu - ia! He's ris - en, al - le - lu - ia! He's ris - en, al - le - lu - ia, al - le - lu - ia!

Be Joyful 223

They worshipped Him, and returned to Jerusalem with great joy. Luke 24:52

2 Part Canon

Be joy - ful, joy - ful, the Lord is a - live,

Come on be joy - ful, joy - ful, the Lord is a - live!

TEXT and MUSIC: Kurt Kaiser

BE JOYFUL
Irregular meter

224 Jesus Lives, and So Shall I

Now is Christ risen from the dead . . . the firstfruits of them that slept. 1 Cor. 15:20

1. Je - sus lives, and so shall I: Death, thy sting is gone for -
2. Je - sus lives and reigns su - preme: And, His king - dom still re -
3. Je - sus lives—and by His grace, Vic - t'ry o'er my pas - sions
4. Je - sus lives— I know full well Naught from Him my heart can
5. Je - sus lives—and death is now But my en - trance in - to

ev - er! He for me hath deigned to die, Lives the
main - ing, I shall al - so be with Him, Ev - er
giv - ing, I will change my heart and ways, Ev - er
sev - er, Life nor death nor pow'rs of hell, Joy nor
glo - ry; Cour - age, then, my soul, for thou Hast a

bands of death to sev - er. He shall raise me
liv - ing, ev - er reign - ing. God has prom - ised—
to His glo - ry liv - ing. Me He rais - es
grief, hence - forth for - ev - er. None of all His
crown of life be - fore thee. Thou shalt find thy

from the dust: Je - sus is my hope and trust.
be it must: Je - sus is my hope and trust.
from the dust: Je - sus is my hope and trust.
saints is lost: Je - sus is my hope and trust.
hopes were just: Je - sus is my hope and trust. A - men.

TEXT: Christian F. Gellert; translated by Philip Schaff
MUSIC: Johann Crüger

ZUVERSICHT
7.8.7.8.7.7.

Worship Christ the Risen King 225

My Lord and my God. John 20:28

1. Rise, O Church, and lift your voi - ces, Christ has con - quered
2. See the tomb where death had laid Him, Emp - ty now, its
3. Hear the earth pro - test and trem - ble, See the stone re -
4. Doubt may lift its head to mur - mur, Scof - fers mock and
5. We ac - claim Your life, O Je - sus, Now we sing Your

death and hell. Sing as all the earth re - joi - ces;
mouth de - clares; "Death and I could not con - tain Him,
moved with pow'r; All hell's min - ions may as - sem - ble
sin - ners jeer; But the truth pro - claims a won - der
vic - to - ry; Sin or hell may seek to seize us

Re - sur - rec - tion an - thems swell. Come and wor - ship,
For the Throne of Life He shares." Come and wor - ship,
But can - not with - stand His hour. He has con - quered,
Thought-ful hearts re - ceive with cheer. He is ris - en,
But Your con - quest keeps us free. Stand in tri - umph,

come and wor - ship, Wor - ship Christ, the Ris - en King!
come and wor - ship, Wor - ship Christ, the Ris - en King!
He has con - quered, Christ the Lord, the Ris - en King!
He is ris - en, Now re - ceive the Ris - en King!
Stand in tri - umph, Wor - ship Christ, the Ris - en King! A - men.

TEXT: Jack W. Hayford
MUSIC: Henry T. Smart
    A lower setting may be found at No. 241

REGENT SQUARE
8.7.8.7.8.7.

226 The Day of Resurrection

Behold, Jesus met them, saying, "All hail". Matt. 28:9

1. The day of res - ur - rec - tion! Earth, tell it out a - broad;
2. Our hearts be pure from e - vil, That we may see a - right
3. Now let the heav'ns be joy - ful! Let earth her song be - gin!

The Pass - o - ver of glad - ness, The Pass - o - ver of God.
The Lord in rays e - ter - nal Of res - ur - rec - tion light;
The world re - sound in tri - umph, And all that is there - in;

From death to life e - ter - nal, From earth un - to the sky,
And, lis - t'ning to His ac - cents, May hear, so calm and plain,
Let all things seen and un - seen Their notes of glad - ness blend;

Our Christ hath brought us o - ver With hymns of vic - to - ry.
His own "All hail!" and, hear - ing, May raise the vic - tor strain.
For Christ the Lord hath ris - en, Our Joy that hath no end.

TEXT: John of Damascus, 8th century; translated by John M. Neale
MUSIC: Henry T. Smart
       A lower setting may be found at No. 483

LANCASHIRE
7.6.7.6.D.

Thine Is the Glory 227

Death is swallowed up in victory. 1 Cor. 15:54

1. Thine is the glo-ry, Ris-en, con-qu'ring Son; End-less is the
2. Lo! Je-sus meets us, Ris-en, from the tomb; Lov-ing-ly He
3. No more we doubt Thee, Glo-rious Prince of Life! Life is naught with-

vic-t'ry Thou o'er death hast won. An-gels in bright rai-ment
greets us, Scat-ters fear and gloom; Let His church with glad-ness
out Thee; Aid us in our strife; Make us more than con-qu'rors,

Rolled the stone a-way, Kept the fold-ed grave-clothes Where Thy
Hymns of tri-umph sing, For her Lord now liv-eth; Death hath
Through Thy death-less love; Bring us safe through Jor-dan With Thy

Refrain

bod-y lay.
lost its sting. Thine is the glo-ry, Ris-en, con-qu'ring Son;
power and love.

End-less is the vic-t'ry Thou o'er death hast won. A-men.

TEXT: Edmund L. Budry; translated by Richard B. Hoyle
MUSIC: George Frederick Handel

MACCABEUS
10.11.11.11. with Refrain

Words from PSALMS, HYMNS, and SPIRITUAL SONGS. Copyright World Student Christian Federation. Used by Permission.

228 Rejoice, the Lord Is King

Rejoice in the Lord always: and again I say, Rejoice. Phil. 4:4

Descant - last stanza

4. Re-joice, our Lord shall come a-gain.

1. Re - joice, the Lord is King! Your Lord and King a - dore!
2. The Lord, our Sav - ior, reigns, The God of truth and love;
3. His king-dom can - not fail, He rules o'er earth and heav'n;
4. Re - joice in glo - rious hope! Our Lord the Judge shall come

And take His ser - vants to their e - ter - nal home:

Re - joice, give thanks, and sing, And tri - umph ev - er - more:
When He had purged our stains, He took His seat a - bove:
The keys of death and hell Are to our Je - sus giv'n:
And take His ser - vants up To their e - ter - nal home:

Lift up your heart, Re -

Lift up your heart, lift up your voice! Re -

TEXT: Charles Wesley; based on Philippians 4:4
MUSIC: John Darwall;
    Descant and choral ending by Camp Kirkland
    A higher setting may be found at No. 111

DARWALL
6.6.6.6.8.8.

joice, a - gain I say, I say re - joice! A - men.

joice, a - gain I say, re - joice! A - men.

*Do not sing "Amen" if
choral ending is utilized.

Optional choral ending
Unison

Lift up your voice! Re - joice, a - gain I say, re -

Keyboard

joice, re - joice! A - men.

229 Our God Reigns

How beautiful . . . are the feet of him that bringeth good tidings . . . "Thy God reigneth!" Isa. 52:7

1. How love-ly on the moun-tains are the feet of him
2. He had no state-ly form, He had no maj-es-ty,
3. Out from the tomb He came with grace and maj-es-ty,

who brings good news, good news An-nounc-ing
That we should be drawn to Him. He was de-
He is a-live, He is a-live. God loves us

peace, pro-claim-ing news of hap-pi-ness. Our God
spised and we took no ac-count of Him, Yet now He
so, see here His hands, His feet, His side. Yes, we

Refrain

reigns, Our God reigns!
reigns with the Most High. Our God reigns!
know, He is a-live.

TEXT and MUSIC: Leonard E. Smith, Jr.; arranged by Eugene Thomas

OUR GOD REIGNS
Irregular meter

Our God reigns!   Our God reigns!   Our God   reigns!

OPTIONAL STANZAS: *To be sung after verse 2. Verse 3 is to be sung last.*

It was our sin and guilt that bruised and wounded Him.
It was our sin that brought Him down.
When we like sheep had gone astray, our Shepherd came
And on His shoulders bore our shame.

Refrain

Meek as a lamb that's led out to the slaughterhouse,
Dumb as a sheep before its shearer,
His life ran down upon the ground like pouring rain,
That we might be born again.

Refrain

Jesus Is King 230

I am a King. To this end was I born. John 18:37

3 Part Canon

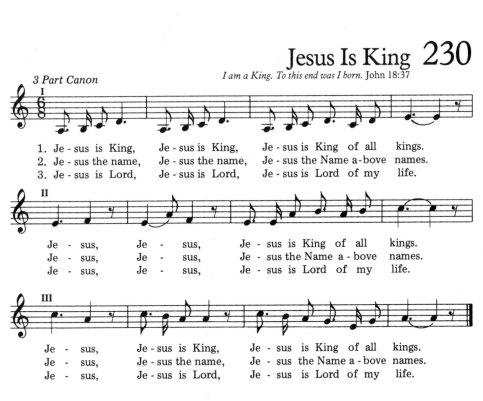

1. Je - sus is King,   Je - sus is King,   Je - sus is King of all   kings.
2. Je - sus the name,   Je - sus the name,   Je - sus the Name a-bove   names.
3. Je - sus is Lord,   Je - sus is Lord,   Je - sus is Lord of my   life.

Je - sus,   Je - sus,   Je - sus is King of all   kings.
Je - sus,   Je - sus,   Je - sus the Name a - bove   names.
Je - sus,   Je - sus,   Je - sus is Lord of my   life.

Je - sus,   Je - sus is King,   Je - sus is King of all   kings.
Je - sus,   Je - sus the name,   Je - sus the Name a - bove   names.
Je - sus,   Je - sus is Lord,   Je - sus is Lord of my   life.

TEXT: Gerald S. Henderson
MUSIC: Traditional Appalachian melody; adapted by Gerald S. Henderson

JESUS IS KING
Irregular meter

231 Jesus Shall Reign

He shall have dominion . . . from sea to sea, . . . from the river unto the ends of the earth. Ps. 72:8

1. Je-sus shall reign wher-e'er the sun Does His suc-ces-sive jour-neys run;
2. To Him shall end-less prayer be made, And end-less prais-es crown His head;
3. Peo-ple and realms of ev-'ry tongue Dwell on His love with sweet-est song;
4. Let ev-'ry crea-ture rise and bring His grate-ful hon-ors to our King;

His king-dom spread from shore to shore, Till moons shall wax and wane no more.
His name like sweet per-fume shall rise With ev-'ry morn-ing sac-ri-fice.
And in-fant voic-es shall pro-claim Their ear-ly bless-ings on His name.
An-gels de-scend with songs a-gain, And earth re-peat the loud "A-men!"

Optional last stanza harmonization

Descant

4. Let ev-'ry crea-ture

Broader
Unison

4. Let ev-'ry crea-ture rise and

Broaden

TEXT: Isaac Watts, altered; based on Psalm 72
MUSIC: John Hatton; Descant and last stanza harmonization by Ken Barker

DUKE STREET
L.M.

Descant and last stanza harm. © 1986 WORD MUSIC (a div. of WORD, INC.). All Rights Reserved. International Copyright Secured.

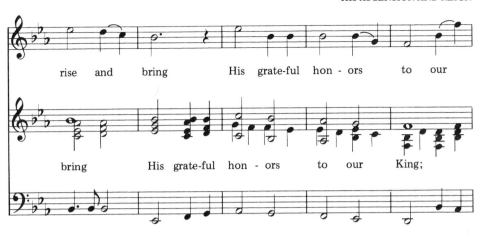

rise and bring His grate-ful hon - ors to our

bring His grate-ful hon - ors to our King;

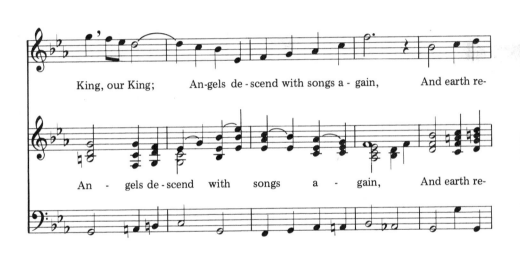

King, our King; An-gels de - scend with songs a - gain, And earth re-

An - gels de - scend with songs a - gain, And earth re-

Choir divide

peat the loud "A - men!" A - men.

peat the loud "A - men!" A - men.

232 Hail the Day That Sees Him Rise

When He ascended up on high, He led captivity captive. Eph. 4:8

1. Hail the day that sees Him rise, Al - le - lu - ia!
2. There for Him high tri - umph waits; Al - le - lu - ia!
3. See, He lifts His hands a - bove! Al - le - lu - ia!
4. Lord, be - yond our mor - tal sight, Al - le - lu - ia!

To His throne a - bove the skies; Al - le - lu - ia!
Lift your heads, e - ter - nal gates, Al - le - lu - ia!
See, He shows the prints of love! Al - le - lu - ia!
Raise our hearts to reach Thy height, Al - le - lu - ia!

Christ, the Lamb for sin - ners giv'n, Al - le - lu - ia!
He hath con - quered death and sin, Al - le - lu - ia!
Hark! His gra - cious lips be - stow, Al - le - lu - ia!
There Thy face un - cloud - ed see, Al - le - lu - ia!

En - ters now the high - est heav'n. Al - le - lu - ia!
Take the King of glo - ry in! Al - le - lu - ia!
Bless-ings on His church be - low. Al - le - lu - ia!
Find our heav'n of heav'ns in Thee! Al - le - lu - ia! A - men.

TEXT: Charles Wesley
MUSIC: Welsh Hymn melody; arranged by John Roberts

LLANFAIR
7.7.7.7. with Alleluias

Alleluia! Sing to Jesus 233

A great multitude . . . of all nations . . . stood . . . before the Lamb. Rev. 7:9

1. Al - le - lu - ia! sing to Je - sus! His the scep - tre, His the throne;
2. Al - le - lu - ia! not as or - phans Are we left in sor - row now;
3. Al - le - lu - ia! Bread of Heav - en, You on earth our food, and stay!

Al - le - lu - ia! His the tri - umph, His the vic - to - ry a - lone;
Al - le - lu - ia! He is near us, Faith be - lieves, nor ques - tions how:
Al - le - lu - ia! here the sin - ful Flee to You from day to day;

Hark! the songs of peace - ful Zi - on Thun - der like a might - y flood;
Though the clouds from sight re - ceived Him When the for - ty days were o'er,
In - ter - ces - sor, Friend of sin - ners, Earth's Re - deem - er, plead for me,

"Je - sus, out of ev - 'ry na - tion Has re - deemed us by His blood."
Shall our hearts for - get His prom - ise, "I am with you ev - er - more"?
Where the songs of all the sin - less Sweep a - cross the crys - tal sea. A - men.

TEXT: William C. Dix
MUSIC: Rowland H. Prichard; arranged by Robert Harkness
A lower setting may be found at No. 89

HYFRYDOL
8.7.8.7.D.

234 Crown Him with Many Crowns

On His head were many crowns. Rev. 19:12

1. Crown Him with man-y crowns, The Lamb up-on His throne:
2. Crown Him the Lord of love: Be-hold His hands and side—
3. Crown Him the Lord of life: Who tri-umphed o'er the grave,
4. Crown Him the Lord of heav'n: One with the Fa-ther known,

Hark! how the heav'n-ly an-them drowns All mu-sic but its own!
Rich wounds, yet vis-i-ble a-bove, In beau-ty glo-ri-fied.
Who rose vic-to-rious to the strife For those He came to save.
One with the Spir-it thru Him giv'n From yon-der glo-rious throne.

A-wake, my soul, and sing Of Him who died for thee, And
No an-gel in the sky Can ful-ly bear that sight, But
His glo-ries now we sing, Who died and rose on high, Who
To Thee be end-less praise, For Thou for us hast died; Be

hail Him as thy match-less King Thru all e-ter-ni-ty.
down-ward bends his won-d'ring eye At mys-ter-ies so bright.
died e-ter-nal life to bring And lives that death may die.
Thou, O Lord, thru end-less days A-dored and mag-ni-fied. A-men.

TEXT: Matthew Bridges, stanzas 1, 2, 4; Godfrey Thring, stanza 3
MUSIC: George J. Elvey; Last stanza harmonization by Mark Hayes
A higher setting may be found at No. 478

DIADEMATA
S.M.D.

Optional last stanza harmonization

Unison

die. *Broaden* 4. Crown Him the Lord of heav'n: One

with the Fa - ther known, One with the Spir - it thru Him giv'n

From yon-der glo - rious throne. To Thee be end - less praise,

For Thou for us hast died; Be Thou, O Lord, thru

Optional choir divisi-sing cued notes

ff

end - less days A - dored and mag - ni - fied. A - men.

235 At the Name of Jesus

Whosoever . . . shall confess Me before men, him will I confess also before My Father. Matt. 10:32

1. At the name of Je - sus
2. At His voice cre - a - tion
3. Hum-bled for a sea - son,
4. In your hearts en - throne Him;
5. Broth-ers, this Lord Je - sus

Ev - 'ry knee shall bow,
Sprang at once to sight,
To re - ceive a name
There let Him sub - due
Shall re - turn a - gain,

Ev - 'ry tongue con - fess Him
All the an - gel fac - es,
From the lips of sin - ners,
All that is not ho - ly,
With the Fa - ther's glo - ry

King of glo - ry now;
All the hosts of light,
Un - to whom He came,
All that is not true:
O'er the earth to reign;

'Tis the Fa - ther's pleas - ure
Thrones and dom-i - na - tions,
Faith-ful-ly He bore it
Crown Him as your Cap - tain
For all wreaths of em - pire

We should call Him Lord,
Stars up - on their way,
Spot - less to the last,
In temp - ta - tion's hour;
Meet up - on His brow,

Who from the be - gin - ning
All the heav'n-ly or - ders
Brought it back vic - to - rious,
Let His will en - fold you
All our hearts con - fess Him

Was the might-y Word.
In their great ar - ray.
When from death He passed.
In its light and power.
King of glo - ry now. A - men.

TEXT: Caroline M. Noel; based on Philippians 2:5-11
MUSIC: Ronn Huff

ASHLYNE
6.5.6.5.D.

Is It the Crowning Day? 236

Unto them that look for Him shall He appear the second time . . . unto salvation. Heb. 9:28

1. Je - sus may come to - day, Glad day! Glad day! And I would
2. I may go home to - day, Glad day! Glad day! Seem-eth I
3. Why should I anx - ious be? Glad day! Glad day! Lights ap -pear
4. Faith-ful I'll be to - day, Glad day! Glad day! And I will

see my Friend; Dan - gers and trou-bles would end If Je - sus should
hear their song; Hail to the ra - di - ant throng! If I should go
on the shore, Storms will af -fright nev - er - more, For He is "at
free - ly tell Why I should love Him so well, For He is my

Refrain

come to - day.
home to - day.
hand" to - day. Glad day! Glad day! Is it the crown - ing
all to - day.

day? I'll live for to - day, nor anx - ious be, Je - sus my Lord I

soon shall see; Glad day! Glad day! Is it the crown - ing day?

TEXT: George Walker Whitcomb
MUSIC: Charles H. Marsh

CROWNING DAY
Irregular meter

237 We Shall Behold Him

We shall be like Him; for we shall see Him as He is. 1 John 3:2

1. The sky shall un - fold, pre - par - ing His en - trance; The stars shall ap-
2. The an - gel shall sound the shout of His com - ing; The sleeping shall

plaud Him with thun-ders of praise. The sweet light in His eyes shall en-
rise from their slum-ber-ing place. And those who re -main shall be

hance those a - wait- ing; And we shall be-hold Him then face to face.
changed in a mo - ment; And we shall be-hold Him then face to face.

Refrain

And we shall be - hold Him, We shall be - hold Him Face to

face in all of His glo - ry. O we shall be - hold Him, We shall be-

TEXT and MUSIC: Dottie Rambo; arranged by Tom Fettke

WE SHALL BEHOLD HIM
Irregular meter

hold Him Face to face, our Sav-ior and Lord.

Optional choral ending
Broaden   *rit.*

And we shall be - hold Him, our Sav - ior and Lord.

The King Is Coming 238

The Lord cometh with ten thousands of His saints. Jude 14

O the King is com-ing, the King is com-ing! I just

heard the trum-pets sound-ing, And now His face I see; O the King is

com-ing, the King is com-ing! Praise God, He's com-ing for me!

TEXT: Gloria Gaither, William J. Gaither and Charles Millhuff
MUSIC: William J. Gaither

KING IS COMING
Irregular meter

239 Jesus Is Coming Again

I will come again, and receive you unto Myself. John 14:3

1. Mar - vel - ous mes - sage we bring, Glo - ri - ous car - ol we sing,
2. For - est and flow - er ex - claim, Moun - tain and mead - ow the same,
3. Stand - ing be - fore Him at last, Tri - al and trou - ble all past,

Won - der - ful word of the King— Je - sus is com - ing a - gain! (a - gain!)
All earth and heav - en pro - claim— Je - sus is com - ing a - gain! (a - gain!)
Crowns at His feet we will cast— Je - sus is com - ing a - gain! (a - gain!)

Refrain—Unison

Com - ing a - gain, Com - ing a - gain;

May - be morn - ing, may - be noon, May - be eve - ning and may - be soon!

Com - ing a - gain, Com - ing a - gain;

TEXT and MUSIC: John W. Peterson

COMING AGAIN
7.7.7.7. with Refrain

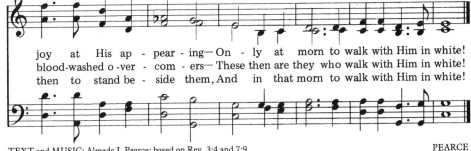

Parts

O what a won-der-ful day it will be— Je-sus is com-ing a - gain!

When He Shall Come 240

They shall walk with Me in white: for they are worthy. Rev. 3:4

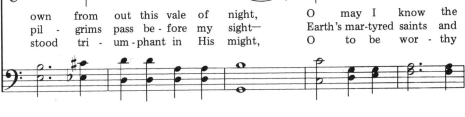

1. When He shall come, re - splen-dent in His glo - ry, To take His
2. When I shall stand with - in the court of heav - en Where white-robed
3. When He shall call, from earth's re - mot-est cor - ners, All who have

own from out this vale of night, O may I know the
pil - grims pass be - fore my sight— Earth's mar-tyred saints and
stood tri - um-phant in His might, O to be wor - thy

joy at His ap - pear - ing—On - ly at morn to walk with Him in white!
blood-washed o -ver - com - ers— These then are they who walk with Him in white!
then to stand be - side them, And in that morn to walk with Him in white!

TEXT and MUSIC: Almeda J. Pearce; based on Rev. 3:4 and 7:9

PEARCE
11.10.11.10.

241 Lo, He Comes with Clouds Descending

They shall see the Son of Man coming in the clouds of heaven. Matt. 24:30

1. Lo, He comes with clouds de-scend-ing, Once for fa - vored sin - ners slain;
2. Ev - ery eye shall now be-hold Him, Robed in dread-ful maj - es - ty;
3. Now re-demp - tion, long ex-pect - ed, See in sol - emn pomp ap-pear:
4. Yea, A - men! let all a-dore Thee, High on Thine e - ter - nal throne;

Thou-sand thou-sand saints at-tend-ing, Swell the tri - umph of His train:
Those who set at naught and sold Him, Pierced and nailed Him to the tree,
All His saints, by men re - ject - ed, Now shall meet Him in the air:
Sav - ior, take the pow'r and glo - ry, Claim the king - dom for Thine own:

Al - le - lu - ia! al - le - lu - ia! God ap-pears on earth to reign.
Deep-ly wail - ing, deep - ly wail - ing, Shall the true Mes - si - ah see.
Al - le - lu - ia! al - le - lu - ia! See the day of God ap-pear.
O, come quick-ly, O, come quick-ly! Ev - er - last - ing God, come down. A-men.

TEXT: Charles Wesley and Martin Madan; based on John Cennick
MUSIC: Henry T. Smart
A higher setting may be found at No. 225

REGENT SQUARE
8.7.8.7.8.7.

242 While We Are Waiting, Come

Behold, I come quickly; and My reward is with Me. Rev. 22:12

1. While we are wait - ing, come; While we are wait - ing, come.
2. With pow'r and glo - ry, come; With pow'r and glo - ry, come.
3. Come, Sav-ior, quick - ly come; Come, Sav-ior, quick - ly come.

TEXT: Claire Cloninger
MUSIC: Don Cason

WAITING
S.M.

© Copyright 1986 WORD MUSIC (a div. of WORD, INC.). All Rights Reserved. International Copyright Secured.

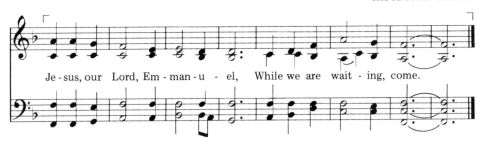

Je - sus, our Lord, Em - man - u - el, While we are wait - ing, come.

O Come, Messiah, Come Again 243

From henceforth expecting till His enemies be made His footstool. Heb. 10:13

Unison

O come, Mes - si - ah, come a - gain, And

rid the world of death and sin. Re - turn, Thou ris - en Sav - ior and

Refrain—*parts optional*

King. That heav'n and earth at last may sing Re - joice, re -

joice, Em - man - u - el has come to thee, O Is - ra - el!

TEXT: Vann Trapp
MUSIC: Adapted from Plainsong by Thomas Helmore;
    arranged by Tom Fettke

VENI EMMANUEL
L.M. with Refrain

244 The Trees of the Field

Ye shall go out with joy . . . and all the trees of the field shall clap. Isa. 55:12

Unison

You shall go out with joy and be led forth with peace;

The moun-tains and the hills will break forth be-

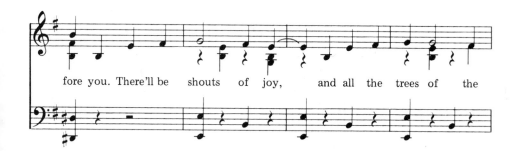

fore you. There'll be shouts of joy, and all the trees of the

field Will clap, will clap their hands.

TEXT: Steffi Geiser Rubin; based on Isaiah 55:12
MUSIC: Stuart Dauermann

THE TREES OF THE FIELD
Irregular meter

245 What If It Were Today?

Lift up your heads; for your redemption draweth nigh. Luke 21:28

1. Je - sus is com-ing to earth a-gain— What if it were to - day?
2. Sa - tan's do-min-ion will then be o'er— O that it were to - day!
3. Faith-ful and true would He find us here If He should come to - day?

Com - ing in pow-er and love to reign— What if it were to - day?
Sor - row and sigh-ing shall be no more— O that it were to - day!
Watch-ing in glad-ness and not in fear, If He should come to - day?

Com - ing to claim His cho - sen Bride, All the re - deemed and pu - ri - fied,
Then shall the dead in Christ a - rise, Caught up to meet Him in the skies;
Signs of His com - ing mul - ti - ply, Morn-ing light breaks in east-ern sky;

rit.   *a tempo*

O - ver this whole earth scat - tered wide— What if it were to - day?
When shall these glo - ries meet our eyes? What if it were to - day?
Watch, for the time is draw - ing nigh— What if it were to - day?

Refrain

Glo - ry, glo - ry! Joy to my heart 'twill bring; Glo - ry, glo - ry!

TEXT and MUSIC: Lelia N. Morris
© 1912. Renewal 1940 by Hope Publishing Co., Carol Stream, IL 60188. All Rights Reserved. Used by Permission.

SECOND COMING
Irregular meter

When we shall crown Him King; Glo - ry! glo - ry! Haste to pre -

pare the way; Glo - ry, glo - ry! Je - sus will come some-day.

He Is Coming 246

He cometh with clouds; and every eye shall see Him. Rev. 1:7

3 Part Canon

I

1. Oh, Je - sus my Sav - ior, He is com - ing a - gain.
2. In clouds of great glo - ry, He is com - ing a - gain.
3. And we shall be like Him, He is com - ing a - gain.

II

Oh, Je - sus my Sav - ior, He is com - ing a - gain.
In clouds of great glo - ry, He is com - ing a - gain.
And we shall be like Him, He is com - ing a - gain.

III

Com - ing, com - ing, com - ing a - gain.

TEXT: Gerald S. Henderson; based on 1 Thessalonians 4:16-17;
1 John 3:2; Revelation 1:7
MUSIC: From *The Diapason*, 1860; adapted by Gerald S. Henderson

DIAPASON
Irregular meter

247 Spirit of the Living God

Walk in the Spirit, and ye shall not fulfill the lust of the flesh. Gal. 5:16

Spir - it of the Liv - ing God, fall fresh on me. Spir - it of the

Liv - ing God, fall fresh on me. Melt me, mold me, fill me,

use me. Spir - it of the Liv - ing God, fall fresh on me.

TEXT and MUSIC: Daniel Iverson
Copyright 1935, 1963 by the Moody Bible Institute of Chicago. Used by permission of Moody Press.

IVERSON
Irregular meter

248 Holy Ghost, with Light Divine

"Not by might, nor by power, but by My Spirit," saith the Lord of hosts. Zech. 4:6

1. Ho - ly Ghost, with light di - vine, Shine up - on this heart of mine;
2. Ho - ly Ghost, with pow'r di - vine, Cleanse this guilt-y heart of mine;
3. Ho - ly Ghost, with joy di - vine, Cheer this sad-dened heart of mine;
4. Ho - ly Spir - it, all di - vine, Dwell with-in this heart of mine;

TEXT: Andrew Reed
MUSIC: Louis M. Gottschalk; adapted by Edwin P. Parker

MERCY
7.7.7.7.

Chase the shades of night a - way, Turn my dark-ness in - to day.
Long hath sin with-out con - trol Held do - min - ion o'er my soul.
Bid my man - y woes de - part, Heal my wound-ed, bleed-ing heart.
Cast down ev - 'ry i - dol - throne, Reign su-preme and reign a - lone. A-men.

Spirit of God, Descend upon My Heart 249

If we live in the Spirit, let us also walk in the Spirit. Gal. 5:25

1. Spir - it of God, de - scend up - on my heart: Wean it from earth, thro'
2. Hast Thou not bid us love Thee, God and King? All, all Thine own—soul,
3. Teach me to feel that Thou art al - ways nigh; Teach me the strug-gles
4. Teach me to love Thee as Thine an - gels love, One ho - ly pas - sion

all its puls - es move. Stoop to my weak - ness, might-y as Thou
heart and strength and mind. I see Thy cross— there teach my heart to
of the soul to bear— To check the ris - ing doubt, the reb - el
fill - ing all my frame: The bap - tism of the heav'n-de-scend-ed

art, And make me love Thee as I ought to love.
cling; O let me seek Thee, and O let me find.
sigh; Teach me the pa - tience of un - an - swered prayer.
Dove— My heart an al - tar and Thy love the flame. A - men.

TEXT: George Croly
MUSIC: Frederick C. Atkinson

MORECAMBE
10.10.10.10.

250 Come, Holy Spirit

The law of the Spirit of life . . . hath made me free from the law of sin and death. Rom. 8:2

1. Come as a wis-dom to chil-dren, Come as new sight to the
2. Come as a rest to the wea-ry, Come as a balm for the
3. Come like a spring in the des-ert, Come to the with-ered of

blind, Come, Lord, as strength to my weak-ness,
sore, Come as a dew to my dry-ness:
soul; O let Your sweet heal-ing pow-er

Refrain

Take me: soul, bod-y and mind.
Fill me with joy ev-er-more.
Touch me and make me whole. Come, Ho-ly Spir-it, I

need You, Come, sweet Spir-it, I pray; Come in Your

strength and Your pow-er, Come in Your own gen-tle way.

TEXT: Gloria Gaither and William J. Gaither
MUSIC: William J. Gaither

COME, HOLY SPIRIT
8.7.8.7.D.

Breathe on Me 251

He breathed on them, and saith unto them, "Receive ye the Holy Ghost." John 20:22

1. Ho - ly Spir - it, breathe on me, Un - til my heart is clean;
2. Ho - ly Spir - it, breathe on me, My stub-born will sub - due;
3. Ho - ly Spir - it, breathe on me, Fill me with pow'r di - vine;
4. Ho - ly Spir - it, breathe on me, Till I am all Thine own,

Let sun-shine fill its in - most part, With not a cloud be - tween.
Teach me in words of liv - ing flame What Christ would have me do.
Kin - dle a flame of love and zeal With - in this heart of mine.
Un - til my will is lost in Thine, To live for Thee a - lone.

Refrain

Breathe on me, breathe on me, Ho - ly Spir - it, breathe on me;

Take Thou my heart, cleanse ev - 'ry part, Ho - ly Spir - it, breathe on me.

TEXT: Edwin Hatch; adapted by B. B. McKinney; based on John 20:22
MUSIC: B. B. McKinney

TRUETT
7.6.8.6. with Refrain

252 Sweet, Sweet Spirit

The fruit of the Spirit is love, joy, peace. Gal. 5:22

There's a sweet, sweet Spir-it in this place, And I
sweet ex-pres-sions on each face, And I

know that it's the Spir-it of the Lord; There are
know that it's the pres-ence of the Lord.

Refrain

Sweet Ho-ly Spir-it, Sweet heav-en-ly Dove,

Stay right here with us, Fill-ing us with Your love; And for these

bless-ings We lift our hearts in praise: With-out a doubt we'll know

TEXT and MUSIC: Doris Akers

MANNA
Irregular meter

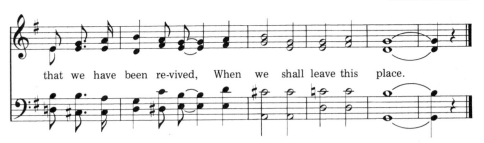

that we have been re-vived, When we shall leave this place.

Where the Spirit of the Lord Is 253

Where the Spirit of the Lord is, there is liberty. 2 Cor. 3:17

Where the Spir-it of the Lord is, there is peace; Where the

Spir-it of the Lord is, there is love. There is com-fort in life's

dark-est hour, there is light and life; There is help and

pow-er in the Spir-it, in the Spir-it of the Lord.

TEXT and MUSIC: Stephen R. Adams; based on 2 Corinthians 3:17

ADAMS
Irregular meter

254 Heavenly Spirit, Gentle Spirit

[The Spirit] shall take of Mine, and shall shew it unto you. John 16:15

1. Heaven-ly Spir - it, gen - tle Spir - it, O de - scend on us, we pray;
2. Hear us plead-ing, in - ter - ced - ing, Thou in - ter - pre - ter of love;
3. Come to cheer us, be Thou near us, Kin - dle in us heav-en's love;
4. Pil - grims, stran-gers, 'mid life's dan-gers, We on Thee would e'er de - pend;

Come, con - sole us, and con - trol us, Christ, most fair, to us por-tray.
With Thy fire, us in - spire, Ho - ly flame from God a - bove.
Keep us burn-ing, hum-ble, yearn-ing, Dwell in us, O heav-en-ly Dove.
Spir - it ten - der, our De-fend - er, Guide us, keep us to the end.

TEXT: Joel Blomquist; translated by Gerhard W. Palmgren
MUSIC: Joel Blomquist

HIMLADUVA
8.7.8.7.

Words © 1950 by Covenant Press. Used by Permission.

255 Greater Is He That Is in Me

Greater is He that is in you, than he that is in the world. 1 John 4:4

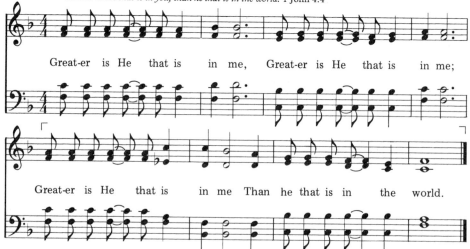

Great-er is He that is in me, Great-er is He that is in me;

Great-er is He that is in me Than he that is in the world.

TEXT and MUSIC: Lanny Wolfe; based on 1 John 4:4

GREATER IS HE
8.8.8.7.

He Is Here, He Is Here 256

Where two or three are gathered . . . in My name, there am I in the midst of them. Matt. 18:20

1. He is here, He is here, He is mov-ing a-mong us. He is here, He is here, as we gath-er in His name! He is here, He is here and He wants to work a won-der. He is here as we gath-er in His name. He is here praise and a-dore Him—yes-ter-day and to-day and for-ev-er-more the same.

2. He is Lord, He is Lord, let us wor-ship be-fore Him. He is Lord, He is Lord, as we gath-er in His name! He is Lord, He is Lord, let us

TEXT and MUSIC: Jimmy Owens; arranged by Lee Herrington

HE IS HERE
Irregular meter

257 The Comforter Has Come

I will pray the Father, and He shall give you another Comforter. John 14:16

1. O spread the ti-dings 'round wher-ev-er man is found, Wher-
2. Lo, the great King of kings, with heal-ing in His wings, To
3. O bound-less love di-vine! how shall this tongue of mine To

ev-er hu-man hearts and hu-man woes a-bound; Let ev-'ry Christian
ev-'ry cap-tive soul a full de-liv-'rance brings; And thru the vacant
won-d'ring mor-tals tell the match-less grace di-vine— That I, a child of

tongue pro-claim the joy-ful sound: The Com-fort-er has come!
cells the song of tri-umph rings: The Com-fort-er has come!
hell, should in His im-age shine! The Com-fort-er has come!

Refrain

The Com-fort-er has come, the Com-fort-er has come! The

Ho-ly Ghost from heav'n—the Fa-ther's prom-ise giv'n; O spread the ti-dings

TEXT: Frank Bottome
MUSIC: William J. Kirkpatrick

COMFORTER
12.12.12.6. with Refrain

'round wher-ev-er man is found—The Com-fort-er has come!

We Are Gathered for Thy Blessing 258

My preaching was . . . in demonstration of the Spirit and of power. 1 Cor. 2:4

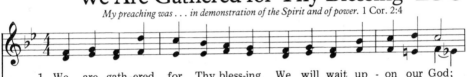

1. We are gath-ered for Thy bless-ing, We will wait up-on our God;
2. We will glo-ry in Thy pow-er, We will sing of won-drous grace;
3. Bring us low in prayer be-fore Thee, And with faith our souls in-spire,

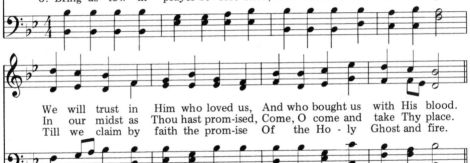

We will trust in Him who loved us, And who bought us with His blood.
In our midst as Thou hast prom-ised, Come, O come and take Thy place.
Till we claim by faith the prom-ise Of the Ho-ly Ghost and fire.

Refrain

Spir-it, now melt and move All of our hearts with love,

Breathe on us from a-bove With old-time pow'r. A-men.

TEXT and MUSIC: Paul Rader

TABERNACLE
8.7.8.7. with Refrain

259 Breathe on Me, Breath of God

He breathed on them, and saith unto them, "Receive ye the Holy Ghost." John 20:22

1. Breathe on me, Breath of God, Fill me with life a-new, That I may love what Thou dost love, And do what Thou wouldst do.
2. Breathe on me, Breath of God, Un-til my heart is pure, Un-til my will is one with Thine, To do and to en-dure.
3. Breathe on me, Breath of God, Till I am whol-ly Thine, Un-til this earth-ly part of me Glows with Thy fire di-vine.
4. Breathe on me, Breath of God, So shall I nev-er die, But live with Thee the per-fect life Of Thine e-ter-ni-ty. A-men.

TEXT: Edwin Hatch
MUSIC: Robert Jackson

TRENTHAM
S.M.

260 Welcome, Welcome

Ye are the temple of God, and . . . the Spirit of God dwelleth in you. 1 Cor. 3:16

Wel-come, wel-come, wel-come, wel-come! Ho-ly Ghost we wel-come Thee.

Come in power and fill this tem-ple; Ho-ly Ghost we wel-come Thee.

TEXT: Lelia N. Morris
MUSIC: Daniel Read; arranged by Kurt Kaiser

WELCOME
8.7.8.7.

Fill Me Now 261

Be filled with the Spirit. Eph. 5:18

1. Hov - er o'er me, Ho - ly Spir - it, Bathe my trem - bling heart and brow;
2. Thou canst fill me, gra - cious Spir - it, Tho I can - not tell Thee how;
3. I am weak - ness, full of weak - ness, At Thy sa - cred feet I bow;
4. Cleanse and com - fort, bless and save me, Bathe, O bathe my heart and brow;

Fill me with Thy hal-low'd pres - ence, Come, O come and fill me now.
But I need Thee, great - ly need Thee, Come, O come and fill me now.
Blest, di - vine, e - ter - nal Spir - it, Fill with pow'r, and fill me now.
Thou art com - fort - ing and sav - ing, Thou art sweet - ly fill - ing now.

Refrain

Fill me now, fill me now, Je - sus, come and fill me now;

Fill me with Thy hal-lowed pres - ence—Come, O come and fill me now.

TEXT: Elwood H. Stokes
MUSIC: John R. Sweney

FILL ME NOW
8.7.8.7. with Refrain

262 Holy, Holy, Holy

Holy, holy, holy, Lord God Almighty. Rev. 4:8

Descant - last stanza

4. Ho - ly, ho - ly, ho - ly, ho - ly! Lord God Al - might - y!

1. Ho - ly, ho - ly, ho - ly! Lord God Al - might - y!
2. Ho - ly, ho - ly, ho - ly! all the saints a - dore Thee,
3. Ho - ly, ho - ly, ho - ly! though the dark - ness hide Thee,
4. Ho - ly, ho - ly, ho - ly! Lord God Al - might - y!

All Thy works shall praise Thy name in earth and sky;

Ear - ly in the morn - ing our song shall rise to
Cast - ing down their gold - en crowns a - round the glass - y
Though the eye of sin - ful man Thy glo - ry may not
All Thy works shall praise Thy name in earth and sky and

We praise Thy name, O Lord, most Ho - ly, ho - ly, ho - ly, ho - ly!

Thee;   Ho - ly, ho - ly, ho - ly!
sea;   Cher - u - bim and ser - a - phim
see;   On - ly Thou art ho - ly—
sea;   Ho - ly, ho - ly, ho - ly!

TEXT: Reginald Heber
MUSIC: John B. Dykes; Descant by Gary Rhodes

NICAEA
11.12.12.10.

mer - ci - ful and might - y! God in three Per - sons,

mer - ci - ful and might - y! God in three Per - sons,
fall - ing down be - fore Thee, Which wert and art and
there is none be - side Thee, Per - fect in pow'r, in
mer - ci - ful and might - y! God in three Per - sons,

bless - ed Trin - i - ty. A - men.

bless - ed Trin - i - ty!
ev - er - more shalt be.
love and pu - ri - ty.
bless - ed Trin - i - ty! A - men.

Sing Praise 263

Sing praises unto the Lord. Ps. 68:32

3 Part Canon

I   II   III

Sing praise to the Fa - ther, praise to the Son; Sing praise, sing praise.

Sing praise to the Spir - it, Three in One; Sing praise, sing praise.

TEXT: Gerald S. Henderson
MUSIC: Israeli Folk song; adapted by Gerald S. Henderson

SING PRAISE
Irregular meter

264 Praise Ye the Triune God

I will . . . praise Thy name for Thy lovingkindness and for Thy truth. Ps. 138:2

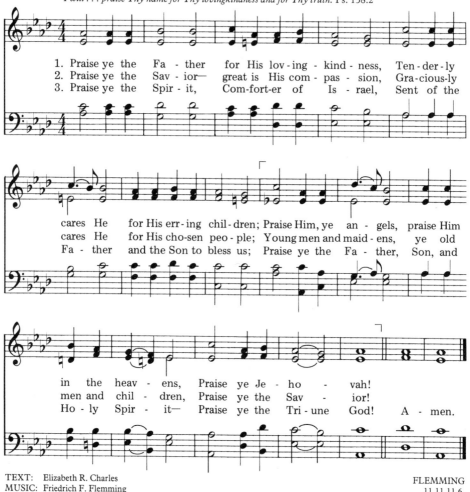

1. Praise ye the Fa - ther for His lov-ing - kind - ness, Ten-der-ly
2. Praise ye the Sav - ior— great is His com - pas - sion, Gra-cious-ly
3. Praise ye the Spir - it, Com-fort-er of Is - rael, Sent of the

cares He for His err-ing chil-dren; Praise Him, ye an - gels, praise Him
cares He for His cho-sen peo - ple; Young men and maid - ens, ye old
Fa - ther and the Son to bless us; Praise ye the Fa - ther, Son, and

in the heav - ens, Praise ye Je - ho - vah!
men and chil - dren, Praise ye the Sav - ior!
Ho - ly Spir - it— Praise ye the Tri - une God! A - men.

TEXT: Elizabeth R. Charles
MUSIC: Friedrich F. Flemming

FLEMMING
11.11.11.6.

265 Father, I Adore You

True worshippers shall worship the Father in spirit and in truth. John 4:23

3 Part Round

1. Fa-ther, I a - dore You, Lay my life be - fore You, How I love You.
2. Je - sus, I a - dore You, Lay my life be - fore You, How I love You.
3. Spir-it, I a - dore You, Lay my life be - fore You, How I love You.

TEXT and MUSIC: Terrye Coelho

MARANATHA
Irregular meter

Holy, Holy 266

Thou only art holy: for all nations shall . . . worship before Thee. Rev. 15:4

1. Ho - ly, ho - ly, ho - ly, ho - ly, Ho - ly, ho - ly,
2. Gra - cious Fa - ther, gra - cious Fa - ther, We're so blest to be Your
3. Pre - cious Je - sus, pre - cious Je - sus, We're so glad that You've re-
4. Ho - ly Spir - it, Ho - ly Spir - it, Come and fill our hearts a-
5. Ho - ly, ho - ly, ho - ly, ho - ly, Ho - ly, ho - ly,
6. Hal - le - lu - jah, hal - le - lu - jah, Hal - le - lu - jah,

Lord God Al - might - y; And we lift our hearts be - fore You as a
child-ren, gra - cious Fa - ther; And we lift our heads be - fore You as a
deemed us, pre-cious Je - sus; And we lift our hands be - fore You as a
new, Ho - ly Spir - it; And we lift our voice be - fore You as a
Lord God Al - might - y; And we lift our hearts be - fore You as a
hal - le - lu - jah; And we lift our hearts be - fore You as a

tok - en of our love, Ho - ly, ho - ly, ho - ly, ho - ly.
tok - en of our love, Gra - cious Fa - ther, gra - cious Fa - ther.
tok - en of our love, Pre - cious Je - sus, pre - cious Je - sus.
tok - en of our love, Ho - ly Spir - it, Ho - ly Spir - it.
tok - en of our love, Ho - ly, ho - ly, ho - ly, ho - ly.
tok - en of our love, Hal - le - lu - jah, hal - le - lu - jah.

TEXT and MUSIC: Jimmy Owens

HOLY, HOLY
Irregular meter

267 Come, Thou Almighty King

The Lord is a great God, and a great King. Ps. 95:3

1. Come, Thou Almighty King,
2. Come, Thou Incarnate Word,
3. Come, Holy Comforter,
4. To Thee, great One in Three,

TEXT: Source unknown
MUSIC: Felice de Giardini;
Last stanza harmonization by O. D. Hall, Jr.

ITALIAN HYMN
6.6.4.6.6.6.4.

Optional last stanza harmonization   *Broader Unison*

rall.

4. To Thee, great One in Three,

E - ter - nal prais - es be, Hence ev - er - more;

Thy sov-'reign maj - es-ty May we in glo - ry see, And to e -

rit.   *a tempo*   *Optional choral ending cresc.*

ter - ni - ty Love and a - dore.

play cued notes if opt. choral ending is used.

A - men.

A - men.

tenor: Come, Thou Al - might - y King.

A - men.

268 God, Our Father, We Adore Thee

Our Father which art in heaven, Hallowed be Thy name. Matt. 6:9

1. God, our Fa - ther, we a - dore Thee! We, Thy chil - dren, bless Thy name!
2. Son E - ter - nal, we a - dore Thee! Lamb up - on the throne on high!
3. Ho - ly Spir - it, we a - dore Thee! Par - a - clete and heav'n - ly guest!
4. Fa - ther, Son, and Ho - ly Spir - it— Three in One! we give Thee praise!

Cho - sen in the Christ be - fore Thee, We are "ho - ly with - out blame."
Lamb of God, we bow be - fore Thee, Thou hast brought Thy peo - ple nigh!
Sent from God and from the Sav - ior, Thou hast led us in - to rest.
For the rich - es we in - her - it, Heart and voice to Thee we raise!

We a - dore Thee! we a - dore Thee! Ab - ba's prais - es we pro - claim!
We a - dore Thee! we a - dore Thee! Son of God, who came to die!
We a - dore Thee! we a - dore Thee! By Thy grace for - ev - er blest:
We a - dore Thee! we a - dore Thee! Thee we bless, thro' end - less days!

We a - dore Thee! we a - dore Thee! Ab - ba's prais - es we pro - claim!
We a - dore Thee! we a - dore Thee! Son of God, who came to die!
We a - dore Thee! we a - dore Thee! By Thy grace for - ev - er blest!
We a - dore Thee! we a - dore Thee! Thee we bless, thro' end - less days! A - men.

TEXT: George W. Frazier; Alfred S. Loizeaux, stanza 3
MUSIC: John Zundel
A lower setting may be found at No. 92; Alternate tune: HYFRYDOL, No. 89

BEECHER
8.7.8.7.D.

O Word of God Incarnate 269

The entrance of Thy words giveth light. Ps. 119:130

1. O Word of God in-car-nate, O Wis-dom from on high,
2. The Church from her dear Mas-ter Re-ceived the gift di-vine,
3. It float-eth like a ban-ner Be-fore God's host un-furled;
4. O make Thy Church, dear Sav-ior, A lamp of pur-est gold,

O Truth un-changed, un-chang-ing, O Light of our dark sky;
And still that light she lift-eth O'er all the earth to shine.
It shin-eth like a bea-con A-bove the dark-ling world.
To bear be-fore the na-tions Thy true light as of old.

We praise Thee for the ra-diance That from the hal-lowed page,
It is the gold-en cas-ket Where gems of truth are stored;
It is the chart and com-pass That o'er life's surg-ing sea,
O teach Thy wan-d'ring pil-grims By this their path to trace,

A lan-tern to our foot-steps, Shines on from age to age.
It is the heav'n-drawn pic-ture Of Christ, the liv-ing Word.
'Mid mists and rocks and quick-sands, Still guides, O Christ, to Thee.
Till, clouds and dark-ness end-ed, They see Thee face to face. A-men.

TEXT: William W. How
MUSIC: *Neuvermehrtes Gesangbuch*, Meiningen, 1693; arranged by Felix Mendelssohn

MUNICH
7.6.7.6.D.

270 Wonderful Words of Life

The words that I speak unto you, they are spirit, and they are life. John 6:63

1. Sing them o-ver a-gain to me, Won-der-ful words of Life;
2. Christ, the bless-ed One, gives to all Won-der-ful words of Life;
3. Sweet-ly ech-o the gos-pel call, Won-der-ful words of Life;

Let me more of their beau-ty see, Won-der-ful words of Life.
Sin-ner, list to the lov-ing call, Won-der-ful words of Life.
Of-fer par-don and peace to all, Won-der-ful words of Life.

Words of life and beau-ty, Teach me faith and du-ty;
All so free-ly giv-en, Woo-ing us to Heav-en:
Je-sus, on-ly Sav-ior, Sanc-ti-fy for-ev-er:

Refrain

Beau-ti-ful words, won-der-ful words, Won-der-ful words of Life.

Beau-ti-ful words, won-der-ful words, Won-der-ful words of Life.

TEXT and MUSIC: Philip P. Bliss

WORDS OF LIFE
8.6.8.6.6.6. with Refrain

Standing on the Promises 271

. . . Whereby are given unto us exceeding great and precious promises. 2 Pet. 1:4

1. Stand-ing on the prom - is - es of Christ my King, Thro' e - ter - nal a - ges
2. Stand-ing on the prom - is - es that can - not fail, When the howl-ing storms of
3. Stand-ing on the prom - is - es of Christ the Lord, Bound to Him e - ter - nal-
4. Stand-ing on the prom - is - es I can - not fall, Lis-t'ning ev - ery mo-ment

let His prais - es ring; Glo - ry in the high - est, I will shout and sing,
doubt and fear as - sail, By the liv - ing Word of God I shall pre - vail,
ly by love's strong cord, O - ver-com-ing dai - ly with the Spir - it's sword,
to the Spir - it's call, Rest - ing in my Sav - ior as my all in all,

Refrain

Stand-ing on the prom-is-es of God. Stand-ing, stand - ing,
stand-ing on the prom-is-es,

Stand-ing on the prom - is - es of God my Sav - ior; Stand - ing,

stand - ing, I'm stand-ing on the prom-is - es of God.
stand-ing on the prom-is-es,

TEXT and MUSIC: R. Kelso Carter

PROMISES
11.11.11.9. with Refrain

272 Thy Word

Thy Word is a lamp unto my feet, and a light unto my path. Ps. 119:105

Thy Word is a lamp un-to my feet and a light un-to my path.

Thy Word is a lamp un-to my feet and a light un-to my path.

2nd time rit.

2nd time Fine

Thy Word is a lamp un-to my feet and a light un-to my path.

TEXT: Amy Grant; based on Psalm 119:105
MUSIC: Michael W. Smith; arranged by Keith Phillips

THY WORD
Irregular meter

273 Holy Bible, Book Divine

All Scripture is given by inspiration of God, and is profitable. 2 Tim. 3:16

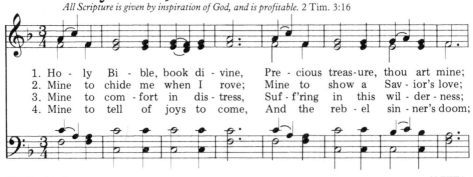

1. Ho - ly Bi - ble, book di - vine, Pre - cious treas-ure, thou art mine;
2. Mine to chide me when I rove; Mine to show a Sav - ior's love;
3. Mine to com - fort in dis - tress, Suf - f'ring in this wil - der - ness;
4. Mine to tell of joys to come, And the reb - el sin - ner's doom;

TEXT: John Burton
MUSIC: William B. Bradbury

ALETTA
7.7.7.7.

Mine to tell me whence I came; Mine to teach me what I am.
Mine thou art to guide and guard; Mine to pun-ish or re-ward.
Mine to show, by liv-ing faith, Man can tri-umph o-ver death.
O thou Ho-ly Book di-vine, Pre-cious treas-ure, thou art mine. A-men.

Break Thou the Bread of Life 274

He looked up to heaven, and blessed, and brake the loaves. Mark 6:41

1. Break Thou the bread of life, Dear Lord, to me, As Thou didst
2. Bless Thou the truth, dear Lord, To me, to me, As Thou didst
3. Thou art the bread of life, O Lord, to me, Thy ho-ly
4. O send Thy Spir-it, Lord, Now un-to me, That He may

break the loaves Be-side the sea; Be-yond the sa-cred page
bless the bread By Gal-i-lee; Then shall all bond-age cease,
Word the truth That sav-eth me; Give me to eat and live
touch my eyes And make me see: Show me the truth con-cealed

I seek Thee, Lord, My spir-it pants for Thee, O liv-ing Word.
All fet-ters fall; And I shall find my peace, My All in all.
With Thee a-bove; Teach me to love Thy truth, For Thou art love.
With-in Thy Word, And in Thy Book re-vealed I see the Lord. A-men.

TEXT: Mary A. Lathbury, stanzas 1, 2; Alexander Groves, stanzas 3, 4;
based on Matthew 14:19
MUSIC: William F. Sherwin

BREAD OF LIFE
6.4.6.4.D.

275 How Firm a Foundation

The foundation of God standeth sure . . . The Lord knoweth them that are His. 2 Tim. 2:19

1. How firm a foun-da-tion, ye saints of the Lord,
2. "Fear not, I am with thee; O be not dis-mayed,
3. "When through fier-y tri-als thy path-way shall lie,
4. "The soul that on Je-sus hath leaned for re-pose

Is laid for your faith in His ex-cel-lent Word!
For I am thy God, and will still give thee aid;
My grace, all suf-fi-cient, shall be thy sup-ply:
I will not, I will not de-sert to its foes;

What more can He say than to you He hath said,
I'll strength-en thee, help thee, and cause thee to stand,
The flame shall not hurt thee; I on-ly de-sign
That soul, though all hell should en-deav-or to shake,

To you who for ref-uge to Je-sus have fled?
Up-held by My right-eous, om-nip-o-tent hand.
Thy dross to con-sume and thy gold to re-fine.
I'll nev-er, no, nev-er, no, nev-er for-sake!"

TEXT: Rippon's *Selection of Hymns*, 1787
MUSIC: Traditional American melody; Caldwell's *Union Harmony*, 1837

FOUNDATION
11.11.11.11.

Christ Is Made the Sure Foundation 276

Other foundation can no man lay than . . . Jesus Christ. 1 Cor. 3:11

1. Christ is made the sure foun-da-tion, Christ the head and cor - ner - stone, Chos - en of the Lord and pre - cious, Bind - ing all the Church in one, Ho - ly Zi - on's help for-ev - er, And her con - fi - dence a - lone.

2. To this tem - ple, where we call Thee, Come, O Lord of hosts, to - day; With ac - cus - tomed lov - ing - kind - ness Hear Thy peo - ple as they pray, And Thy full - est ben - e - dic - tion Shed with - in its walls al - way.

3. Here vouch-safe to all Thy serv - ants What they ask of Thee to gain, What they gain from Thee for - ev - er With the bless - ed to re - tain, And here - aft - er in Thy glo - ry Ev - er - more with Thee to reign.

4. Laud and hon - or to the Fa - ther, Laud and hon - or to the Son, Laud and hon - or to the Spir - it, Ev - er Three and ev - er One, One in might and One in glo - ry While un - end - ing a - ges run. A - men.

TEXT: Latin Hymn, 7th century; translated by John M. Neale
MUSIC: Henry T. Smart
        A lower setting may be found at No. 241

REGENT SQUARE
8.7.8.7.8.7.

277 The Church's One Foundation

I lay . . . for a foundation . . . a precious corner stone. Isa. 28:16

1. The Church-'s one foun - da - tion Is Je - sus Christ her Lord;
2. E - lect from ev - 'ry na - tion, Yet one o'er all the earth,
3. 'Mid toil and trib - u - la - tion And tu - mult of her war,
4. Yet she on earth hath un - ion With God the Three in One,

She is His new cre - a - tion By wa - ter and the Word:
Her char - ter of sal - va - tion One Lord, one faith, one birth;
She waits the con - sum - ma - tion Of peace for - ev - er - more;
And mys - tic sweet com - mun - ion With those whose rest is won:

From heav'n He came and sought her To be His ho - ly bride; With
One ho - ly name she bless - es, Par - takes one ho - ly food, And
Till with the vi - sion glo - rious Her long - ing eyes are blest, And
O hap - py ones and ho - ly! Lord, give us grace that we, Like

His own blood He bought her, And for her life He died.
to one hope she press - es, With ev - 'ry grace en - dued.
the great Church vic - to - rious Shall be the Church at rest.
them, the meek and low - ly, On high may dwell with Thee. A - men.

TEXT: Samuel J. Stone
MUSIC: Samuel S. Wesley
A lower setting may be found at No. 567

AURELIA
7.6.7.6.D.

Glorious Things of Thee Are Spoken 278

Glorious things are spoken of thee, O city of God. Ps. 87:3

1. Glo - rious things of thee are spo - ken, Zi - on, cit - y of our God;
2. See, the streams of liv - ing wa - ters, Spring-ing from e - ter - nal Love,
3. Round each hab - i - ta - tion hov-ering, See the cloud and fire ap - pear

He whose word can - not be bro - ken Formed thee for His own a - bode.
Well sup-ply thy sons and daugh-ters, And all fear of want re - move.
For a glo - ry and a cov-ering, Show - ing that the Lord is near!

On the Rock of A - ges found-ed, What can shake thy sure re - pose?
Who can faint while such a riv - er Ev - er flows their thirst to assuage?
Thus de - riv - ing from their ban - ner Light by night and shade by day,

With sal - va - tion's walls sur-round-ed, Thou mayst smile at all thy foes.
Grace which, like the Lord, the Giv - er, Nev - er fails from age to age!
Safe they feed up - on the man - na Which He gives them when they pray. A - men.

TEXT: John Newton; based on Psalm 87:3 and Isaiah 33:20, 21
MUSIC: Franz Joseph Haydn
A lower setting may be found at No. 9

AUSTRIAN HYMN
8.7.8.7.D.

279 Faith of Our Fathers

Contend for the faith which was once delivered unto the saints. Jude 3

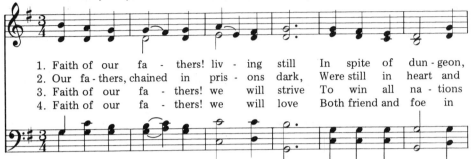

1. Faith of our fa - thers! liv - ing still In spite of dun - geon,
2. Our fa - thers, chained in pris - ons dark, Were still in heart and
3. Faith of our fa - thers! we will strive To win all na - tions
4. Faith of our fa - thers! we will love Both friend and foe in

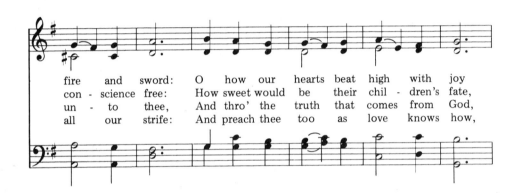

fire and sword: O how our hearts beat high with joy
con - science free: How sweet would be their chil - dren's fate,
un - to thee, And thro' the truth that comes from God,
all our strife: And preach thee too as love knows how,

Optional Descant - Ladies Trio

Faith of our fa - thers,

When-e'er we hear that glo - rious word! Faith of our fa - thers,
If they like them could die for thee! Faith of our fa - thers,
Man-kind shall then be tru - ly free. Faith of our fa - thers,
By kind - ly words and vir - tuous life: Faith of our fa - thers,

TEXT: Frederick W. Faber
MUSIC: Henry F. Hemy; arranged by James G. Walton
Descant and choral ending by Ken Barker

ST. CATHERINE
8.8.8.8.8.8.

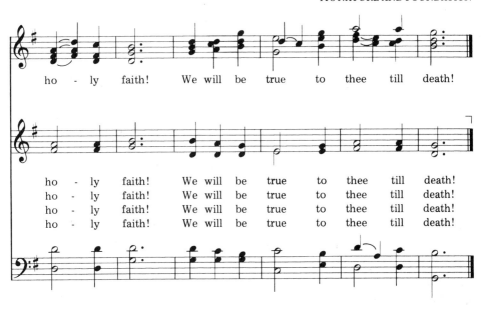

ho - ly faith! We will be true to thee till death!

ho - ly faith! We will be true to thee till death!
ho - ly faith! We will be true to thee till death!
ho - ly faith! We will be true to thee till death!
ho - ly faith! We will be true to thee till death!

Optional choral ending

mf   *cresc.*

We will be true, We will be true,

f   *cresc.*   *ff*

We will be true to thee till death! A - men.

280 I Love Thy Kingdom, Lord

Lord, I have loved the habitation of Thy house. Ps. 26:8

1. I love Thy king - dom, Lord, The house of Thine a - bode, The
2. I love Thy Church, O God! Her walls be - fore Thee stand, Dear
3. For her my tears shall fall; For her my prayers as - cend; To
4. Be - yond my high - est joy I prize her heav'n - ly ways, Her
5. Sure as Thy truth shall last, To Zi - on shall be giv'n The

Church our blest Re - deem-er saved With His own pre - cious blood.
as the ap - ple of Thine eye, And grav - en on Thy hand.
her my cares and toils be giv'n, Till toils and cares shall end.
sweet com-mun-ion, sol - emn vows, Her hymns of love and praise.
bright - est glo - ries earth can yield, And bright - er bliss of heav'n. A - men.

TEXT: Timothy Dwight
MUSIC: Aaron Williams
  A higher setting may be found at No. 21

ST. THOMAS
S.M.

281 The Bond of Love

We know that we have passed from death unto life, because we love the brethren. 1 John 3:14

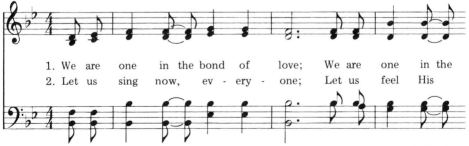

1. We are one in the bond of love; We are one in the
2. Let us sing now, ev - ery - one; Let us feel His

TEXT and MUSIC: Otis Skillings

BOND OF LOVE
Irregular meter

bond of love. We have joined our spir-it with the
love be - gun. Let us join our hands that the

Spir - it of God; We are one in the bond of love.
world will know We are one in the bond of love.

The Family of God 282

. . . the whole family in heaven and earth. Eph. 3:15

I'm so glad I'm a part of the fam-ily of God— I've been washed in the

foun-tain, cleansed by His blood! Joint heirs with Je-sus as we trav-el this

sod, For I'm part of the fam-ily, the fam-ily of God.

TEXT: Gloria Gaither and William J. Gaither
MUSIC: William J. Gaither

FAMILY OF GOD
Irregular meter

283 We Are God's People

Ye are a chosen generation . . . a peculiar people. 1 Pet. 2:9

Unison

1. We are God's peo - ple, the cho - sen of the Lord,
2. We are God's loved ones, the Bride of Christ our Lord,
3. We are the Bod - y of which the Lord is Head,
4. We are a Tem - ple, the Spir - it's dwell - ing place,

Born of His Spir - it, es - tab - lished by His Word; Our
For we have known it, the love of God out - poured; Now
Called to o - bey Him, now ris - en from the dead; He
Formed in great weak - ness, a cup to hold God's grace; We

cor - ner-stone is Christ a - lone, And strong in Him we stand: O let us
let us learn how to re - turn The gift of love once given: O let us
wills us be a fam - i - ly Di - verse yet tru - ly one: O let us
die a - lone, for on its own Each em - ber los - es fire: Yet joined in

live trans - par - ent - ly, And walk heart to heart and hand in hand.
share each joy and care, And live with a zeal that pleas - es Heaven.
give our gifts to God, And so shall His work on earth be done.
one the flame burns on To give warmth and light, and to in - spire.

TEXT: Bryan Jeffery Leech
MUSIC: Johannes Brahms; arranged by Fred Bock

SYMPHONY
11.11.13.8.9.

They'll Know We Are Christians by Our Love 284

By this shall all men know that ye are My disciples, if ye have love one to another. John 13:35

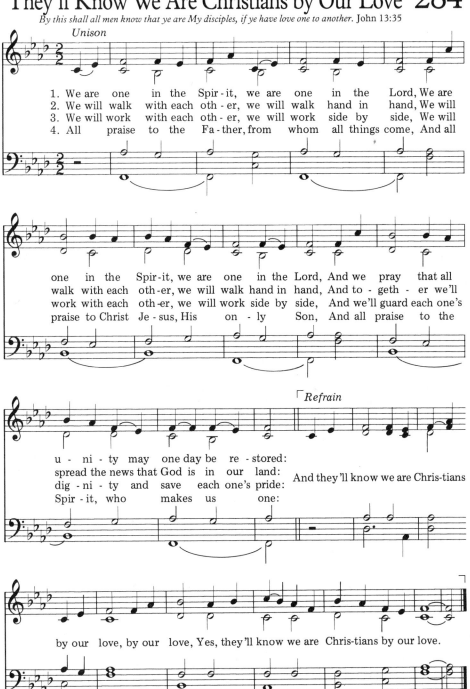

Unison

1. We are one in the Spir-it, we are one in the Lord, We are
2. We will walk with each oth-er, we will walk hand in hand, We will
3. We will work with each oth-er, we will work side by side, We will
4. All praise to the Fa-ther, from whom all things come, And all

one in the Spir-it, we are one in the Lord, And we pray that all
walk with each oth-er, we will walk hand in hand, And to-geth-er we'll
work with each oth-er, we will work side by side, And we'll guard each one's
praise to Christ Je-sus, His on-ly Son, And all praise to the

Refrain

u-ni-ty may one day be re-stored:
spread the news that God is in our land:
dig-ni-ty and save each one's pride: And they'll know we are Chris-tians
Spir-it, who makes us one:

by our love, by our love, Yes, they'll know we are Chris-tians by our love.

TEXT and MUSIC: Peter Scholtes; based on John 13:35

ST. BRENDAN'S
Irregular meter

285 In Christ There Is No East or West

In every nation he that feareth Him . . . is accepted with Him. Acts 10:35

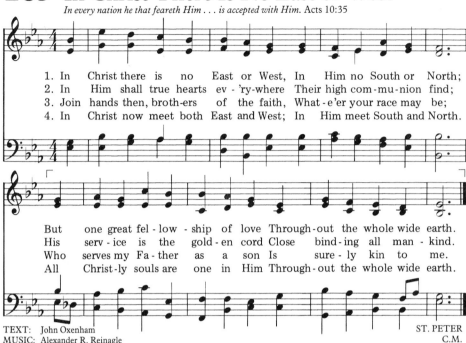

1. In Christ there is no East or West, In Him no South or North;
2. In Him shall true hearts ev-'ry-where Their high com-mu-nion find;
3. Join hands then, broth-ers of the faith, What-e'er your race may be;
4. In Christ now meet both East and West; In Him meet South and North.

But one great fel-low-ship of love Through-out the whole wide earth.
His serv-ice is the gold-en cord Close bind-ing all man-kind.
Who serves my Fa-ther as a son Is sure-ly kin to me.
All Christ-ly souls are one in Him Through-out the whole wide earth.

TEXT: John Oxenham
MUSIC: Alexander R. Reinagle
ST. PETER
C.M.

A lower setting may be found at No. 94; Alternate setting: McKEE, No. 547

Words used by permission of Desmond Dunkerley, 23 Haslemere Rd., Southsea, Portsmouth, Hants. PO4-8BB, England.

286 Blest Be the Tie That Binds

Ye are all one in Christ Jesus. Gal. 3:28

1. Blest be the tie that binds Our hearts in Chris-tian love;
2. Be-fore our Fa-ther's throne We pour our ar-dent prayers;
3. When we a-sun-der part, It gives us in-ward pain;

The fel-low-ship of kin-dred minds Is like to that a-bove.
Our fears, our hopes, our aims are one, Our com-forts and our cares.
But we shall still be joined in heart, And hope to meet a-gain. A-men.

TEXT: John Fawcett
MUSIC: Johann G. Naegeli; arranged by Lowell Mason
DENNIS
S.M.

Our God Has Made Us One 287

Keep the unity of the Spirit in the bond of peace. Eph. 4:3

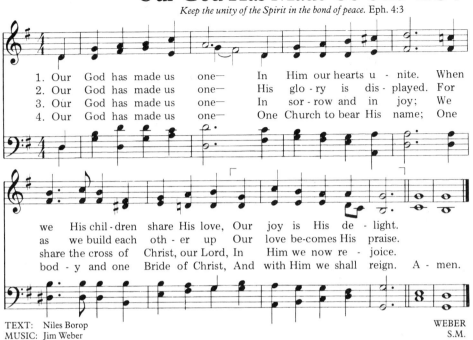

1. Our God has made us one— In Him our hearts u - nite. When
2. Our God has made us one— His glo - ry is dis - played. For
3. Our God has made us one— In sor - row and in joy; We
4. Our God has made us one— One Church to bear His name; One

we His chil - dren share His love, Our joy is His de - light.
as we build each oth - er up Our love be - comes His praise.
share the cross of Christ, our Lord, In Him we now re - joice.
bod - y and one Bride of Christ, And with Him we shall reign. A - men.

TEXT: Niles Borop
MUSIC: Jim Weber

WEBER
S.M.

RENEWAL AND REVIVAL

Faithful Men 288

Pray . . . the Lord of the harvest, that He will send forth labourers into His harvest. Matt. 9:38

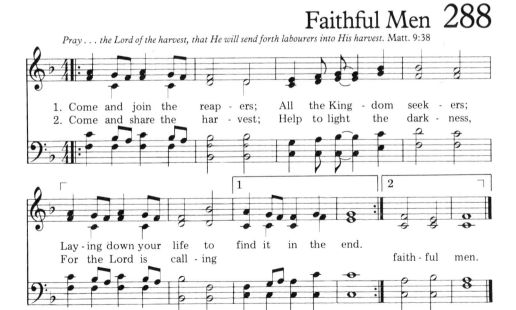

1. Come and join the reap - ers; All the King - dom seek - ers;
2. Come and share the har - vest; Help to light the dark - ness,

1

2

Lay - ing down your life to find it in the end.
For the Lord is call - ing faith - ful men.

TEXT and MUSIC: Twila Paris

FAITHFUL MEN
6.6.11.6.6.9.

289 There Shall Be Showers of Blessing

There shall be showers of blessing. Ezek. 34:26

1. "There shall be show-ers of bless - ing"— This is the prom-ise of love;
2. "There shall be show-ers of bless - ing"— Pre - cious re - viv - ing a - gain;
3. "There shall be show-ers of bless - ing"— Send them up - on us, O Lord;
4. "There shall be show-ers of bless - ing"— O that to - day they might fall,

There shall be sea - sons re - fresh - ing, Sent from the Sav - ior a - bove.
O - ver the hills and the val - leys, Sound of a - bun-dance of rain.
Grant to us now a re - fresh - ing, Come and now hon - or Your Word.
Now as to God we're con - fess - ing, Now as on Je - sus we call!

Refrain

Show - ers of bless - ing, Show-ers of bless-ing we need;
Show - ers, show-ers of bless - ing,

Mer - cy-drops round us are fall - ing, But for the show-ers we plead.

TEXT: Daniel W. Whittle; based on Ezekiel 34:26
MUSIC: James McGranahan

SHOWERS OF BLESSING
8.7.8.7. with Refrain

THE LIVING CHURCH

A Brief Service of
Prayer and Challenge

Suggested Hymn Stanzas

To facilitate an uninterrupted flow from stanza to stanza,
the suggested stanzas have been marked with an arrow: ▶

O Breath of Life, stanzas 1, 2, 3
God of Grace and God of Glory, stanza 1
Rise Up, O Church of God, complete

WORSHIP LEADER:
God of the living church empow'r,
   Thine ancient might reveal;
Give wisdom for this crucial hour,
   And in Thy mercy, heal.

PEOPLE:
God of the living church forgive,
   Renew, perfect, translate,
In Thee to be, and move, and live,
   Immanuel, we wait.

WORSHIP LEADER:
God of the living church renew,
   Fresh vision now impart,
And as we strive to live for You
   Sustain each faithful heart.

ALL:
God of the living church, we plead,
   Bestow Thy mighty pow'r,
Thy loving presence, Lord, we need,
   To guide us in this hour.

"God of the Living Church"
by Alfred H. Ackley

Optional Introduction to "O Breath of Life"

mf

291 O Breath of Life

O Lord, revive Thy work in the midst of the years. Hab. 3:2

1. O Breath of Life, come sweep-ing thru us, Re - vive Thy
2. O Wind of God, come bend us, break us, Till hum - bly
3. O Breath of Love, come breathe with - in us, Re - new - ing
4. O Heart of Christ, once bro - ken for us, 'Tis there we
5. Re - vive us, Lord! Is zeal a - bat - ing, While har - vest

Church with life and pow'r; O Breath of Life, come, cleanse, re-
we con - fess our need; Then in Thy ten - der - ness re -
thought and will and heart; Come, Love of Christ, a - fresh to
find our strength and rest; Our bro - ken, con - trite hearts now
fields are vast and white? Re - vive us, Lord, the world is

new us, And fit Thy Church to meet this hour.
make us, Re - vive, re - store, for this we plead.
win us, Re - vive Thy Church in ev - 'ry part.
so - lace, And let Thy wait - ing Church be blest.
wait - ing, E - quip Thy Church to spread the light. A - men.

TEXT: Bessie Porter Head
MUSIC: Joel Blomquist

DET AR ETT FAST ORD
9.8.9.8.

Optional transition to "God of Grace and God of Glory"

accel. poco a poco

God of Grace and God of Glory 292

Be not afraid . . . for the Lord thy God is with thee. Josh. 1:9

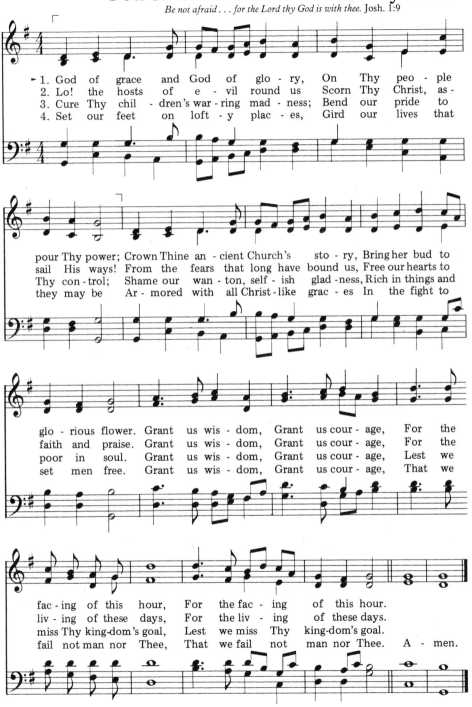

1. God of grace and God of glo - ry, On Thy peo - ple
2. Lo! the hosts of e - vil round us Scorn Thy Christ, as -
3. Cure Thy chil - dren's war - ring mad - ness; Bend our pride to
4. Set our feet on loft - y plac - es, Gird our lives that

pour Thy power; Crown Thine an - cient Church's sto - ry, Bring her bud to
sail His ways! From the fears that long have bound us, Free our hearts to
Thy con - trol; Shame our wan - ton, self - ish glad - ness, Rich in things and
they may be Ar - mored with all Christ - like grac - es In the fight to

glo - rious flower. Grant us wis - dom, Grant us cour - age, For the
faith and praise. Grant us wis - dom, Grant us cour - age, For the
poor in soul. Grant us wis - dom, Grant us cour - age, Lest we
set men free. Grant us wis - dom, Grant us cour - age, That we

fac - ing of this hour, For the fac - ing of this hour.
liv - ing of these days, For the liv - ing of these days.
miss Thy king-dom's goal, Lest we miss Thy king-dom's goal.
fail not man nor Thee, That we fail not man nor Thee. A - men.

TEXT: Harry Emerson Fosdick
MUSIC: John Hughes

CWM RHONDDA
8.7.8.7.8.7.7.

Optional transition to "Rise Up, O Church of God"

293 Rise Up, O Church of God

Be watchful, and strengthen the things which remain, that are ready to die. Rev. 3:2

1. Rise up, O Church of God! Have done with less - er things;
2. Rise up, O Church of God! His king-dom tar - ries long;
3. Rise up, O sons of God! The Church for you doth wait,
4. Lift high the cross of Christ! Tread where His feet have trod;

Give heart and mind and soul and strength To serve the King of kings.
Bring in the day of broth-er - hood And end the night of wrong.
Her strength un - e - qual to her task, Rise up, and make her great!
As fol - l'wers of the Son of Man, Rise up, O Church of God!

Optional last stanza setting
Descant

Rise up!

Broader

rit.   4. Lift high the cross of Christ! Tread

TEXT: William P. Merrill, altered
MUSIC: Aaron Williams; Last stanza setting by Eugene Thomas

ST. THOMAS
S.M.

Rise up! As fol-l'wers of the Son of Man, Rise
where His feet have trod; As fol-l'wers of the Son of Man, Rise

f *Optional choral ending*

up, O Church of God! Rise up, O Church of
up, O Church of God! Rise up O Church of

cresc. *ff*

God! Rise up! Rise up! Rise up!
God! Rise up! Rise up! Rise up!

The end of "THE LIVING CHURCH—A Brief Service of Prayer and Challenge"

294 Set My Soul Afire

His Word was in mine heart as a burning fire . . . I could not stay. Jer. 20:9

1. Set my soul a - fire, Lord, for Thy ho - ly Word, Burn it deep with - in me, let Thy voice be heard; Mil - lions grope in dark - ness in this day and hour, I will be a wit - ness, fill me with Thy pow'r.

2. Set my soul a - fire, Lord, for the lost in sin, Give to me a pas - sion as I seek to win; Help me not to fal - ter, nev - er let me fail, Fill me with Thy Spir - it, let Thy will pre - vail.

3. Set my soul a - fire, Lord, in my dai - ly life, Far too long I've wan - dered in this day of strife; Noth - ing else will mat - ter but to live for Thee, I will be a wit - ness, for Christ lives in me.

Refrain

Set my soul a - fire, Lord, set my soul a - fire, Make my life a wit - ness of Thy sav - ing pow'r. Mil - lions grope in dark - ness,

TEXT and MUSIC: Gene Bartlett

SCALES
11.11.11.11. with Refrain

wait-ing for Thy Word, Set my soul a - fire, Lord, Set my soul a - fire.

Revive Us Again 295

Wilt Thou not revive us again: that Thy people may rejoice in Thee? Ps. 85:6

1. We praise Thee, O God, for the Son of Thy love, For Je - sus who
2. We praise Thee, O God, for Thy Spir - it of light, Who has shown us our
3. All glo - ry and praise to the Lamb that was slain, Who has borne all our
4. Re - vive us a - gain— fill each heart with Thy love; May each soul be re -

died and is now gone a - bove.
Sav - ior and scat-tered our night.
sins and has cleansed ev - 'ry stain.
kin - dled with fire from a - bove.

Refrain

Hal-le - lu - jah, Thine the glo - ry! Hal-le -

lu - jah, a - men! Hal-le - lu - jah, Thine the glo - ry! Re - vive us a - gain.

TEXT: William P. Mackay
MUSIC: John J. Husband

REVIVE US AGAIN
11.11. with Refrain

296 We've a Story to Tell to the Nations

Go ye therefore, and teach all nations. Matt. 28:19

1. We've a sto-ry to tell to the na - tions That shall turn their
2. We've a song to be sung to the na - tions That shall lift their
3. We've a mes-sage to give to the na - tions That the Lord who
4. We've a Sav-ior to show to the na - tions Who the path of

hearts to the right, A sto - ry of truth and mer - cy, A
hearts to the Lord, A song that shall con - quer e - vil And
reign-eth a - bove Hath sent us His Son to save us, And
sor - row hath trod, That all of the world's great peo - ples Might

sto - ry of peace and light, A sto - ry of peace and light.
shat - ter the spear and sword, And shat - ter the spear and sword.
show us that God is love, And show us that God is love.
come to the truth of God, Might come to the truth of God.

Refrain

For the dark-ness shall turn to dawn-ing, And the dawn-ing to noon-day bright,

And Christ's great king-dom shall come to earth, The king-dom of love and light.

TEXT and MUSIC: H. Ernest Nichol

MESSAGE
10.8.8.7.7. with Refrain

I Love to Tell the Story 297

They that were scattered abroad went every where preaching the Word. Acts 8:4

1. I love to tell the sto - ry of un - seen things a - bove, Of Je - sus
2. I love to tell the sto - ry—'tis pleas-ant to re - peat What seems, each
3. I love to tell the sto - ry, for those who know it best Seem hun - ger-

and His glo - ry, of Je - sus and His love; I love to tell the
time I tell it, more won - der-ful - ly sweet; I love to tell the
ing and thirst-ing to hear it like the rest; And when in scenes of

sto - ry be - cause I know 'tis true, It sat - is - fies my long-ings
sto - ry, for some have nev - er heard The mes - sage of sal - va - tion
glo - ry I sing the new, new song, 'Twill be the old, old sto - ry

Refrain

as noth-ing else can do.
from God's own ho - ly Word. I love to tell the sto - ry! 'Twill be my
that I have loved so long.

theme in glo - ry— To tell the old, old sto - ry Of Je-sus and His love.

TEXT: A. Catherine Hankey
MUSIC: William G. Fischer

HANKEY
7.6.7.6.D. with Refrain

298 O Zion, Haste

O Zion, that bringest good tidings . . . lift up thy voice. Isa. 40:9

1. O *Zi - on, haste, thy mis - sion high ful - fill - ing, To tell to all the
2. Be - hold how man - y thou-sands still are ly - ing, Bound in the dark-some
3. Pro-claim to ev - ery peo - ple, tongue and na - tion That God, in whom they
4. Give of thy sons to bear the mes - sage glo - rious; Give of thy wealth to

world that God is Light; That He who made all na - tions is not will - ing
pris - on-house of sin, With none to tell them of the Sav - ior's dy - ing,
live and move, is love: Tell how He stooped to save His lost cre - a - tion,
speed them on their way; Pour out thy soul for them in prayer vic - to - rious;

⌐Refrain

One soul should per - ish, lost in shades of night.
Or of the life He died for them to win. Pub - lish glad ti - dings,
And died on earth that man might live a - bove.
And all thy spend-ing Je - sus will re - pay.

ti - dings of peace; Ti - dings of Je - sus, re - demp-tion, and re - lease.

TEXT: Mary A. Thomson
MUSIC: James Walch

TIDINGS
11.10.11.10. with Refrain

*Isaiah 40:9. By extension the word refers to the People of God.

Rescue the Perishing 299

Others save with fear, pulling them out of the fire. Jude 23

1. Res - cue the per - ish - ing, care for the dy - ing, Snatch them in pit - y from sin and the grave; Weep o'er the err - ing one, lift up the fall - en, Tell them of Je - sus, the might - y to save.

2. Tho they are slight-ing Him, still He is wait - ing, Wait - ing the pen - i - tent child to re - ceive; Plead with them ear-nest-ly, plead with them gen - tly, He will for - give if they on - ly be - lieve.

3. Down in the hu - man heart, crushed by the tempt - er, Feel - ings lie bur - ied that grace can re - store; Touched by a lov - ing heart, wak-ened by kind - ness, Cords that are bro - ken will vi-brate once more.

4. Res - cue the per - ish - ing, du - ty de-mands it— Strength for your la - bor the Lord will pro - vide; Back to the nar - row way pa - tient - ly win them, Tell the poor wan-d'rer a Sav - ior has died.

Refrain

Res - cue the per - ish-ing, Care for the dy - ing; Je - sus is mer - ci - ful, Je - sus will save.

TEXT: Fanny J. Crosby
MUSIC: William H. Doane

RESCUE
11.10.11.10. with Refrain

300 I'll Tell the World That I'm a Christian

I am not ashamed of the gospel of Christ. Rom. 1:16

1. I'll tell the world that I'm a Chris-tian— I'm not a-shamed His name to
2. I'll tell the world that He is com-ing— It may be near or far a-

bear; I'll tell the world that I'm a Chris-tian— I'll take Him with me
way; But we must live as if His com-ing Would be to-mor-row

an-y-where. I'll tell the world how Je-sus saved me, And how He
or to-day. For when He comes and life is o-ver, For those who

gave me a life brand-new; And I know that if you trust Him
love Him there's more to be; Eyes have nev-er seen the won-ders

That all He gave me He'll give to you. I'll tell the world
That He's pre-par-ing for you and me. O tell the world

TEXT and MUSIC: Baynard L. Fox

TUCKER
Irregular meter

that He's my Sav-ior,   No oth-er one   could love me so;   My life, my
that you're a Chris-tian,   Be not a-shamed   His name to bear;   O tell the

all   is His for-ev-er,   And where He leads me   I will go.
world   that you're a Chris-tian,   And take Him with you   ev-ery-where.

Go Ye into All the World 301

All power is given unto Me in heaven and in earth. Matt. 28:18

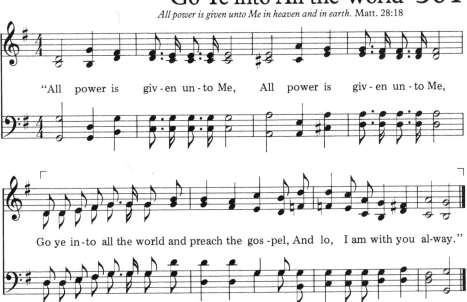

"All   power is   giv-en un-to Me,   All   power is   giv-en un-to Me,

Go ye in-to all the world and preach the gos-pel, And lo,   I am with you al-way."

TEXT and MUSIC: James McGranahan; based on Matthew 28:18-20

GO YE
8.8.12.8.

302 Share His Love

He . . . spared not His own Son, but delivered Him up for us all. Rom. 8:32

Unison

1. The love of God is broad-er than earth's vast ex-panse,
2. All those who have trust-ed in God's on-ly Son,
3. We show the love of God each day we live,

'Tis deep - er and wid - er than the sea.
And hold this pre - cious trea - sure in their hearts,
Re - veal Christ's pres - ence in our lives;

Love reach-es out to all to bring a - bun-dant life,
Seek ways to make it known to all who need to know
And how the Ho - ly Spir - it guides us day by day,

For God so loved the world His on - ly Son He gave.
That God so loved the world His on - ly Son He gave.
For God so loved the world His on - ly Son He gave.

Refrain

Share His love by tell - ing what the Lord has done for you,

TEXT and MUSIC: William J. Reynolds

SULLIVAN
Irregular meter

Share His love by shar-ing of your faith, and show the world that

Je-sus Christ is real to you ev-'ry mo-ment, ev-'ry day.

People Need the Lord 303

I am poor and needy . . . Thou art my help and my deliverer. Ps. 40:17

Unison

1. Peo-ple need the Lord, peo-ple need the
2. Peo-ple need the Lord, peo-ple need the

Lord; At the end of bro - ken dreams,
Lord; When will we re - al - ize

He's the o - pen door. peo-ple need the Lord.

TEXT and MUSIC: Greg Nelson and Phill McHugh;
arranged by David Allen

PEOPLE NEED THE LORD
Irregular meter

304 Lift High the Cross

I, if I be lifted up from the earth, will draw all men unto Me. John 12:32

Refrain - Unison

Lift high the Cross, the love of Christ pro - claim, Till all the world a - dore His sa - cred name.

Fine

Parts Optional

1. Come, Chris - tians, fol - low where our Sav - ior trod,
2. Led on their way by this tri - um - phant sign,
3. O Lord, once lift - ed on this glo - rious Tree,
4. Set up Thy throne, that earth's de - spair may cease
5. For Thy blest Cross which doth for all a - tone,

Return to Refrain

Our King vic - to - rious, Christ, the Son of God.
The hosts of God in con - qu'ring ranks com - bine.
As Thou hast prom - ised, draw men un - to Thee.
Be - neath the shad - ow of its heal - ing peace.
Cre - a - tion's prais - es rise be - fore Thy throne.

TEXT: George W. Kitchin and Michael R. Newbolt
MUSIC: Sydney H. Nicholson

CRUCIFER
10.10.10.10.

Copyright used by permission of Hymns Ancient and Modern LTD.

Lord, Thy Church on Earth Is Seeking 305

Lift up your eyes, and look on the fields; for they are white already to harvest. John 4:35

1. Lord, Thy church on earth is seek - ing Thy re - new - al
2. Free - dom, give to those in bond - age, Lift the bur - dens
3. In the streets of ev - 'ry cit - y Where the bruised and

from a - bove; Teach us all the art of speak - ing With the
caused by sin; Give new hope, new strength and cour - age, Grant re -
lone - ly dwell, We shall show the Sav - ior's pit - y, We shall

ac - cent of Thy love. We would heed Thy great com - mis - sion:
lease from fears with - in. Light for dark - ness, joy for sor - row;
of His mer - cy tell. In all lands and with all rac - es,

"Go ye in - to ev - 'ry place; Preach, bap - tize, ful - fill My
Love for ha - tred, peace for strife. These and count - less bless - ings
We shall serve and seek to bring All the world to ren - der

mis - sion, Serve with love and share My grace."
fol - low As the Spir - it gives new life.
prais - es, Christ, to Thee, Re - deem - er, King. A - men.

TEXT: Hugh Sherlock
MUSIC: William David Young

KINGSTON
8.7.8.7.D.

306 Jesus Saves!

Christ Jesus came into the world to save sinners. 1 Tim. 1:15

1. We have heard the joy - ful sound— Je - sus saves! Je - sus saves!
2. Waft it on the roll - ing tide— Je - sus saves! Je - sus saves!
3. Sing a - bove the bat - tle strife— Je - sus saves! Je - sus saves!
4. Give the winds a might - y voice— Je - sus saves! Je - sus saves!

Spread the ti - dings all a - round— Je - sus saves! Je - sus saves!
Tell to sin - ners far and wide— Je - sus saves! Je - sus saves!
By His death and end - less life— Je - sus saves! Je - sus saves!
Let the na - tions now re - joice— Je - sus saves! Je - sus saves!

Bear the news to ev - 'ry land, Climb the steeps and cross the waves;
Sing, ye is - lands of the sea! Ech - o back, ye o - cean caves!
Sing it soft - ly thru the gloom, When the heart for mer - cy craves;
Shout sal - va - tion full and free, High - est hills and deep - est caves;

On - ward! 'tis our Lord's com - mand— Je - sus saves! Je - sus saves!
Earth shall keep her ju - bi - lee— Je - sus saves! Je - sus saves!
Sing in tri - umph o'er the tomb— Je - sus saves! Je - sus saves!
This our song of vic - to - ry— Je - sus saves! Je - sus saves!

TEXT: Priscilla J. Owens
MUSIC: William J. Kirkpatrick

JESUS SAVES
7.6.7.6.7.7.7.6.

Send the Light 307

. . . the light of the glorious gospel of Christ. 2 Cor. 4:4

1. There's a call comes ring-ing o'er the rest-less wave, "Send the light!
2. We have heard the Mac-e-do-nian call to-day, "Send the light!
3. Let us pray that grace may ev-ery-where a-bound, Send the light!
4. Let us not grow wea-ry in the work of love, Send the light!

Send the light!" There are souls to res-cue, there are souls to save,
Send the light!" And a gold-en of-fering at the cross we lay,
Send the light! And a Christ-like spir-it ev-ery-where be found,
Send the light! Let us gath-er jew-els for a crown a-bove,

Refrain

Send the light! Send the light! Send the light, the bless-ed gos-pel light;

1. Let it shine from shore to shore!

2. shine from shore to shore!

TEXT and MUSIC: Charles H. Gabriel

McCABE
11.6.11.6. with Refrain

308 Go

Lo, I am with you always, even unto the end of the world. Matt. 28:20

1. Go ye there-fore and teach all na - tions, go, go, go.
2. If you love Me, real - ly love Me, feed My sheep.
3. Go ye there-fore and teach all na - tions, go, go, go.

Go ye there-fore and teach all na - tions, go, go,
If you love Me, real - ly love Me, feed My
Go ye there-fore and teach all na - tions, go, go,

go. Bap-tiz-ing them in the name of the Fa-ther and Son, and
sheep. Lo, I'll be with you for-ev-er and ev-er, un-til the
go. Bap-tiz-ing them in the name of the Fa-ther and Son, and

Ho - ly Ghost. Go, go, go.
end of the world. Go, go, go.
Ho - ly Ghost. Go, go, go.

TEXT and MUSIC: Leon Patillo; arranged by Eugene Thomas

GO
Irregular meter

Pass It On 309

If God so loved us, we ought also to love one another. 1 John 4:11

1. It only takes a spark to get a fire go-ing,
2. What a won-drous time is spring—when all the trees are bud-ding,
3. I wish for you, my friend, this hap-pi-ness that I've found—

pass it on!

And soon all those a-round can warm up in its glow-ing;
The birds be-gin to sing, the flow-ers start their bloom-ing;
You can de-pend on Him, it mat-ters not where you're bound;

pass it on!

That's how it is with God's love, once you've ex-per-i-enced it: You
That's how it is with God's love, once you've ex-per-i-enced it: You
I'll shout it from the moun-tain top, I want my world to know: The

spread His love to ev-'ry-one, you want to pass it on.
want to sing, it's fresh like spring, you want to pass it on.
Lord of love has come to me, I want to pass it on.

TEXT and MUSIC: Kurt Kaiser

PASS IT ON
Irregular meter

310 So Send I You

As My Father hath sent Me, even so send I you. John 20:21

1. So send I you— to la-bor un-re-ward-ed, To serve un-
2. So send I you— to bind the bruised and bro-ken, O'er wan-d'ring
3. So send I you— to lone-li-ness and long-ing, With heart a-
4. So send I you— to leave your life's am-bi-tion, To die to
5. So send I you— to hearts made hard by ha-tred, To eyes made

paid, un-loved, un-sought, un-known, To bear re-buke, to suf-fer
souls to work, to weep, to wake, To bear the bur-dens of a
hun-g'ring for the loved and known, For-sak-ing home and kin-dred,
dear de-sire, self-will re-sign, To la-bor long, and love where
blind be-cause they will not see, To spend, tho it be blood, to

1-4 *D.C.*

scorn and scoff-ing— So send I you, to toil for Me a-lone.
world a-wea-ry— So send I you, to suf-fer for My sake.
friend and dear one— So send I you, to know My love a-lone.
men re-vile you— So send I you, to lose your life in Mine.
spend and spare not— So send I you, to taste of Cal-va-

5 ⌜ *Coda*

ry. "As the Fa-ther hath sent Me, So send I you."

TEXT: Margaret Clarkson; based on John 20:21
MUSIC: John W. Peterson
Alternate tune: adaptable, without Coda, to FINLANDIA, No. 347

TORONTO
11.10.11.10. with Coda

So Send I You - by Grace Made Strong 311

As My Father hath sent Me, even so send I you. John 20:21

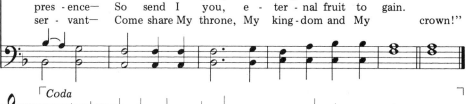

1. So send I you— by grace made strong to tri - umph O'er hosts of hell,
2. So send I you— to take to souls in bond - age The Word of Truth
3. So send I you— My strength to know in weak - ness, My joy in grief,
4. So send I you— to bear My cross with pat - ience, And then one day

o'er dark - ness, death and sin, My name to bear and in that name to
that sets the cap - tive free, To break the bonds of sin, to loose death's
My per - fect peace in pain, To prove My pow'r, My grace, My prom - ised
with joy to lay it down, To hear My voice, "Well done, My faith-ful

1-3 **4**
D.C.

con - quer— So send I you, My vic - to - ry to win.
fet - ters— So send I you, to bring the lost to Me.
pres - ence— So send I you, e - ter - nal fruit to gain.
ser - vant— Come share My throne, My king - dom and My crown!"

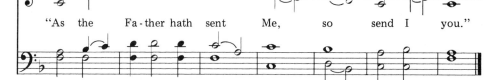

Coda

"As the Fa - ther hath sent Me, so send I you."

TEXT: Margaret Clarkson; based on John 20:21
MUSIC: Kurt Kaiser
Alternate tunes: adaptable, without Coda to FINLANDIA, No. 347; TORONTO, No. 310

BY GRACE MADE STRONG
11.10.11.10. with Coda

312 To Be God's People

Ye shine as lights in the world; holding forth the Word of life. Phil. 2:15-16

Unison

1. Al-might-y Fa-ther give us a vis-ion
2. And when we fal-ter be Thou our com-fort;

of a dy-ing world that needs Your love and care.
guide us as Your chil-dren that our lives may be

We see the need, the yearn-ing for a Sav-ior,
A bea-con in this dark-ness that sur-rounds us,

In Je-sus' name, grant this our prayer. To be God's
A light that oth-ers then may see.

Refrain

peo-ple in this place, live His

TEXT and MUSIC: Charles F. Brown

GOD'S PEOPLE
10.11.11.8. with Refrain

good - ness, share His grace, Pro -claim God's

mer - cy through His Son, be His

love to ev - 'ry - one.

Lord, Lay Some Soul upon My Heart 313

I made myself servant unto all, that I might gain the more. 1 Cor. 9:19

Lord lay some soul up - on my heart, And love that soul through me;

And may I no - bly do my part To win that soul for Thee.

TEXT: Dr. Leon Tucker
MUSIC: Ira D. Sankey

IRA
C.M.

314 Reach Out and Touch

Let us not love in word . . . but in deed and in truth. 1 John 3:18

Unison

1. Reach out and touch a soul that is hun-gry; Reach out and touch a
2. Reach out and touch a friend who is wea-ry; Reach out and touch a

spir - it in de - spair; Reach out and touch a life torn and dirt - y, A
seek - er un-a - ware; Reach out and touch tho' touch-ing means los-ing A

man who is lone - ly— If you care! Reach out and touch that
part of your own self— If you dare! Reach out and give your

neigh-bor who hates you; Reach out and touch that stran-ger who meets you;
love to the love - less; Reach out and make a home for the home-less;

Reach out and touch the broth-er who needs you; Reach out and let the smile of
Reach out and shed God's light in the dark - ness; Reach out and let the smile of

TEXT and MUSIC: Charles F. Brown

REACH OUT
Irregular meter

God touch thro' you.

you.

Let Your Heart Be Broken 315

When He saw the multitudes, He was moved with compassion on them. Matt. 9:36

1. Let your heart be bro - ken For a world in need— Feed the mouths that
2. Here on earth ap - ply - ing Prin - ci - ples of love— Vis - i - ble ex -
3. Blest to be a bless - ing, Priv - i - leged to care, Chal-lenged by the
4. Add to your be - liev - ing Deeds that prove it true— Know-ing Christ as
5. Let your heart be ten - der And your vi - sion clear— See man - kind as

hun - ger, Soothe the wounds that bleed, Give the cup of wa - ter And the
pres - sion God still rules a - bove, Liv - ing il - lus - tra - tion Of the
need Ap - par - ent ev - 'ry - where, Where mankind is want - ing Fill the
Sav - ior, Make Him Mas - ter too: Fol - low in His foot-steps, Go where
God sees, Serve Him far and near; Let your heart be bro - ken By a

loaf of bread— Be the hands of Je - sus, Serv - ing in His stead.
Liv - ing Word To the minds of all who've Nev - er seen and heard.
va - cant place, Be the means thru which the Lord re - veals His grace.
He has trod, In the world's great trou - ble Risk your-self for God.
broth-er's pain, Share your rich re - sourc - es— Give and give a - gain.

TEXT: Bryan Jeffery Leech
MUSIC: James Mountain

WYE VALLEY (abridged)
6.5.6.5.D.

Words copyright © 1976 by THE EVANGELICAL COVENANT CHURCH. Used by Permission.

316 Macedonia

Come over into Macedonia, and help us. Acts 16:9

1. The vi-sion of a dy-ing world Is vast be-fore our eyes; We
2. The sav-age hugs his god of stone And fears de-scent of night; The
3. To-day, as un-der-stand-ing's bounds Are stretch'd on ev-ery hand, O
4. The warn-ing bell of judg-ment tolls, A-bove us looms the cross; A-

feel the heart-beat of its need, We hear its fee-ble cries: Lord
cit-y dwell-er cring-es lone A-mid the gar-ish light: Lord
clothe Thy Word in bright, new sounds, And speed it o'er the land; Lord
round are ev-er-dy-ing souls—How great, how great the loss! O

Je-sus Christ, re-vive Thy church In this, her cru-cial hour! Lord
Je-sus Christ, a-rouse Thy church To see their mute dis-tress! Lord
Je-sus Christ, em-pow-er us To preach by ev-ery means! Lord
Lord, con-strain and move Thy church The glad news to im-part! And

Je-sus Christ, a-wake Thy church With Spir-it-giv-en pow'r.
Je-sus Christ, e-quip Thy church With love and ten-der-ness.
Je-sus Christ, em-bold-en us In near and dis-tant scenes.
Lord, as Thou dost stir Thy church, Be-gin with-in my heart. A-men.

TEXT: Anne Ortlund
MUSIC: Henry S. Cutler

ALL SAINTS, NEW
C.M.D.

This Child We Dedicate to Thee 317

Bring them up in the nurture and admonition of the Lord. Eph. 6:4

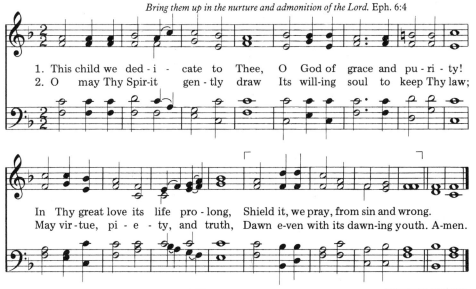

1. This child we ded-i-cate to Thee, O God of grace and pu-ri-ty!
2. O may Thy Spir-it gen-tly draw Its will-ing soul to keep Thy law;

In Thy great love its life pro-long, Shield it, we pray, from sin and wrong.
May vir-tue, pi-e-ty, and truth, Dawn e-ven with its dawn-ing youth. A-men.

TEXT: From the German; translated by Samuel Gilman
MUSIC: Henry K. Oliver

FEDERAL STREET
L.M.

Good Shepherd, Take This Little Child 318

He took them up in His arms, put His hands upon them, and blessed them. Mark 10:16

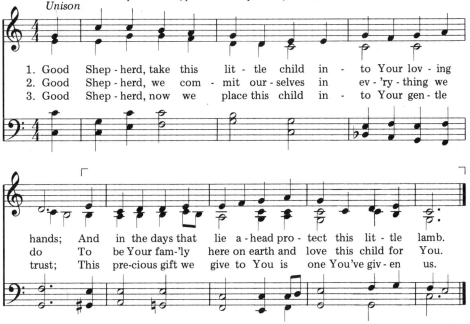

Unison

1. Good Shep-herd, take this lit-tle child in-to Your lov-ing
2. Good Shep-herd, we com-mit our-selves in ev-'ry-thing we
3. Good Shep-herd, now we place this child in-to Your gen-tle

hands; And in the days that lie a-head pro-tect this lit-tle lamb.
do To be Your fam-'ly here on earth and love this child for You.
trust; This pre-cious gift we give to You is one You've giv-en us.

TEXT: Claire Cloninger
MUSIC: Ken Barker

AMY
C.M.

319 We Bless the Name of Christ, the Lord

It becometh us to fulfill all righteousness. Matt. 3:15

Unison

1. We bless the name of Christ the Lord, We bless Him
2. We fol - low Him with pure de - light To sanc - ti -
3. Bap - tized in God the Fa - ther, Son And Ho - ly
4. By grace we "Ab - ba, Fa - ther," cry; By grace the

for His ho - ly Word, Who loved to do His
fy His sa - cred rite, And thus our faith with
Spir - it, Three in One, With con - science free we
Com - fort - er comes nigh; And for Thy grace our

Fa - ther's will, And all His righ - teous - ness ful - fill.
wa - ter seal To prove o - be - dience that we feel.
rest in God, In love and peace, thro' Je - sus' blood.
love shall be For - ev - er, on - ly, Lord, for Thee.

TEXT: Samuel F. Coffman
MUSIC: Thomas Hastings
An alternate setting of this tune may be found at No. 432

RETREAT
L.M.

320 Come Holy Spirit, Dove Divine

Therefore we are buried with Him by baptism into death. Rom. 6:4

1. Come, Ho-ly Spir - it, Dove di - vine, On these bap - tis-mal wa - ters shine,
2. We love Thy name, we love Thy laws, And joy - ful - ly em-brace Thy cause,
3. We sink be - neath the wa - ter's face, And thank Thee for Thy sav - ing grace;
4. And as we rise with Thee to live, O let the Ho - ly Spir - it give

TEXT: Adoniram Judson
MUSIC: H. Percy Smith
A higher setting may be found at No. 451

MARYTON
L.M.

And teach our hearts, in high - est strain, To praise the Lamb for sin - ners slain.
We love Thy cross, the shame, the pain, O Lamb of God for sin - ners slain.
We die to sin and seek a grave With Thee, be-neath the yield-ing wave.
The seal - ing unc - tion from a - bove, The joy of life, the fire of love. A-men.

THE LORD'S SUPPER

According to Thy Gracious Word 321

This is My body, which is broken for you: this do in remembrance of Me. 1 Cor. 11:24

1. Ac - cord - ing to Thy gra-cious word, In meek hu - mil - i - ty,
2. Thy bod - y, bro - ken for my sake, My bread from heav'n shall be;
3. When to the cross I turn mine eyes And rest on Cal - va - ry,
4. Re - mem - ber Thee and all Thy pains And all Thy love to me;
5. And when these fail - ing lips grow dumb And mind and mem - 'ry flee,

This will I do, my dy - ing Lord: I will re - mem - ber Thee.
Thy tes - ta - men - tal cup I take, And thus re - mem - ber Thee.
O Lamb of God, my sac - ri - fice, I must re - mem - ber Thee.
Yea, while a breath, a pulse re - mains, Will I re - mem - ber Thee.
When Thou shalt in Thy king - dom come, Je - sus, re - mem - ber me!

TEXT: James Montgomery
MUSIC: From Henry W. Greatorex's *Collection of Church Music*, 1851
    A higher setting may be found at No. 70

MANOAH
C.M.

322 In Remembrance

This is My body which is given for you: this do in remembrance of Me. Luke 22:19

Introduction

In re- mem-brance of Me,
(In re-) mem-brance of Me,

eat this bread. In re - mem-brance of Me, drink this wine. In re-
heal the sick. In re - mem-brance of Me, feed the poor. In re-

mem-brance of Me, pray for the time when God's own will is
mem-brance of Me, o - pen the door and let your broth - er

1 done. In re-
2 in, Let him in.

Take, eat, and be com - fort - ed; drink and re - mem - ber

TEXT: Ragan Courtney
MUSIC: Buryl Red; arranged by Robert F. Douglas

RED
Irregular meter

© Copyright 1972 Broadman Press. International Copyright Secured. All Rights Reserved. Used by Permission.

323 Let Us Break Bread Together

They continued steadfastly . . . in breaking of bread. Acts 2:42

1. Let us break bread to-geth-er on our knees; (on our knees;)
2. Let us drink the cup to-geth-er on our knees; (on our knees;)
3. Let us praise God to-geth-er on our knees; (on our knees;)

Let us break bread to-geth-er on our knees; (on our knees;)
Let us drink the cup to-geth-er on our knees; (on our knees;)
Let us praise God to-geth-er on our knees; (on our knees;)

Refrain

When I fall on my knees with my face to the ris-ing sun,

O Lord, have mer-cy on me. (on me.)

TEXT: Traditional Spiritual
MUSIC: Traditional Spiritual; arranged by Keith Phillips

LET US BREAK BREAD
Irregular meter

Come Celebrate Jesus 324

This do . . . in remembrance of Me. 1 Cor. 11:25

Come cel-e-brate Je-sus, come cel-e-brate Je-sus,

The bread and the wine, the mo-ment in time. Come cel-e-brate

Je-sus, the Spir-it that frees us, His ta-ble

1

D.C.

has been laid, come now and cel-e-brate Him.

2

cel-e-brate Him. (cel-e-brate Him.)

TEXT: Claire Cloninger
MUSIC: John Rosasco; arranged by David Allen

CELEBRATE JESUS
Irregular meter

325 Here, O My Lord, I See Thee Face to Face

Thy face, Lord, will I seek. Ps. 27:8

1. Here, O my Lord, I see Thee face to face,
2. Here would I feed up - on the bread of God,
3. I have no help but Thine, nor do I need
4. Mine is the sin, but Thine the right - eous - ness,

Here would I touch and han - dle things un - seen;
Here drink with Thee the roy - al wine of heaven;
An - oth - er arm save Thine to lean up - on;
Mine is the guilt, but Thine the cleans - ing blood;

Here grasp with firm - er hand e - ter - nal grace,
Here would I lay a - side each earth - ly load,
It is e - nough, my Lord, e - nough in - deed—
Here is my robe, my ref - uge, and my peace—

And all my wea - ri - ness up - on Thee lean.
Here taste a - fresh the calm of sin for - giv'n.
My strength is in Thy might, Thy might a - lone.
Thy blood, Thy right - eous - ness, O Lord, my God. A - men.

TEXT: Horatius Bonar
MUSIC: Edward Dearle

PENITENTIA
10.10.10.10.

Softly and Tenderly 326

Come unto Me, all ye that labour and are heavy laden, and I will give you rest. Matt. 11:28

1. Soft - ly and ten - der - ly Je - sus is call - ing, Call - ing for
2. Why should we tar - ry when Je - sus is plead - ing, Plead - ing for
3. Time is now fleet - ing, the mo - ments are pass - ing, Pass - ing from
4. O for the won - der - ful love He has prom - ised, Prom - ised for

you and for me; See, on the por - tals He's wait - ing and watch - ing,
you and for me? Why should we lin - ger and heed not His mer - cies,
you and from me; Shad - ows are gath - er - ing, death's night is com - ing,
you and for me! Though we have sinned, He has mer - cy and par - don,

Refrain

Watch - ing for you and for me.
Mer - cies for you and for me?
Com - ing for you and for me.
Par - don for you and for me.

Come home, come home,
Come home, come home,

Ye who are wea - ry, come home; Ear - nest - ly, ten - der - ly,

Je - sus is call - ing, Call - ing, O sin - ner, come home!

TEXT and MUSIC: Will L. Thompson

THOMPSON
11.7.11.7. with Refrain

327 Jesus Is Calling

Today, if ye will hear His voice, harden not your hearts. Heb. 4:7

1. Je - sus is ten - der - ly call - ing you home, Call - ing to - day,
2. Je - sus is call - ing the wea - ry to rest, Call - ing to - day,
3. Je - sus is wait - ing, O come to Him now, Wait - ing to - day,
4. Je - sus is plead - ing, O list to His voice: Hear Him to - day,

call - ing to - day, Why from the sun - shine of love will you roam
call - ing to - day, Bring Him your bur - den and you shall be blest;
wait - ing to - day, Come with your sins, at His feet low - ly bow;
hear Him to - day, They who be - lieve on His name shall re - joice;

Refrain

Far - ther and far - ther a - way? Call - ing to - day,
He will not turn you a - way.
Come, and no long - er de - lay.
Quick - ly a - rise and a - way. Call - ing, call - ing to - day, to - day,

Call - ing to - day, Je - sus is
Call - ing, call - ing to - day, to - day, Je - sus is ten - der - ly

call - ing, Is ten - der - ly call - ing to - day.
call - ing to - day,

TEXT: Fanny J. Crosby
MUSIC: George C. Stebbins

CALLING TODAY
10.8.10.7. with Refrain

Have You Any Room for Jesus? 328

Now is the accepted time; behold, now is the day of salvation. 2 Cor. 6:2

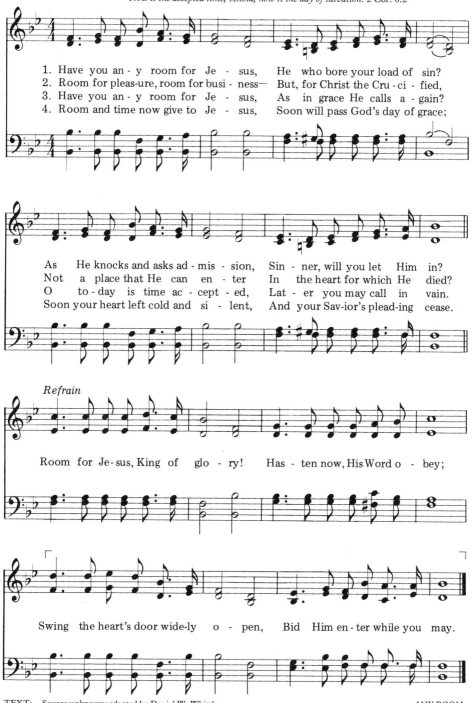

1. Have you an-y room for Je - sus, He who bore your load of sin?
2. Room for pleas-ure, room for busi - ness— But, for Christ the Cru - ci - fied,
3. Have you an-y room for Je - sus, As in grace He calls a - gain?
4. Room and time now give to Je - sus, Soon will pass God's day of grace;

As He knocks and asks ad - mis - sion, Sin - ner, will you let Him in?
Not a place that He can en - ter In the heart for which He died?
O to - day is time ac - cept - ed, Lat - er you may call in vain.
Soon your heart left cold and si - lent, And your Sav-ior's plead-ing cease.

Refrain

Room for Je-sus, King of glo - ry! Has - ten now, His Word o - bey;

Swing the heart's door wide-ly o - pen, Bid Him en - ter while you may.

TEXT: Source unknown; adapted by Daniel W. Whittle
MUSIC: C. C. Williams

ANY ROOM
8.7.8.7. with Refrain

329 The Savior Is Waiting

Today if ye will hear His voice, harden not your hearts. Heb. 3:15

1. The Sav - ior is wait - ing to en - ter your heart— Why don't you
2. If you'll take one step toward the Sav - ior, my friend, You'll find His

let Him come in? There's noth - ing in this world to keep you a -
arms o - pen wide; Re - ceive Him and all of your dark - ness will

Refrain

part— What is your an - swer to Him? Time af - ter time He has
end, With - in your heart He'll a - bide.

wait - ed be - fore, And now He is wait - ing a - gain To see if you're

will - ing to o - pen the door— O how He wants to come in.

TEXT and MUSIC: Ralph Carmichael;
arranged by Michael James

CARMICHAEL
11.7.11.7. with Refrain

Optional choral ending
Slowly

Oh, how He wants to come in.
wants to come in.
in.

Only Trust Him 330

Believe on the Lord Jesus Christ, and thou shalt be saved. Acts 16:31

1. Come, ev-'ry soul by sin op-pressed—There's mer-cy with the Lord,
2. For Je-sus shed His pre-cious blood, Rich bless-ings to be-stow;
3. Yes, Je-sus is the Truth, the Way, That leads you in-to rest:

And He will sure-ly give you rest By trust-ing in His Word.
Plunge now in-to the crim-son flood That wash-es white as snow.
Be-lieve in Him with-out de-lay And you are ful-ly blest.

Refrain

On-ly trust Him, on-ly trust Him, On-ly trust Him now;

He will save you, He will save you, He will save you now.

TEXT and MUSIC: John H. Stockton

MINERVA
C.M. with Refrain

331 Room at the Cross for You

Yet there is room. Luke 14:22

1. The cross up-on which Je-sus died Is a shel-ter in
2. Tho mil-lions have found Him a friend And have turned from the
3. The hand of my Sav-ior is strong, And the love of my

which we can hide; And its grace so free is suf-
sins they have sinned, The Sav-ior still waits to
Sav-ior is long; Through sun-shine or rain, through

fi-cient for me, And deep is its foun-tain—as wide as the sea.
o-pen the gates And wel-comes a sin-ner be-fore it's too late.
loss or in gain, The blood flows from Cal-v'ry to cleanse ev-'ry stain.

Refrain

There's room at the cross for you, There's room at the cross for you; Tho

mil-lions have come, There's still room for one—Yes, there's room at the cross for you.

TEXT and MUSIC: Ira F. Stanphill

ROOM AT THE CROSS
Irregular meter

Without Him 332

Without Me ye can do nothing. John 15:5

1. With-out Him I could do noth-ing, With-out Him I'd sure-
2. With-out Him I would be dy-ing, With-out Him I'd be

ly fail; With-out Him I would be drift-ing Like a
en-slaved; With-out Him life would be hope-less, But with

Refrain

ship with-out a sail.
Je-sus, thank God, I'm saved. Je - sus, O Je - sus!

Do you know Him to-day? Do not turn Him a-way. O Je-

sus, O Je - sus, With-out Him, how lost I would be.

TEXT and MUSIC: Mylon R. LeFevre

WITHOUT HIM
8.7.8.7. with Refrain

333 His Way with Thee

As for God, His way is perfect . . . God . . . maketh my way perfect. Ps. 18:30,32

1. Would you live for Je - sus and be al-ways pure and good? Would you walk with
2. Would you have Him make you free and fol-low at His call? Would you know the
3. Would you in His king-dom find a place of con-stant rest? Would you prove Him

Him with - in the nar - row road? Would you have Him bear your bur - den,
peace that comes by giv - ing all? Would you have Him save you, so that
true in prov - i - den - tial test? Would you in His serv - ice la - bor

Refrain

car - ry all your load? Let Him have His way with thee.
you need nev-er fall? Let Him have His way with thee. His pow'r can make you what you
al-ways at your best? Let Him have His way with thee.

ought to be; His blood can cleanse your heart and make you free; His love can

fill your soul, and you will see 'Twas best for Him to have His way with thee.

TEXT and MUSIC: Cyrus S. Nusbaum

NUSBAUM
Irregular meter

Come, Ye Sinners, Poor and Needy 334

Come . . . take the water of life freely. Rev. 22:17

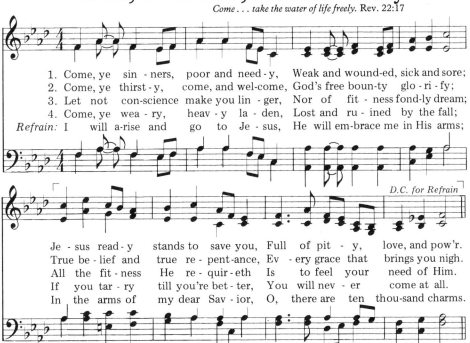

1. Come, ye sin-ners, poor and need-y, Weak and wound-ed, sick and sore;
2. Come, ye thirst-y, come, and wel-come, God's free boun-ty glo-ri-fy;
3. Let not con-science make you lin-ger, Nor of fit-ness fond-ly dream;
4. Come, ye wea-ry, heav-y la-den, Lost and ru-ined by the fall;

Refrain: I will a-rise and go to Je-sus, He will em-brace me in His arms;

D.C. for Refrain

Je-sus read-y stands to save you, Full of pit-y, love, and pow'r.
True be-lief and true re-pent-ance, Ev-ery grace that brings you nigh.
All the fit-ness He re-quir-eth Is to feel your need of Him.
If you tar-ry till you're bet-ter, You will nev-er come at all.
In the arms of my dear Sav-ior, O, there are ten thou-sand charms.

TEXT: Joseph Hart; Refrain, source unknown
MUSIC: Traditional American melody; Walker's *Southern Harmony*, 1835

ARISE
8.7.8.7. with Refrain

Turn Your Eyes upon Jesus 335

We all, . . . beholding . . . the glory of the Lord, are changed into the same image. 2 Cor. 3:18

Turn your eyes up-on Je - sus, Look full in His won-der-ful face,

won-der-ful face,

And the things of earth will grow strange-ly dim In the light of His glo-ry and grace.

TEXT and MUSIC: Helen H. Lemmel

LEMMEL (Refrain only)
Irregular meter

336 Jesus, I Come

He hath sent Me . . . to proclaim liberty to the captives. Isa. 61:1

1. Out of my bond-age, sor-row and night, Je-sus, I come, Je-sus, I come;
2. Out of my shame-ful fail-ure and loss, Je-sus, I come, Je-sus, I come;
3. Out of un-rest and ar-ro-gant pride, Je-sus, I come, Je-sus, I come;
4. Out of the fear and dread of the tomb, Je-sus, I come, Je-sus, I come;

In-to Thy free-dom, glad-ness and light, Je-sus, I come to Thee.
In-to the glo-rious gain of Thy cross, Je-sus, I come to Thee.
In-to Thy bless-ed will to a-bide, Je-sus, I come to Thee.
In-to the joy and light of Thy home, Je-sus, I come to Thee.

Out of my sick-ness in-to Thy health, Out of my want and in-to Thy wealth,
Out of earth's sor-rows in-to Thy balm, Out of life's storms and in-to Thy calm,
Out of my-self to dwell in Thy love, Out of de-spair in-to rap-tures a-bove,
Out of the depths of ru-in un-told, In-to the peace of Thy shel-ter-ing fold,

Out of my sin and in-to Thy-self, Je-sus, I come to Thee.
Out of dis-tress to ju-bi-lant psalm, Je-sus, I come to Thee.
Up-ward for aye on wings like a dove, Je-sus, I come to Thee.
Ev-er Thy glo-rious face to be-hold, Je-sus, I come to Thee.

TEXT: William T. Sleeper
MUSIC: George C. Stebbins

JESUS, I COME
Irregular meter

Pass Me Not 337

The Lord is not slack concerning His promise . . . not willing that any should perish. 2 Pet. 3:9

1. Pass me not, O gen - tle Sav - ior— Hear my hum - ble cry!
2. Let me at a throne of mer - cy Find a sweet re - lief;
3. Trust - ing on - ly in Thy mer - it, Would I seek Thy face;
4. Thou the spring of all my com - fort, More than life to me!

While on oth - ers Thou art call - ing, Do not pass me by.
Kneel - ing there in deep con - tri - tion— Help my un - be - lief.
Heal my wound - ed, bro - ken spir - it, Save me by Thy grace.
Whom have I on earth be - side Thee? Whom in heav'n but Thee?

Refrain

Sav - ior, Sav - ior, Hear my hum - ble cry!

While on oth - ers Thou art call - ing, Do not pass me by.

TEXT: Fanny J. Crosby
MUSIC: William H. Doane

PASS ME NOT
8.5.8.5. with Refrain

338 At Calvary

When they were come to the place, which is called Calvary, there they crucified Him. Luke 23:33

1. Years I spent in van - i - ty and pride, Car - ing not my Lord was
2. By God's Word at last my sin I learned— Then I trem-bled at the
3. Now I've giv'n to Je - sus ev - 'ry - thing, Now I glad - ly own Him
4. O the love that drew sal - va - tion's plan! O the grace that bro't it

cru - ci - fied, Know-ing not it was for me He died On Cal - va - ry.
law I'd spurned, Till my guilt-y soul im-plor-ing turned To Cal - va - ry.
as my King, Now my rap-tured soul can on - ly sing Of Cal - va - ry.
down to man! O the might-y gulf that God did span At Cal - va - ry.

Refrain

Mer - cy there was great and grace was free, Par - don there was mul - ti -

plied to me, There my bur-dened soul found lib - er - ty—At Cal - va - ry.

TEXT: William R. Newell
MUSIC: Daniel B. Towner

CALVARY
9.9.9.4. with Refrain

Since I Have Been Redeemed 339

Christ hath redeemed us from the curse of the law. Gal. 3:13

1. I have a song I love to sing, Since I have been re-deemed,
2. I have a Christ who sat-is-fies, Since I have been re-deemed,
3. I have a wit-ness bright and clear, Since I have been re-deemed,
4. I have a home pre-pared for me, Since I have been re-deemed,

Of my Re-deem-er, Sav-ior, King, Since I have been re-deemed.
To do His will my high-est prize, Since I have been re-deemed.
Dis-pel-ling ev-ery doubt and fear, Since I have been re-deemed.
Where I shall dwell e-ter-nal-ly, Since I have been re-deemed.

Refrain

Since I have been re-deemed, Since I have been re-
Since I have been re-deemed, Since I have been re-deemed,

deemed, I will glo-ry in His name; Since I have been re-
Since I have been re-deemed, Since

deemed, I will glo-ry in my Sav-ior's name.
I have been re-deemed,

TEXT and MUSIC: Edwin O. Excell

OTHELLO
C.M. with Refrain

340 I Lay My Sins on Jesus

The Lord hath laid on Him the iniquity of us all. Isa. 53:6

1. I lay my sins on Je - sus, The spot-less Lamb of God;
2. I lay my wants on Je - sus— All full - ness dwells in Him;
3. I long to be like Je - sus— Meek, lov - ing, low - ly, mild;

He bears them all, and frees us From the ac - curs - ed load.
He heals all my dis - eas - es, He doth my soul re - deem.
I long to be like Je - sus—The Fa - ther's ho - ly Child.

I bring my guilt to Je - sus, To wash my crim - son stains
I lay my griefs on Je - sus, My bur - dens and my cares;
I long to be with Je - sus, A - mid the heav'n - ly throng,

White in His blood most pre - cious, Till not a spot re - mains.
He from them all re - leas - es, He all my sor - rows shares.
To sing with saints His prais - es, To learn the an - gels' song.

TEXT: Horatius Bonar
MUSIC: Traditional Greek melody

CRUCIFIX
7.6.7.6.D.

Lord, I'm Coming Home 341

I will arise and go to my father. Luke 15:18

1. I've wan-dered far a-way from God— Now I'm com-ing home;
2. I've wast-ed man-y pre-cious years— Now I'm com-ing home;
3. I've tired of sin and stray-ing, Lord— Now I'm com-ing home;
4. My soul is sick, my heart is sore— Now I'm com-ing home;

The paths of sin too long I've trod— Lord, I'm com-ing home.
I now re-pent with bit-ter tears— Lord, I'm com-ing home.
I'll trust Thy love, be-lieve Thy word— Lord, I'm com-ing home.
My strength re-new, my hope re-store— Lord, I'm com-ing home.

Refrain

Com-ing home, com-ing home, Nev-er-more to roam;

O-pen now Thine arms of love— Lord, I'm com-ing home.

TEXT and MUSIC: William J. Kirkpatrick

COMING HOME
8.5.8.5. with Refrain

342 Just As I Am

Him that cometh to Me I will in no wise cast out. John 6:37

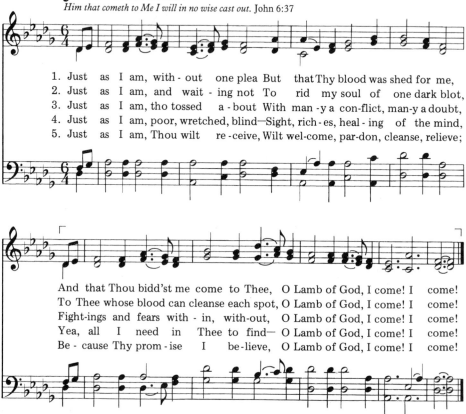

1. Just as I am, with-out one plea But that Thy blood was shed for me,
2. Just as I am, and wait-ing not To rid my soul of one dark blot,
3. Just as I am, tho tossed a-bout With man-y a con-flict, man-y a doubt,
4. Just as I am, poor, wretched, blind—Sight, rich-es, heal-ing of the mind,
5. Just as I am, Thou wilt re-ceive, Wilt wel-come, par-don, cleanse, relieve;

And that Thou bidd'st me come to Thee, O Lamb of God, I come! I come!
To Thee whose blood can cleanse each spot, O Lamb of God, I come! I come!
Fight-ings and fears with-in, with-out, O Lamb of God, I come! I come!
Yea, all I need in Thee to find— O Lamb of God, I come! I come!
Be-cause Thy prom-ise I be-lieve, O Lamb of God, I come! I come!

TEXT: Charlotte Elliott
MUSIC: William B. Bradbury

WOODWORTH
L.M.

343 Be Still and Know

I am the Lord that healeth thee. Ex. 15:26

1. Be still and know that I am God. Be still and know that
2. I am the Lord that heal-eth thee. I am the Lord that

TEXT and MUSIC: Anonymous; based on Psalm 46:10, Exodus 15:26;
arranged by Lee Herrington

BE STILL AND KNOW
8.8.8.

I am God. Be still and know that I am God.
heal - eth thee. I am the Lord that heal - eth thee.

He's Got the Whole World in His Hands 344

In whose hand is the soul of every living thing. Job 12:10

Unison

1. He's got the whole world in His hands, He's got the
2. He's got the wind and the rain in His hands, He's got the
3. He's got the ti - ny lit - tle ba - by in His hands, He's got the
4. He's got you and me, broth-er, in His hands, He's got

whole world in His hands, He's got the whole
wind and the rain in His hands, He's got the wind and the
ti - ny lit - tle ba - by in His hands, He's got the ti - ny lit - tle
you and me, sis - ter, in His hands, He's got you and me,

world in His hands, He's got the whole world in His hands.
rain in His hands, He's got the whole world in His hands.
ba - by in His hands, He's got the whole world in His hands.
broth - er, in His hands, He's got the whole world in His hands.

TEXT and MUSIC: Traditional Spiritual; arranged by Eugene Thomas

WHOLE WORLD
Irregular meter

345 Blessed Assurance

Is any merry? let him sing psalms. James 5:13

1. Bless-ed as - sur-ance, Je - sus is mine! O what a fore-taste of
2. Per - fect sub - mis - sion, per - fect de - light! Vi-sions of rap - ture now
3. Per - fect sub - mis - sion—all is at rest, I in my Sav - ior am

glo - ry di - vine! Heir of sal - va - tion, pur-chase of God,
burst on my sight; An - gels de - scend-ing bring from a - bove
hap - py and blest; Watch-ing and wait - ing, look-ing a - bove,

Descant

This is my sto - ry,

Refrain

Born of His Spir - it, washed in His blood.
Ech - oes of mer - cy, whis-pers of love.
Filled with His good-ness, lost in His love.

This is my sto - ry,

this is my song, Prais-ing my Sav - ior all the day long; This is my

this is my song, Prais-ing my Sav - ior all the day long; This is my

TEXT: Fanny J. Crosby
MUSIC: Phoebe P. Knapp; Descant by James C. Gibson

ASSURANCE
9.10.9.9. with Refrain

sto - ry, this is my song, Prais-ing my Sav - ior all the day long.

sto - ry, this is my song, Prais-ing my Sav - ior all the day long.

I Am Trusting Thee, Lord Jesus 346

. . . the Lord, on whom they believed. Acts 14:23

1. I am trust - ing Thee, Lord Je - sus—Trust - ing on - ly Thee;
2. I am trust - ing Thee to guide me—Thou a - lone shalt lead,
3. I am trust - ing Thee for pow - er—Thine can nev - er fail;
4. I am trust - ing Thee, Lord Je - sus—Nev - er let me fall;

Trust - ing Thee for full sal - va - tion, Great and free.
Ev - 'ry day and hour sup - ply - ing All my need.
Words which Thou Thy - self shalt give me Must pre - vail.
I am trust - ing Thee for - ev - er, And for all. A - men.

TEXT: Frances Ridley Havergal
MUSIC: Ethelbert W. Bullinger

BULLINGER
8.5.8.3.

347 Be Still, My Soul

Be still, and know that I am God. Ps. 46:10

1. Be still, my soul! the Lord is on thy side; Bear pa-tient-ly the cross of grief or pain; Leave to thy God to or-der and pro-vide; In ev-ery change He faith-ful will re-main. Be still, my soul! thy best, thy heaven-ly Friend Thro' thorn-y ways leads to a joy-ful end.

2. Be still, my soul! thy God doth un-der-take To guide the fu-ture as He has the past. Thy hope, thy con-fi-dence let noth-ing shake; All now mys-te-rious shall be bright at last. Be still, my soul! the waves and winds still know His voice who ruled them while He dwelt be-low.

3. Be still, my soul! the hour is has-tening on When we shall be for-ev-er with the Lord, When dis-ap-point-ment, grief, and fear are gone, Sor-row for-got, love's pur-est joys re-stored. Be still, my soul! when change and tears are past, All safe and bless-ed we shall meet at last.

TEXT: Katharina von Schlegel; translated by Jane L. Borthwick
MUSIC: Jean Sibelius
A lower setting may be found at No. 535

FINLANDIA
10.10.10.10.10.10.

Music copyright used by permission of G. Schirmer, Inc.

Hiding in Thee 348

Lead me to the Rock that is higher than I. Ps. 61:2

1. O safe to the Rock that is high - er than I, My
2. In the calm of the noon - tide, in sor - row's lone hour, In
3. How oft in the con - flict, when pressed by the foe, I have

soul in its con - flicts and sor - rows would fly; So
times when temp - ta - tion casts o'er me its power; In the
fled to my Ref - uge and breathed out my woe; How

sin - ful, so
tem - pests of
of - ten, when

wea - ry, Thine, Thine would I be; Thou blest Rock of A - ges, I'm
life, on its wide, heav - ing sea, Thou blest Rock of A - ges, I'm
tri - als like sea bil - lows roll, Have I hid - den in Thee, O Thou

Refrain

hid - ing in Thee.
hid - ing in Thee. Hid - ing in Thee, Hid - ing in
Rock of my soul.

Thee, Thou blest Rock of A - ges, I'm hid - ing in Thee.

TEXT: William O. Cushing
MUSIC: Ira D. Sankey

HIDING IN THEE
11.11.11.11. with Refrain

349 Trust and Obey

. . . made known to all nations for the obedience of faith. Rom. 16:26

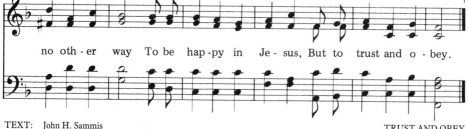

1. When we walk with the Lord in the light of His Word, What a glo - ry He
2. Not a shad-ow can rise, not a cloud in the skies, But His smile quick-ly
3. Not a bur-den we bear, not a sor - row we share, But our toil He doth
4. But we nev-er can prove the de - lights of His love Un - til all on the
5. Then in fel - low-ship sweet we will sit at His feet, Or we'll walk by His

sheds on our way! While we do His good will He a - bides with us still,
drives it a - way; Not a doubt nor a fear, not a sigh nor a tear,
rich - ly re - pay; Not a grief nor a loss, not a frown nor a cross,
al - tar we lay; For the fa - vor He shows and the joy He be - stows
side in the way; What He says we will do, where He sends we will go—

Refrain

And with all who will trust and o - bey.
Can a - bide while we trust and o - bey.
But is blest if we trust and o - bey. Trust and o - bey, for there's
Are for them who will trust and o - bey.
Nev - er fear, on - ly trust and o - bey.

no oth - er way To be hap - py in Je - sus, But to trust and o - bey.

TEXT: John H. Sammis
MUSIC: Daniel B. Towner

TRUST AND OBEY
6.6.9.D. with Refrain

'Tis So Sweet to Trust in Jesus 350

Ye believe in God, believe also in Me. John 14:1

1. 'Tis so sweet to trust in Je - sus, Just to take Him at His word,
2. O how sweet to trust in Je - sus, Just to trust His cleans - ing blood,
3. Yes, 'tis sweet to trust in Je - sus, Just from sin and self to cease,
4. I'm so glad I learned to trust Him, Pre - cious Je - sus, Sav - ior, Friend;

Just to rest up - on His prom - ise, Just to know "Thus saith the Lord."
Just in sim - ple faith to plunge me 'Neath the heal - ing, cleans - ing flood!
Just from Je - sus sim - ply tak - ing Life and rest and joy and peace.
And I know that He is with me, Will be with me to the end.

Refrain

Je - sus, Je - sus, how I trust Him! How I've proved Him o'er and o'er!

Je - sus, Je - sus, pre - cious Je - sus! O for grace to trust Him more!

TEXT: Louisa M. R. Stead
MUSIC: William J. Kirkpatrick

TRUST IN JESUS
8.7.8.7. with Refrain

351 Moment by Moment

Having loved His own . . . He loved them unto the end. John 13:1

1. Dy-ing with Je-sus, by death reck-oned mine;
2. Nev-er a tri-al that He is not there,
3. Nev-er a weak-ness that He doth not feel,

Liv-ing with Je-sus a
Nev-er a bur-den that
Nev-er a sick-ness that

new life di-vine; Look-ing to Je-sus till glo-ry doth shine, Mo-ment by
He doth not bear, Nev-er a sor-row that He doth not share, Mo-ment by
He can-not heal; Mo-ment by mo-ment, in woe or in weal, Je-sus my

Refrain

mo-ment, O Lord, I am Thine.
mo-ment, I'm un-der His care. Mo-ment by mo-ment I'm kept in His love;
Sav-ior a-bides with me still.

Mo-ment by mo-ment I've life from a-bove; Look-ing to Je-sus till

glo-ry doth shine; Mo-ment by mo-ment, O Lord, I am Thine.

TEXT: Daniel W. Whittle
MUSIC: May Whittle Moody

WHITTLE
10.10.10.10. with Refrain

A Child of the King 352

...if children, then... heirs of God, and joint-heirs with Christ. Rom. 8:17

1. My Fa-ther is rich in hous-es and lands, He hold-eth the
2. My Fa-ther's own Son, the Sav-ior of men, Once wan-dered on
3. I once was an out-cast stran-ger on earth, A sin-ner by
4. A tent or a cot-tage, why should I care? They're build-ing a

wealth of the world in His hands! Of ru-bies and dia-monds, of
earth as the poor-est of them; But now He is reign-ing for-
choice, and an al-ien by birth; But I've been a-dopt-ed, my
pal-ace for me o-ver there; Though ex-iled from home, yet

sil-ver and gold, His cof-fers are full, He has rich-es un-told.
ev-er on high, And will give me a home in heav'n by and by.
name's writ-ten down, An heir to a man-sion, a robe, and a crown.
still I may sing; All glo-ry to God, I'm a child of the King.

Refrain

I'm a child of the King, A child of the King:

With Je-sus my Sav-ior, I'm a child of the King.

TEXT: Harriet E. Buell
MUSIC: John B. Sumner

BINGHAMTON
10.11.11.11. with Refrain

353 A Shelter in the Time of Storm

The Rock of my strength, and my Refuge, is in God. Ps. 62:7

1. The Lord's our Rock, in Him we hide, A shel-ter in the time of storm;
2. A shade by day, de-fense by night, A shel-ter in the time of storm;
3. The rag-ing storms may round us beat, A shel-ter in the time of storm;
4. O Rock di-vine, O Ref-uge dear, A shel-ter in the time of storm;

Se-cure what-ev-er ill be-tide, A shel-ter in the time of storm.
No fears a-larm, no foes af-fright, A shel-ter in the time of storm.
We'll nev-er leave our safe re-treat, A shel-ter in the time of storm.
Be Thou our help-er ev-er near, A shel-ter in the time of storm.

Refrain

O, Je-sus is a Rock in a wea-ry land, A wea-ry land, a wea-ry land;

O, Je-sus is a Rock in a wea-ry land, A shel-ter in the time of storm.

TEXT: Vernon J. Charlesworth; adapted by Ira D. Sankey
MUSIC: Ira D. Sankey

SHELTER
L.M. with Refrain

Leaning on the Everlasting Arms 354

The eternal God is thy Refuge, and underneath are the everlasting arms. Deut. 33:27

1. What a fel - low-ship, what a joy di - vine, Lean - ing on the ev - er -
2. O how sweet to walk in this pil - grim way, Lean - ing on the ev - er -
3. What have I to dread, what have I to fear, Lean - ing on the ev - er -

last - ing arms; What a bless - ed-ness, what a peace is mine,
last - ing arms; O, how bright the path grows from day to day,
last - ing arms? I have bless - ed peace with my Lord so near,

Refrain

Lean - ing on the ev - er - last - ing arms. Lean - ing,
Lean - ing on the ev - er - last - ing arms. Lean-ing on Je - sus,
Lean - ing on the ev - er - last - ing arms.

lean - ing, Safe and se - cure from all a - larms; Lean -
lean - ing on Je - sus, Lean - ing on

ing, lean - ing, Lean - ing on the ev - er - last - ing arms.
Je - sus, lean - ing on Je - sus,

TEXT: Elisha A. Hoffman
MUSIC: Anthony J. Showalter

SHOWALTER
10.9.10.9. with Refrain

355 Trusting Jesus

. . . beholding . . . the stedfastness of your faith in Christ. Col. 2:5

1. Sim - ply trust - ing ev - ery day, Trust - ing through a storm - y way;
2. Bright-ly doth His Spir - it shine In - to this poor heart of mine.
3. Sing - ing if my way is clear, Pray - ing if the path be drear;
4. Trust-ing Him while life shall last, Trust - ing Him till earth be past;

E - ven when my faith is small, Trust - ing Je - sus— that is all.
While He leads I can - not fall, Trust - ing Je - sus— that is all.
If in dan - ger, for Him call, Trust - ing Je - sus— that is all.
Till with - in the jas - per wall, Trust - ing Je - sus— that is all.

Refrain

Trust - ing as the mo - ments fly, Trust - ing as the days go by;

Trust - ing Him what - e'er be - fall, Trust - ing Je - sus— that is all.

TEXT: Edgar P. Stites
MUSIC: Ira D. Sankey

TRUSTING JESUS
7.7.7.7. with Refrain

Under His Wings 356

Under His wings shalt thou trust. Ps. 91:4

1. Un-der His wings I am safe-ly a-bid-ing, Tho the night
2. Un-der His wings, what a ref-uge in sor-row! How the heart
3. Un-der His wings, O what pre-cious en-joy-ment! There will I

deep-ens and tem-pests are wild; Still I can trust Him, I
yearn-ing-ly turns to His rest! Of-ten when earth has no
hide till life's tri-als are o'er; Shel-tered, pro-tect-ed, no

know He will keep me, He has re-deemed me and I am His child.
balm for my heal-ing, There I find com-fort and there I am blest.
e-vil can harm me, Rest-ing in Je-sus I'm safe ev-er-more.

Refrain

Un-der His wings, un-der His wings, Who from His love can sev-er?

Un-der His wings my soul shall a-bide, Safe-ly a-bide for-ev-er.

TEXT: William O. Cushing
MUSIC: Ira D. Sankey

HINGHAM
11.10.11.10. with Refrain

357 Jesus Loves Even Me

Christ also loved the church, and gave Himself for it. Eph. 5:25

1. I am so glad that our Fa - ther in heav'n Tells of His
2. Tho I for - get Him and wan - der a - way, Still He doth
3. O if there's on - ly one song I can sing When in His

love in the Book He has giv'n; Won - der - ful things in the
love me wher - ev - er I stray; Back to His dear lov - ing
beau - ty I see the great King, This shall my song in e -

Bi - ble I see— This is the dear - est, that Je - sus loves me.
arms would I flee When I re - mem - ber that Je - sus loves me.
ter - ni - ty be: "O what a won - der, that Je - sus loves me!"

Refrain

I am so glad that Je - sus loves me, Je - sus loves me, Je - sus loves me;

I am so glad that Je - sus loves me, Je - sus loves e - ven me.

TEXT and MUSIC: Philip P. Bliss

GLADNESS
10.10.10.10. with Refrain

I Am Thine, O Lord 358

Let us draw near with a true heart in full assurance of faith. Heb. 10:22

1. I am Thine, O Lord, I have heard Thy voice, And it
2. Con - se - crate me now to Thy serv - ice, Lord, By the
3. O, the pure de - light of a sin - gle hour That be -
4. There are depths of love that I can - not know Till I

told Thy love to me; But I long to rise in the arms of faith,
pow'r of grace di - vine; Let my soul look up with a stead-fast hope,
fore Thy throne I spend, When I kneel in prayer, and with Thee, my God,
cross the nar - row sea; There are heights of joy that I may not reach

Refrain

And be clos - er drawn to Thee.
And my will be lost in Thine.
I com - mune as friend with friend!
Till I rest in peace with Thee.

Draw me near - er,

near - er, bless - ed Lord, To the cross where Thou hast died; Draw me

near - er, near - er, near-er, bless - ed Lord, To Thy pre - cious, bleed-ing side.

TEXT: Fanny J. Crosby
MUSIC: William H. Doane

I AM THINE
10.7.10.7. with Refrain

359 Jesus Is Lord of All

No man can serve two masters . . . Ye cannot serve God and mammon. Matt. 6:24

1. All my to-mor-rows, all my past, Je-sus is Lord of
2. All of my con-flicts, all my thoughts, Je-sus is Lord of
3. All of my long-ings, all my dreams, Je-sus is Lord of

all. I've quit my strug-gles, con-tent-ment at last,
all. His love wins the bat-tles I could not have fought,
all. All of my fail-ures His pow-er re-deems,

Refrain

Je-sus is Lord of all.
Je-sus is Lord of all. King of kings, Lord of
Je-sus is Lord of all.

lords, Je-sus is Lord of all; All my pos-

sess-ions and all my life, Je-sus is Lord of all.

TEXT: Gloria Gaither and William J. Gaither
MUSIC: William J. Gaither

LORD OF ALL
Irregular meter

Jesus Is Lord of All 360

God hath made that same Jesus, whom ye have crucified, both Lord and Christ. Acts 2:36

1. Je - sus is Sav - ior and Lord of my life,
2. Bless - ed Re - deem - er, all glo - ri - ous King,
3. Will you sur - ren - der your all to Him now?

My hope, my glo - ry, my all; Won - der - ful Mas - ter in
Wor - thy of rev - 'rence I pay; Trib - ute and prais - es I
Fol - low His will and o - bey, Crown Him as Sov - 'reign, be-

joy and in strife, On Him you too may call.
joy - ful - ly bring To Him, the Life, the Way.
fore His throne bow; Give Him your heart to - day.

Refrain

Je - sus is Lord of all, Je - sus is Lord of all, Lord of my

thoughts and my serv - ice each day, Je - sus is Lord of all.

TEXT and MUSIC: LeRoy McClard

LORDSHIP OF CHRIST
10.7.10.6. with Refrain

MY GOD, I LOVE THEE

A Brief Service of Adoration and Commitment

Suggested Hymn Stanzas

To facilitate an uninterrupted flow from stanza to stanza,
the suggested stanzas have been marked with an arrow: ►

I Love Thee, stanzas 1, 2
More Love to Thee, stanza 1
My Jesus, I Love Thee, stanzas 1, 2, 4

ALL:
My God, I love Thee;
    Not because I hope for heaven thereby,
Nor yet because who love Thee not
    Must die eternally.

WORSHIP LEADER:
Thou, O my Jesus, Thou didst me
    Upon the cross embrace,
For me didst bear the nails and spear,
    And manifold disgrace.

PEOPLE:
Then why, O blessed Jesus Christ,
    Should I not love Thee well?
Not for the hope of winning heaven,
    Or of escaping hell.

ALL:
E'en so I love Thee, and will love
    And in Thy praise will sing,
Solely because Thou art my God,
    And my eternal King!

"My Eternal King" by Francis Xavier;
translated by Edward Caswall.

Optional introduction to "I Love Thee"

I Love Thee 362

I will love Thee, O Lord, my strength. Ps. 18:1

1. I love Thee, I love Thee, I love Thee, my Lord; I love Thee, my Savior, I love Thee, my God; I love Thee, I love Thee, and that Thou dost know; But how much I love Thee my ac-tions will show.

2. O Je-sus, my Sav-ior, with Thee I am blest, My life and sal-va-tion, my joy and my rest; Thy name be my theme, and Thy love be my song; Thy grace shall in-spire both my heart and my tongue.

3. O, who's like my Sav-ior? He's Sa-lem's bright King; He smiles and He loves me and helps me to sing; I'll praise Him, I'll praise Him with notes loud and clear, While riv-ers of pleas-ure my spir-it shall cheer.

tongue.

Optional transition to "More Love to Thee"

TEXT: Source unknown
MUSIC: Ingalls' *Christian Harmony,* 1805

I LOVE THEE
11.11.11.11.

363 More Love to Thee

This I pray, that your love may abound yet more and more. Phil. 1:9

1. More love to Thee, O Christ, More love to Thee! Hear Thou the
2. Once earth-ly joy I craved, Sought peace and rest; Now Thee a-
3. Then shall my lat-est breath Whis-per Thy praise; This be the

prayer I make On bend-ed knee; This is my ear - nest plea:
lone I seek, Give what is best; This all my prayer shall be:
part - ing cry My heart shall raise; This still my prayer shall be:

More love, O Christ to Thee, More love to Thee, More love to Thee!

TEXT: Elizabeth P. Prentiss
MUSIC: William H. Doane

MORE LOVE TO THEE
6.4.6.4.6.6.4.

Optional transition to "My Jesus, I Love Thee"

My Jesus, I Love Thee 364

I love the Lord, because He hath heard my voice. Ps. 116:1

1. My Jesus, I love Thee, I know Thou art mine—For Thee all the fol-lies of sin I re-sign; My gra-cious Re-deem-er, my Sav-ior art Thou: If ev-er I loved Thee, my Je-sus, 'tis now.

2. I love Thee be-cause Thou hast first lov-ed me And pur-chased my par-don on Cal-va-ry's tree; I love Thee for wear-ing the thorns on Thy brow: If ev-er I loved Thee, my Je-sus, 'tis now.

3. I'll love Thee in life, I will love Thee in death, And praise Thee as long as Thou lend-est me breath; And say when the death-dew lies cold on my brow, "If ev-er I loved Thee, my Je-sus, 'tis now."

4. In man-sions of glo-ry and end-less de-light, I'll ev-er a-dore Thee in heav-en so bright; I'll sing with the glit-ter-ing crown on my brow, "If ev-er I loved Thee, my Je-sus, 'tis now."

TEXT: William R. Featherston
MUSIC: Adoniram J. Gordon

GORDON
11.11.11.11.

Optional choral ending

mp   *decresc.*

I love Thee, I love Thee, I love Thee, my Lord.

The end of "MY GOD, I LOVE THEE - A Brief Service of Adoration and Commitment."

365 Close to Thee

Draw nigh to God, and He will draw nigh to you. James 4:8

1. Thou my ev - er - last - ing por - tion, More than friend or life to me;
2. Not for ease or world - ly pleas - ure, Nor for fame my prayer shall be;
3. Lead me through the vale of shad - ows, Bear me o'er life's fit - ful sea;

All a - long my pil - grim jour - ney, Sav - ior, let me walk with Thee.
Glad - ly will I toil and suf - fer, On - ly let me walk with Thee.
Then the gate of life e - ter - nal May I en - ter, Lord, with Thee.

Close to Thee, close to Thee, Close to Thee, close to Thee; All a -
Close to Thee, close to Thee, Close to Thee, close to Thee; Glad - ly
Close to Thee, close to Thee, Close to Thee, close to Thee; Then the

long my pil - grim jour - ney, Sav - ior, let me walk with Thee.
will I toil and suf - fer, On - ly let me walk with Thee.
gate of life e - ter - nal May I en - ter, Lord, with Thee.

TEXT: Fanny J. Crosby
MUSIC: Silas J. Vail

CLOSE TO THEE
8.7.8.7.6.6.8.7.

I Surrender All 366

Yield yourselves unto God. Rom. 6:13

1. All to Je - sus I sur-ren - der, All to Him I free - ly give;
2. All to Je - sus I sur-ren - der, Hum-bly at His feet I bow,
3. All to Je - sus I sur-ren - der, Make me, Sav - ior, whol - ly Thine;
4. All to Je - sus I sur-ren - der, Lord, I give my - self to Thee;

I will ev - er love and trust Him, In His pres - ence dai - ly live.
World - ly pleas-ures all for-sak - en, Take me, Je - sus, take me now.
May Thy Ho - ly Spir - it fill me, May I know Thy pow'r di - vine.
Fill me with Thy love and pow - er, Let Thy bless - ing fall on me.

Refrain

I sur-ren - der all, I sur - ren - der all.
I sur-ren-der all, I sur-ren-der all.

All to Thee, my bless - ed Sav - ior, I sur - ren - der all.

TEXT: Judson W. VanDeVenter
MUSIC: Winfield S. Weeden

SURRENDER
8.7.8.7. with Refrain

367 Wherever He Leads I'll Go

If any man will come after Me, let him . . . take up his cross, and follow Me. Matt. 16:24

1. "Take up thy cross and fol-low Me," I heard my Mas-ter say;
2. He drew me clos-er to His side, I sought His will to know,
3. It may be thro' the shad-ows dim, Or o'er the storm-y sea,
4. My heart, my life, my all I bring To Christ who loves me so;

"I gave My life to ran - som thee, Sur - ren-der your all to - day."
And in that will I now a - bide, Wher-ev-er He leads I'll go.
I take the cross and fol - low Him, Wher-ev-er He lead-eth me.
He is my Mas-ter, Lord, and King, Wher-ev-er He leads I'll go.

Refrain

Wher-ev-er He leads I'll go, Wher-ev-er He leads I'll go,

I'll fol-low my Christ who loves me so, Wher-ev-er He leads I'll go.

TEXT and MUSIC: B. B. McKinney

FALLS CREEK
8.6.8.7. with Refrain

All for Jesus 368

Present your bodies a living sacrifice . . . unto God, which is your reasonable service. Rom. 12:1

1. All for Je-sus, all for Je-sus! All my be-ing's ran-somed pow'rs:
2. Let my hands per-form His bid-ding, Let my feet run in His ways;
3. Since my eyes were fixed on Je-sus, I've lost sight of all be-side;
4. Oh, what won-der! how a-maz-ing! Je-sus, glo-rious King of kings,

All my tho'ts and words and do-ings, All my days and all my hours.
Let my eyes see Je-sus on-ly, Let my lips speak forth His praise.
So en-chained my spir-it's vi-sion, Look-ing at the Cru-ci-fied.
Deigns to call me His be-lov-ed, Lets me rest be-neath His wings.

Refrain

All for Je-sus! all for Je-sus! All my days and all my hours;
All for Je-sus! all for Je-sus! Let my lips speak forth His praise;
All for Je-sus! all for Je-sus! Look-ing at the Cru-ci-fied;
All for Je-sus! all for Je-sus! Rest-ing now be-neath His wings;

All for Je-sus! all for Je-sus! All my days and all my hours.
All for Je-sus! all for Je-sus! Let my lips speak forth His praise.
All for Je-sus! all for Je-sus! Look-ing at the Cru-ci-fied.
All for Je-sus! all for Je-sus! Rest-ing now be-neath His wings.

TEXT: Mary D. James
MUSIC: Source unknown

CONSTANCY
8.7.8.7. with Refrain

369 O Jesus, I Have Promised

Shew . . . diligence to the full assurance of hope unto the end. Heb. 6:11

1. O Je-sus, I have prom-ised To serve Thee to the end; Be Thou for-ev - er
2. O let me feel Thee near me, The world is ev - er near; I see the sights that
3. O Je-sus, Thou hast prom-ised To all who fol-low Thee, That where Thou art in

near me, My Mas - ter and my Friend: I shall not fear the bat-tle If Thou art
daz - zle, The tempt-ing sounds I hear: My foes are ev - er near me, A-round me
glo - ry, There shall Thy serv-ant be; And, Je-sus, I have prom-ised To serve Thee

by my side, Nor wan-der from the path-way If Thou wilt be my guide.
and with - in; But, Je - sus, draw Thou near-er, And shield my soul from sin.
to the end; O give me grace to fol - low, My Mas - ter and my Friend.

TEXT: John E. Bode
MUSIC: Arthur H. Mann

ANGEL'S STORY
7.6.7.6.D.

370 I'll Live for Him

Live soberly, righteously, and godly, in this present world. Titus 2:12

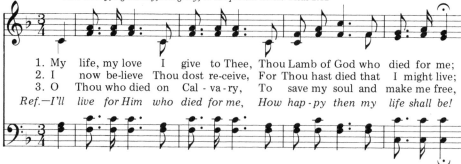

1. My life, my love I give to Thee, Thou Lamb of God who died for me;
2. I now be-lieve Thou dost re-ceive, For Thou hast died that I might live;
3. O Thou who died on Cal - va-ry, To save my soul and make me free,

Ref.—I'll live for Him who died for me, How hap-py then my life shall be!

TEXT: Ralph E. Hudson
MUSIC: C. R. Dunbar

DUNBAR
8.8.8.6. with Refrain

D.C. for Refrain

O may I ev - er faith - ful be, My Sav - ior and my God!
And now hence-forth I'll trust in Thee, My Sav - ior and my God!
I'll con - se - crate my life to Thee, My Sav - ior and my God!
I'll live for Him who died for me, My Sav - ior and my God!

Have Thine Own Way, Lord 371

We are the clay, and Thou our potter. Isa. 64:8

1. Have Thine own way, Lord! Have Thine own way! Thou art the
2. Have Thine own way, Lord! Have Thine own way! Search me and
3. Have Thine own way, Lord! Have Thine own way! Wound-ed and
4. Have Thine own way, Lord! Have Thine own way! Hold o'er my

Pot - ter, I am the clay. Mold me and make me af - ter Thy
try me, Mas - ter, to - day! Whit - er than snow, Lord, wash me just
wea - ry, help me, I pray! Pow - er— all pow - er— sure - ly is
be - ing ab - so - lute sway! Fill with Thy Spir - it till all shall

will, While I am wait - ing, yield - ed and still.
now, As in Thy pres - ence hum - bly I bow.
Thine! Touch me and heal me, Sav - ior di - vine!
see Christ on - ly, al - ways, liv - ing in me! A - men.

TEXT: Adelaide A. Pollard
MUSIC: George C. Stebbins

ADELAIDE
5.4.5.4.D.

372 Living for Jesus

They . . . should not . . . live unto themselves, but unto Him which died for them. 2 Cor. 5:15

1. Liv-ing for Je-sus a life that is true, Striv-ing to please Him in
2. Liv-ing for Je-sus who died in my place, Bear-ing on Cal-v'ry my
3. Liv-ing for Je-sus wher-ev-er I am, Do-ing each du-ty in
4. Liv-ing for Je-sus through earth's lit-tle while, My dear-est treas-ure, the

all that I do; Yield-ing al-le-giance, glad-heart-ed and free,
sin and dis-grace; Such love con-strains me to an-swer His call,
His ho-ly name; Will-ing to suf-fer af-flic-tion and loss,
light of His smile; Seek-ing the lost ones He died to re-deem,

Refrain

This is the path-way of bless-ing for me.
Fol-low His lead-ing and give Him my all. O Je-sus, Lord and
Deem-ing each tri-al a part of my cross.
Bring-ing the wea-ry to find rest in Him.

Sav-ior, I give my-self to Thee; For Thou, in Thy a-tone-ment, Didst

give Thy-self for me. I own no oth-er Mas-ter, My heart shall be Thy

TEXT: Thomas O. Chisholm
MUSIC: C. Harold Lowden

LIVING
10.10.10.10. with Refrain

throne. My life I give, hence-forth to live, O Christ, for Thee a - lone.

Where He Leads Me 373

My sheep hear My voice, and I know them, and they follow Me. John 10:27

1. I can hear my Sav - ior call - ing, I can
2. I'll go with Him thru the judg - ment, I'll go
3. He will give me grace and glo - ry, He will
Refrain: *Where He leads me I will fol - low, where He*

hear my Sav - ior call - ing, I can hear my Sav - ior
with Him thru the judg - ment, I'll go with Him thru the
give me grace and glo - ry, He will give me grace and
leads me I will fol - low, where He leads me I will

D.C. for Refrain

call - ing, "Take thy cross and fol - low, fol - low Me."
judg - ment, I'll go with Him, with Him all the way.
glo - ry, And go with me, with me all the way.
fol - low, I'll go with Him, with Him all the way.

TEXT: E. W. Blandy
MUSIC: John S. Norris

NORRIS
8.8.8.9. with Refrain

374 O Love That Will Not Let Me Go

... nor any other creature, shall be able to separate us from the love of God. Rom. 8:39

1. O Love that will not let me go, I rest my wea-ry soul in Thee; I give Thee back the life I owe, That in Thine o - cean depths its flow May rich - er, full - er be.

2. O Light that fol-l'west all my way, I yield my flick-'ring torch to Thee; My heart re - stores its bor -rowed ray, That in Thy sun-shine's blaze its day May bright-er, fair - er be.

3. O Joy that seek-est me thru pain, I can - not close my heart to Thee; I trace the rain - bow thru the rain, And feel the prom - ise is not vain That morn shall tear - less be.

4. O Cross that lift - est up my head, I dare not ask to fly from Thee; I lay in dust life's glo - ry dead, And from the ground there blos-soms red Life that shall end - less be. A - men.

TEXT: George Matheson
MUSIC: Albert L. Peace

ST. MARGARET
8.8.8.8.6.

375 Jesus Calls Us

He saith unto them, "Follow Me." Matt. 4:19

1. Je-sus calls us; o'er the tu-mult Of our life's wild, rest-less sea, Day by
2. Je-sus calls us from the wor-ship Of the vain world's gold-en store, From each
3. In our joys and in our sor-rows, Days of toil and hours of ease, Still He
4. Je-sus calls us: by Thy mer-cies, Sav-ior, may we hear Thy call, Give our

TEXT: Cecil F. Alexander
MUSIC: William H. Jude

GALILEE
8.7.8.7.

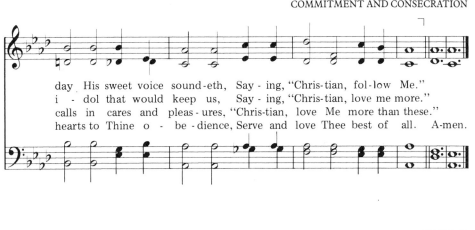

day His sweet voice sound-eth, Say - ing, "Chris-tian, fol-low Me."
i - dol that would keep us, Say - ing, "Chris-tian, love me more."
calls in cares and pleas - ures, "Chris-tian, love Me more than these."
hearts to Thine o - be - dience, Serve and love Thee best of all. A-men.

I Have Decided to Follow Jesus 376

If any man serve Me, let him follow Me. John 12:26

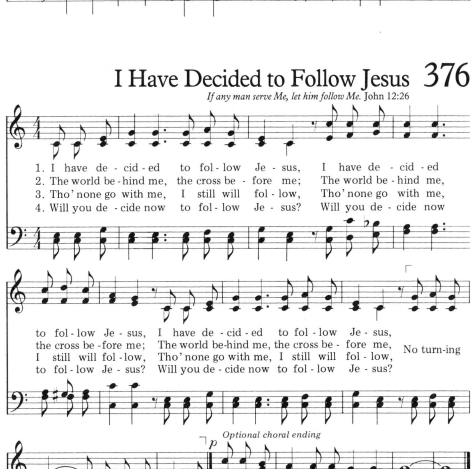

1. I have de - cid - ed to fol - low Je - sus, I have de - cid - ed
2. The world be - hind me, the cross be - fore me; The world be - hind me,
3. Tho' none go with me, I still will fol - low, Tho' none go with me,
4. Will you de - cide now to fol - low Je - sus? Will you de - cide now

to fol - low Je - sus, I have de - cid - ed to fol - low Je - sus,
the cross be - fore me; The world be-hind me, the cross be - fore me,
I still will fol - low, Tho' none go with me, I still will fol - low,
to fol - low Je - sus? Will you de - cide now to fol - low Je - sus?

No turn-ing

Optional choral ending

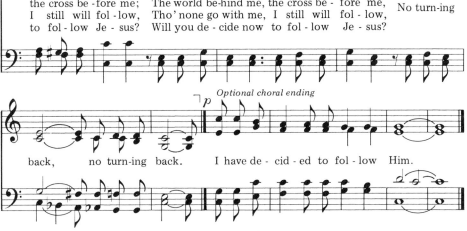

back, no turn-ing back. I have de - cid - ed to fol - low Him.

TEXT: Source unknown
MUSIC: Folk melody from India; arranged by Eugene Thomas

ASSAM
Irregular meter

377 Jesus, I My Cross Have Taken

If any man will come after Me, let him . . . take up his cross daily. Luke 9:23

1. Je - sus, I my cross have tak - en, All to leave and fol - low Thee;
2. Let the world de - spise and leave me, They have left my Sav - ior too;
3. Man may trou - ble and dis - tress me, 'Twill but drive me to Thy breast;
4. Has - ten on from grace to glo - ry, Armed by faith and winged by prayer;

Des - ti - tute, de - spised, for - sak - en, Thou from hence my all shalt be:
Hu - man hearts and looks de - ceive me; Thou art not, like man, un - true;
Life with tri - als hard may press me, Heav'n will bring me sweet - er rest.
Heav'n's e - ter - nal days be - fore me, God's own hand shall guide me there.

Per - ish ev - er - y fond am - bi - tion, All I've sought, and hoped and known;
And, while Thou shalt smile up - on me, God of wis - dom, love, and might,
O 'tis not in grief to harm me, While Thy love is left to me;
Soon shall close my earth - ly mis - sion, Swift shall pass my pil - grim days,

Yet how rich is my con - di - tion, God and heav'n are still my own!
Foes may hate and friends may shun me; Show Thy face, and all is bright.
O 'twere not in joy to charm me, Were that joy un - mixed with Thee.
Hope shall change to glad fru - i - tion, Faith to sight, and prayer to praise. A - men.

TEXT: Henry F. Lyte
MUSIC: Leavitt's *The Christian Lyre*, 1831; attributed to Wolfgang A. Mozart;
arranged by Hubert P. Main
A higher setting may be found at No. 584

ELLESDIE
8.7.8.7.D.

Only One Life 378

He that loseth his life for My sake shall find it. Matt. 10:39

1. On-ly one life to of-fer— Je-sus, my Lord and King;
2. On-ly this hour is mine, Lord— May it be used for Thee;
3. On-ly one life to of-fer— Take it, dear Lord, I pray;

On-ly one tongue to praise Thee And of Thy mer-cy sing (for-ev - er);
May ev-'ry pass-ing mo-ment Count for e-ter-ni-ty (my Sav-ior);
Nothing from Thee with-hold-ing, Thy will I now o-bey (my Je-sus);

On-ly one heart's de-vo-tion— Sav-ior, O may it be Con-se-
Souls all a-bout are dy-ing, Dy-ing in sin and shame; Help me
Thou who hast free-ly giv-en Thine all in all for me, Claim this

crat-ed a-lone to Thy match-less glo-ry, Yield-ed ful-ly to Thee.
bring them the mes-sage of Cal-v'ry's re-demp-tion In Thy glo-ri-ous name.
life for Thine own to be used, my Sav-ior, Ev-'ry mo-ment for Thee.

TEXT: Avis B. Christiansen
MUSIC: Merrill Dunlop

ONLY ONE LIFE
7.6.7.6.7.6.12.6.

379 Take My Life and Let It Be

Sanctify yourselves, and . . . be holy; for I am holy. Lev. 11:44

1. Take my life and let it be Con - se - cra - ted, Lord, to Thee; Take my mo - ments and my days— Let them flow in cease - less praise, Let them flow in cease - less praise.
2. Take my hands and let them move At the im - pulse of Thy love; Take my feet and let them be Swift and beau - ti - ful for Thee, Swift and beau - ti - ful for Thee.
3. Take my voice and let me sing Al - ways, on - ly, for my King; Take my lips and let them be Filled with mes - sag - es from Thee, Filled with mes - sag - es from Thee.
4. Take my sil - ver and my gold— Not a mite would I with - hold; Take my in - tel - lect and use Ev - 'ry pow'r as Thou shalt choose, Ev - 'ry pow'r as Thou shalt choose.
5. Take my will and make it Thine— It shall be no long - er mine; Take my heart— it is Thine own, It shall be Thy roy - al throne, It shall be Thy roy - al throne.
6. Take my love— my Lord, I pour At Thy feet its treas - ure store; Take my - self— and I will be Ev - er, on - ly, all for Thee, Ev - er, on - ly, all for Thee.

Optional last stanza harmonization
Unison

6. Take my love—my Lord, I pour At Thy feet its treas - ure store;

TEXT: Frances Ridley Havergal
MUSIC: Henry A. César Malan; Last verse harmonization by David Allen

HENDON
7.7.7.7. with Repeat

Take my-self— and I will be Ever, on-ly, all for Thee,

Ev - er, on - ly, all for Thee. A - men.

Just a Closer Walk with Thee 380

I can do all things through Christ which strengtheneth me. Phil. 4:13

1. I am weak but Thou art strong; Je - sus, keep me from all wrong;
2. Thro' this world of toil and snares, If I fal - ter, Lord, who cares?
3. When my fee - ble life is o'er, Time for me will be no more;
Refrain: Just a clos-er walk with Thee, Grant it, Je - sus, is my plea,

D.C. for Refrain

I'll be sat - is - fied as long As I walk, let me walk close to Thee.
Who with me my bur-den shares? None but Thee, dear Lord, none but Thee.
Guide me gent-ly, safe-ly o'er To Thy king-dom shore, to Thy shore.
Dai - ly, walk-ing close to Thee, Let it be, dear Lord, let it be.

TEXT and MUSIC: Traditional Folk song

CLOSER WALK
Irregular meter

381 Open My Eyes, That I May See

Open Thou mine eyes, that I may behold wondrous things out of Thy law. Ps. 119:18

1. O-pen my eyes, that I may see Glimp-ses of truth Thou hast for me;
2. O-pen my ears, that I may hear Voic-es of truth Thou send-est clear;
3. O-pen my mouth, and let it bear Glad-ly the warm truth ev-'ry-where;

Place in my hands the won-der-ful key, That shall un-clasp and set me free.
And while the wave-notes fall on my ear, Ev-'ry-thing false will dis-ap-pear.
O-pen my heart, and let me pre-pare Love with Thy chil-dren thus to share.

Si-lent-ly now I wait for Thee, Read-y, my God, Thy will to see;

O-pen my eyes, il-lu-mine me, Spir-it di-vine!
O-pen my ears, il-lu-mine me, Spir-it di-vine!
O-pen my heart, il-lu-mine me, Spir-it di-vine! A-men.

TEXT and MUSIC: Clara H. Scott

SCOTT
Irregular meter

Be Thou My Vision 382

What things were gain to me, those I counted loss for Christ. Phil. 3:7

Unison

1. Be Thou my Vi - sion, O Lord of my heart;
2. Be Thou my Wis - dom, and Thou my true Word;
3. Rich - es I heed not, nor man's emp - ty praise,
4. High King of heav - en, my vic - to - ry won,

Naught be all else to me, save that Thou art—
I ev - er with Thee and Thou with me, Lord;
Thou mine in - her - i - tance, now and al - ways;
May I reach heav - en's joys, O bright heav'n's Sun!

Thou my best thought, by day or by night,
Thou my great Fa - ther, I Thy true son,
Thou and Thou on - ly, first in my heart,
Heart of my own heart, what - ev - er be - fall,

Wak - ing or sleep - ing, Thy pres - ence my light.
Thou in me dwell - ing, and I with Thee one.
High King of heav - en, my Treas - ure Thou art.
Still be my Vi - sion, O Rul - er of all. A - men.

TEXT: Ancient Irish hymn, translated by Mary E. Byrne;
versified by Eleanor H. Hull
MUSIC: Irish Folk melody; arranged by David Allen

SLANE
10.10.10.10.

383 Open Our Eyes, Lord

Blessed are the pure in heart: for they shall see God. Matt. 5:8

1. O - pen our eyes, Lord, we want to see Je - sus,
2. O - pen our ears, Lord, and help us to lis - ten,

to reach out and touch Him, and say that we love
O - pen our eyes,

Him. Lord, we want to see Je - sus.

TEXT and MUSIC: Robert Cull;
arranged by David Allen

OPEN OUR EYES
11.12.11.11.

384 To Be Like Jesus

Be ye followers of me, even as I also am of Christ. 1 Cor. 11:1

To be like Je - sus, to be like Je - sus! My de - sire— to be like Him!

TEXT and MUSIC: Traditional

TO BE LIKE JESUS
10.7.10.7.

All thru life's jour-ney from earth to glo-ry, My de-sire— to be like Him.

Near the Cross 385

God forbid that I should glory, save in the cross of our Lord Jesus Christ. Gal. 6:14

1. Je-sus, keep me near the cross— There a pre-cious foun-tain,
2. Near the cross, a trem-bling soul, Love and mer-cy found me;
3. Near the cross! O Lamb of God, Bring its scenes be-fore me;
4. Near the cross I'll watch and wait, Hop-ing, trust-ing ev-er,

Free to all, a heal-ing stream, Flows from Cal-v'ry's moun-tain.
There the Bright and Morn-ing Star Sheds its beams a-round me.
Help my walk from day to day With its shad-ows o'er me.
Till I reach the gold-en strand Just be-yond the riv-er.

Refrain

In the cross, in the cross Be my glo-ry ev-er,

Till my rap-tured soul shall find Rest, be-yond the riv-er.

TEXT: Fanny J. Crosby
MUSIC: William H. Doane

NEAR THE CROSS
7.6.7.6. with Refrain

IN HIS IMAGE

A Brief Service
of Aspiration and Hope
Suggested Hymn Stanzas

To facilitate an uninterrupted flow from stanza to stanza,
the suggested stanzas have been marked with an arrow: ▶

O to Be Like Thee!, stanzas 1, 2
I Would Be Like Jesus, stanzas 1, 3
More About Jesus, stanzas 1, 2, 4

WORSHIP LEADER:

For whom He did foreknow, He also did predestinate to be conformed to the image of His Son, that He might be the firstborn
among many brethren. For I determined not to know any thing
among you, save Jesus Christ, and Him crucified.

PEOPLE:

But we all, with open face beholding as in a glass the glory of the
Lord, are changed into the same image from glory to glory, even as
by the Spirit of the Lord.

WORSHIP LEADER:

My little children, of whom I travail in birth again until Christ be
formed in you. . . . Let this mind be in you, which was also in Christ
Jesus.

PEOPLE:

Yea doubtless, and I count all things but loss for the excellency of the
knowledge of Christ Jesus my Lord: for whom I have suffered the
loss of all things, and do count them but dung, that I may win Christ.
That I may know Him, and the power of His resurrection, and the
fellowship of His sufferings, being made conformable unto His
death.

WORSHIP LEADER:

For even hereunto were ye called: because Christ also suffered for us,
leaving us an example, that ye should follow His steps. He that saith
he abideth in Him ought himself also so to walk, even as He walked.

Rom. 8:29; 1 Cor. 2:2; 2 Cor. 3:18; Gal. 4:19;
Phil. 2:5; 3:8, 10; 1 Pet. 2:21; 1 John 2:6.

Optional introduction to
"O to Be Like Thee"

mp

O to Be Like Thee! 387

I travail in birth . . . until Christ be formed in you. Gal. 4:19

1. O to be like Thee! bless-ed Re - deem - er, This is my con - stant
2. O to be like Thee! full of com - pas - sion, Lov-ing, for - giv - ing,
3. O to be like Thee! while I am plead - ing, Pour out Thy Spir - it,

long - ing and prayer; Glad-ly I'll for - feit all of earth's treas - ures,
ten - der and kind; Help-ing the help - less, cheer-ing the faint - ing,
fill with Thy love; Make me a tem - ple meet for Thy dwell - ing,

Je - sus, Thy per - fect like-ness to wear.
Seek-ing the wan-d'ring sin - ner to find.
Fit me for life and heav-en a - bove.

Refrain

O to be like Thee!

O to be like Thee, Bless-ed Re - deem-er, pure as Thou art! Come in Thy

sweet-ness, come in Thy full-ness—Stamp Thine own im - age deep on my heart.

TEXT: Thomas O. Chisholm
MUSIC: William J. Kirkpatrick

RONDINELLA
10.9.10.9. with Refrain

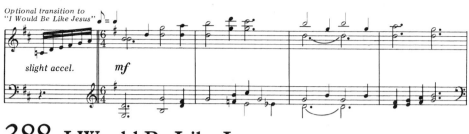

388 I Would Be Like Jesus

Whom He did foreknow, He also did predestinate to be conformed to . . . His Son. Rom. 8:29

1. Earth-ly pleas-ures vain-ly call me— I would be like Je-sus;
2. He has bro-ken ev-'ry fet-ter— I would be like Je-sus;
3. All the way from earth to glo-ry— I would be like Je-sus;
4. That in heav-en He may meet me, I would be like Je-sus;

Noth-ing world-ly shall en-thrall me— I would be like Je-sus:
That my soul may serve Him bet-ter— I would be like Je-sus:
Tell-ing o'er and o'er the sto-ry— I would be like Je-sus:
That His words "Well done" may greet me, I would be like Je-sus:

Refrain

Be like Je-sus— this my song— In the home and in the throng;

Be like Je-sus all day long! I would be like Je-sus.

Opt. segue to "More About Jesus"
Same tempo ♩ = ♪

TEXT: James Rowe
MUSIC: Bentley D. Ackley

SPRING HILL
C.M. with Refrain

More About Jesus 389

Grow in grace, and in the knowledge of our Lord and Saviour Jesus Christ. 2 Pet. 3:18

1. More a-bout Je - sus would I know, More of His grace to oth - ers show,
2. More a-bout Je - sus let me learn, More of His ho - ly will dis-cern;
3. More a-bout Je - sus; in His Word, Hold-ing com-mun-ion with my Lord,
4. More a-bout Je - sus on His throne, Rich - es in glo - ry all His own,

More of His sav - ing full - ness see, More of His love who died for me.
Spir - it of God, my teach-er be, Show-ing the things of Christ to me.
Hear-ing His voice in ev - 'ry line, Mak - ing each faith - ful say - ing mine.
More of His king - dom's sure in - crease, More of His com - ing—Prince of Peace.

Refrain

More, more a - bout Je - sus, More, more a - bout Je - sus;

More of His sav - ing full - ness see, More of His love who died for me!

TEXT: Eliza E. Hewitt
MUSIC: John R. Sweney

SWENEY
L.M. with Refrain

Optional choral ending   *decresc.*   *rit.*

O to be like Thee, Bless-ed Re-deem-er, I want to be like Je-sus, my Lord.

The end of "IN HIS IMAGE—A Brief Service of Aspiration and Hope"

390 May the Mind of Christ, My Savior

Let this mind be in you, which was also in Christ Jesus. Phil. 2:5

1. May the mind of Christ my Sav-ior Live in me from day to day,
2. May the Word of God dwell rich-ly In my heart from hour to hour,
3. May the peace of God my Fa-ther Rule my life in ev-'ry-thing,
4. May the love of Je-sus fill me As the wa-ters fill the sea;
5. May I run the race be-fore me, Strong and brave to face the foe,
6. May His beau-ty rest up-on me As I seek the lost to win,

By His love and pow'r con-trol-ling All I do and say.
So that all may see I tri-umph On-ly thru His pow'r.
That I may be calm to com-fort Sick and sor-row-ing.
Him ex-alt-ing, self a-bas-ing— This is vic-to-ry.
Look-ing on-ly un-to Je-sus As I on-ward go.
And may they for-get the chan-nel, See-ing on-ly Him.

TEXT: Kate B. Wilkinson
MUSIC: A. Cyril Barham-Gould

ST. LEONARDS
8.7.8.5.

391 Aspiration Canon

If ye love Me, keep My commandments. John 14:15

3 Part Canon

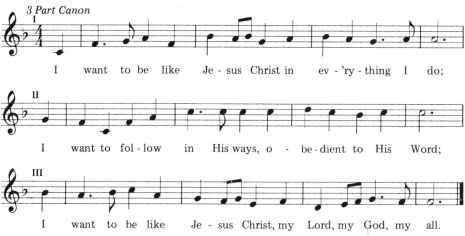

I want to be like Je-sus Christ in ev-'ry-thing I do;

I want to fol-low in His ways, o-be-dient to His Word;

I want to be like Je-sus Christ, my Lord, my God, my all.

TEXT and MUSIC: Bruce Greer

ASPIRATION CANON
8.6.8.6.8.6.

Nearer, Still Nearer 392

. . . a better hope . . . by the which we draw nigh unto God. Heb. 7:19

1. Near - er, still near - er, close to Thy heart, Draw me, my Sav - ior, so pre - cious Thou art; Fold me, O fold me close to Thy breast, Shel - ter me safe in that "Ha - ven of Rest," Shel - ter me safe in that "Ha - ven of Rest."

2. Near - er, still near - er, noth - ing I bring, Naught as an of - fering to Je - sus my King; On - ly my sin - ful, now con-trite heart, Grant me the cleans - ing Thy blood doth im - part, Grant me the cleans - ing Thy blood doth im - part.

3. Near - er, still near - er, while life shall last, 'Til safe in glo - ry my an - chor is cast; Through end-less a - ges, ev - er to be, Near - er, my Sav - ior, still near - er to Thee, Near - er, my Sav - ior, still near - er to Thee. A - men.

TEXT and MUSIC: Lelia N. Morris

MORRIS
9.10.9.10.

393 Nearer, My God, to Thee

Thou art near, O Lord; and all Thy commandments are truth. Ps. 119:151

1. Near - er, my God, to Thee, Near - er to Thee! E'en though it
2. Though like the wan - der - er, The sun gone down, Dark - ness be
3. *There let the way ap - pear Steps un - to heav'n; All that Thou
4. Then, with my wak - ing thoughts Bright with Thy praise, Out of my
5. Or if on joy - ful wing, Cleav - ing the sky, Sun, moon, and

be a cross That rais - eth me; Still all my song shall be, Near-er, my
o - ver me, My rest a stone; Yet in my dreams I'd be Near-er, my
send - est me In mer - cy giv'n; An - gels to beck - on me Near-er, my
ston - y griefs, **Beth - el I'll raise; So by my woes to be Near-er, my
stars for-got, Up - ward I fly, Still all my song shall be Near-er, my

God, to Thee, Near - er, my God, to Thee, Near - er to Thee. A - men.

*Genesis 28:12 **Genesis 35:15
TEXT: Sarah F. Adams; based on Genesis 28:10-22
MUSIC: Lowell Mason

BETHANY
6.4.6.4.6.6.6.4.

394 In My Life Lord, Be Glorified

Christ shall be magnified in my body, whether . . . by life, or by death. Phil. 1:20

1. In my life, Lord, be glo - ri - fied, be glo -ri - fied,
2. In my song, Lord, be glo - ri - fied, be glo -ri - fied,
3. In Your Church, Lord, be glo - ri - fied, be glo -ri - fied,

TEXT and MUSIC: Bob Kilpatrick

BE GLORIFIED
Irregular meter

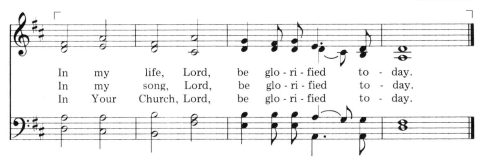

In my life, Lord, be glo-ri-fied to-day.
In my song, Lord, be glo-ri-fied to-day.
In Your Church, Lord, be glo-ri-fied to-day.

Teach Me Thy Way, O Lord 395

Teach me Thy way, O Lord. Ps. 27:11

1. Teach me Thy way, O Lord, Teach me Thy way! Thy guid-ing grace af-ford—
2. When I am sad at heart, Teach me Thy way! When earth-ly joys de-part,
3. When doubts and fears a-rise, Teach me Thy way! When storms o'erspread the skies,
4. Long as my life shall last, Teach me Thy way! Wher-e'er my lot be cast,

Teach me Thy way! Help me to walk a-right, More by faith,
Teach me Thy way! In hours of lone-li-ness, In times of
Teach me Thy way! Shine thro' the cloud and rain, Thro' sor-row,
Teach me Thy way! Un-til the race is run, Un-til the

less by sight; Lead me with heav'n-ly light, Teach me Thy way!
dire dis-tress, In fail-ure or suc-cess, Teach me Thy way!
toil and pain; Make Thou my path-way plain, Teach me Thy way!
jour-ney's done, Un-til the crown is won, Teach me Thy way! A-men.

TEXT and MUSIC: B. Mansell Ramsey

CAMACHA
6.4.6.4.6.6.6.4.

396 Bring Back the Springtime

The winter is past . . . flowers appear on the earth. Song. 2:11-12

1. When in the spring the flow'rs are bloom-ing bright and fair Aft - er the
2. Lord, make me like that stream that flows so cool and clear Down from the

gray of win - ter's gone, Once a - gain the lark be - gins its
mountains high a - bove; I will tell the world that won-drous

tun - ing Back in the mead-ows of my home.
sto - ry Of the streams that flowed from Cal - va - ry.

Refrain

Lord, to my heart bring back the spring - time, Take a - way the

cold and dark of sin; O re - turn to me, sweet Ho - ly

TEXT and MUSIC: Kurt Kaiser

SPRINGTIME
Irregular meter

Spir - it, May I warm and ten - der be a - gain.

Draw Nigh to God 397

Draw nigh to God, and He will draw nigh to you. James 4:8

Draw nigh to God, and He will draw nigh to you.

Draw nigh to God, and He will draw nigh to you. Ac -

quaint thy-self with the Lord, ac - quaint thy-self with the Lord,

Draw nigh to God, and He will draw nigh to you.

TEXT and MUSIC: Colbert and Joyce Croft; based on James 4:8;
arranged by Robert F. Douglas

CROFT
11.11.7.7.11.

398 Fill My Cup, Lord

Whosoever drinketh of the water that I shall give him shall never thirst. John 4:14

1. Like the wom-an at the well I was seek-ing For things that
2. There are mil-lions in this world who are crav-ing The pleas-ures
3. So, my broth-er, if the things this world gave you Leave hun-gers

could not sat-is-fy; And then I heard my Sav-ior speak-ing: "Draw
earth-ly things af-ford; But none can match the won-drous treas-ure
that won't pass a-way, My bless-ed Lord will come and save you,

Refrain

from My well that nev-er shall run dry."
That I find in Je-sus Christ, my Lord. Fill my cup, Lord— I lift it
If you kneel to Him and hum-bly pray:

up, Lord! Come and quench this thirst-ing of my soul; Bread of heav-en,

feed me till I want no more—Fill my cup, fill it up and make me whole!

TEXT and MUSIC: Richard Blanchard

FILL MY CUP
Irregular meter

Higher Ground 399

I press toward the mark for the prize. Phil. 3:14

1. I'm press-ing on the up-ward way, New heights I'm gain-ing ev-'ry day—
2. My heart has no de-sire to stay Where doubts a-rise and fears dis-may;
3. I want to live a-bove the world, Tho Sa-tan's darts at me are hurled;
4. I want to scale the ut-most height And catch a gleam of glo-ry bright;

Still pray-ing as I'm on-ward bound, "Lord, plant my feet on high-er ground."
Tho some may dwell where these a-bound, My pray'r, my aim, is high-er ground.
For faith has caught the joy-ful sound, The song of saints on high-er ground.
But still I'll pray till heav'n I've found, "Lord, lead me on to high-er ground."

Refrain

Lord, lift me up and let me stand By faith on heav-en's ta-ble land;

A high-er plane than I have found—Lord, plant my feet on high-er ground.

TEXT: Johnson Oatman, Jr.
MUSIC: Charles H. Gabriel

HIGHER GROUND
L.M. with Refrain

400 I Want to Be Like Jesus

Ye became followers of us, and of the Lord. 1 Thess. 1:6

1. I have one deep, su-preme de-sire, That I may be like Je-sus.
2. He spent His life in do-ing good; I want to be like Je-sus.
3. A ho-ly, harm-less life He led; I want to be like Je-sus.
4. Oh, per-fect life of Christ, my Lord! I want to be like Je-sus.

To this I fer-vent-ly as-pire, That I may be like Je-sus.
In low-ly paths of ser-vice trod; I want to be like Je-sus.
The Fa-ther's will, His drink and bread; I want to be like Je-sus.
My rec-om-pense and my re-ward, That I may be like Je-sus.

I want my heart His throne to be, So that a watch-ing world may
He sym-pa-thized with hearts dis-tressed; He spoke the words that cheered and
And when at last He comes to die, "For-give them, Fa-ther," hear Him
His Spir-it fill my hun-g'ring soul, His pow-er all my life con-

see His like-ness shin-ing forth in me. I want to be like Je-sus.
blessed; He wel-comed sin-ners to His breast. I want to be like Je-sus.
cry For those who taunt and cru-ci-fy. I want to be like Je-sus.
trol; My deep-est pray'r, my high-est goal, That I may be like Je-sus.

TEXT: Thomas O. Chisholm
MUSIC: David Livingstone Ives

IVES
8.7.8.7.8.8.8.8.7.

Copyright 1945. Renewed 1973 by Lillenas Publishing Co. Used by Permission.

Psalm 42 401

Hope thou in God: for I shall yet praise Him, who is . . . my God. Ps. 42:11

1. As the hart longs for flow-ing streams,
2. My tears have fed me day and night,
3. Why do I mourn and toil with - in,

So longs my soul for You, O God.
While men have said, "Where is your God?"
When it is mine to hope in God?

My soul does thirst for the liv - ing God.
But I re - call as my soul pours dry
I shall a - gain sing praise to Him,

Ritard last stanza

When shall I come to see Your face?
The days of praise with - in Your house.
He is my help, He is my God.

TEXT: Danna Harkin; based on Psalm 42
MUSIC: Appalachian Folk melody; arranged by Michael James

APPALACHIA
8.8.9.8.

402 The Solid Rock

A wise man . . . built his house upon a rock. Matt. 7:24

1. My hope is built on noth - ing less Than Je - sus' blood and
2. When dark - ness veils His love - ly face, I rest on His un -
3. His oath, His cov - e - nant, His blood, Sup - port me in the
4. When He shall come with trum - pet sound, O may I then in

right - eous - ness; I dare not trust the sweet - est frame, But
chang - ing grace; In ev - 'ry high and storm - y gale, My
whelm-ing flood; When all a - round my soul gives way, He
Him be found: Dressed in His right - eous - ness a - lone, Fault-

whol - ly lean on Je - sus' name. On Christ, the sol - id
an - chor holds with - in the veil. On Christ, the sol - id
then is all my hope and stay. On Christ, the sol - id
less to stand be - fore the throne. On Christ, the sol - id

Rock, I stand: All oth - er ground is sink - ing sand.
Rock, I stand: All oth - er ground is sink - ing sand.
Rock, I stand: All oth - er ground is sink - ing sand.
Rock, I stand: All oth - er ground is sink - ing sand. A - men.

TEXT: Edward Mote
MUSIC: John B. Dykes
Alternate tune: SOLID ROCK at No. 404

MELITA
8.8.8.8.8.8.

A LIVING HOPE

A Brief Service of
Affirmation and Renewal

Suggested Hymn Stanzas

To facilitate an uninterrupted flow from stanza to stanza,
the suggested stanzas have been marked with an arrow: ▶

The Solid Rock, stanzas 1, 3, 4
My Faith Has Found a Resting Place, stanzas 1, 2
My Hope Is in the Lord, stanzas 1, 3, 4

WORSHIP LEADER:

Therefore being justified by faith, we have peace with God through
our Lord Jesus Christ; by whom also we have access by faith into this
grace wherein we stand, and rejoice in hope of the glory of God. And
hope maketh not ashamed; because the love of God is shed abroad in
our hearts by the Holy Ghost which is given unto us.

PEOPLE:

For when we were yet without strength, in due time Christ died for
the ungodly. Much more then, being now justified by His blood, we
shall be saved from wrath through Him. For if, when we were enemies, we were reconciled to God by the death of His Son, much
more, being reconciled, we shall be saved by His life.

WORSHIP LEADER:

Wherein God, willing more abundantly to shew unto the heirs of
promise the immutability of His counsel, confirmed it by an oath;
that by two immutable things, in which it was impossible for God to
lie, we might have a strong consolation, who have fled for refuge to
lay hold upon the hope set before us.

ALL:

Which hope we have as an anchor of the soul, both sure and stedfast,
and which entereth into that within the veil; whither the forerunner
is for us entered, even Jesus, made an High Priest for ever.

Rom. 5:1-2, 5-6, 9-10; Heb. 6:17-20.

404 The Solid Rock

A wise man . . . built his house upon a rock. Matt. 7:24

1. My hope is built on noth-ing less Than Je-sus' blood and right-eous-ness;
2. When dark-ness veils His love-ly face, I rest on His un-chang-ing grace;
3. His oath, His cov-e-nant, His blood Sup-port me in the whelm-ing flood;
4. When He shall come with trumpet sound, O may I then in Him be found,

I dare not trust the sweet-est frame, But whol-ly lean on Je-sus' name.
In ev-'ry high and storm-y gale My an-chor holds with-in the veil.
When all a-round my soul gives way, He then is all my hope and stay.
Dressed in His right-eous-ness a-lone, Fault-less to stand be-fore the throne.

Refrain

On Christ, the sol-id Rock, I stand— All oth-er ground is sink-ing sand, All oth-er ground is sink-ing sand.

TEXT: Edward Mote
MUSIC: William B. Bradbury
        Alternate tune: MELITA at No. 402

SOLID ROCK
L.M. with Refrain

Optional transition to
"My Faith Has Found a Resting Place"

mf

Same tempo

My Faith Has Found a Resting Place 405

We which have believed do enter into rest. Heb. 4:3

1. My faith has found a rest-ing place—Not in de-vice or creed:
2. E - nough for me that Je - sus saves—This ends my fear and doubt;
3. My heart is lean - ing on the Word—The writ-ten Word of God:
4. My great Phy - si - cian heals the sick— The lost He came to save;

I trust the Ev - er - liv-ing One— His wounds for me shall plead.
A sin - ful soul I come to Him— He'll nev - er cast me out.
Sal - va-tion by my Sav-ior's name— Sal - va-tion thru His blood.
For me His pre-cious blood He shed— For me His life He gave.

Refrain

I need no oth - er ar - gu-ment, I need no oth - er plea; It
is e - nough that Je - sus died, And that He died for me.

TEXT: Lidie H. Edmunds
MUSIC: André Grétry; arranged by William J. Kirkpatrick

LANDAS
C.M. with Refrain

Optional transition to
"My Hope Is in the Lord"

mf
$d = d$
faster tempo
cresc.

406 My Hope Is in the Lord

... Christ in you, the hope of glory. Col. 1:27

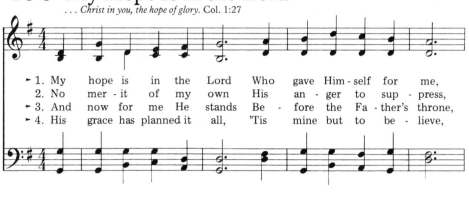

1. My hope is in the Lord Who gave Him-self for me,
2. No mer-it of my own His an-ger to sup-press,
3. And now for me He stands Be-fore the Fa-ther's throne,
4. His grace has planned it all, 'Tis mine but to be-lieve,

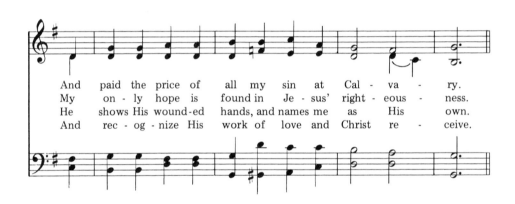

And paid the price of all my sin at Cal-va-ry.
My on-ly hope is found in Je-sus' right-eous-ness.
He shows His wound-ed hands, and names me as His own.
And rec-og-nize His work of love and Christ re-ceive.

Descant

For me He died, For me He lives,

Refrain

For me He died, For me He lives,

For me He died, For me He lives,

TEXT and MUSIC: Norman J. Clayton

WAKEFIELD

Descant and choral ending by Michael James

6.6.12. with Refrain

The end of "A LIVING HOPE—A Brief Service of Affirmation and Renewal"

407 Hear Now the Name

Confess your faults one to another, and pray one for another, that ye may be healed. James 5:16

1. Hear now the Name I'm sing - ing, Here in this
2. Pain and af - flic - tion bear - ing, Frail is the
3. Heart - ache and men - tal an - guish Rip at the
4. Thy King - dom come this ho - ur; Thy King - dom

Name re - veal - ing All of God's love and heal - ing
flesh we're wear - ing, Man - kind this weak - ness shar - ing—
soul, men lan - guish. Hell - ish the sword now brand - ished,
come with pow - er. Pour forth Your love, a show - er,

Comes to you this hour. O - pen your heart re - ceiv - ing,
Cry - ing to be whole. Christ wore the stripes in sor - row,
Pierc - ing hu - man minds. Comes now the Lord of heal - ing,
Drench our thirst - y souls. Rule o - ver sin and sick - ness,

Speak now this Name be - liev - ing; No - thing be -
Paid all that we might bor - row Health for a
Touched with our deep - est feel - ing; Truth from His
Strength - en our ev - ery weak - ness. Son, rise, dis -

TEXT and MUSIC: Jack W. Hayford

ANNAMARIE
7.7.7.5.D. with Refrain

Refrain

yond con - ceiv - ing Lies be - yond His power.
bright to - mor - row, Bod - y, mind and soul.
lips is peal - ing, Free - ing hu - man - kind.
pel all bleak - ness, Come and make us whole.

Je - sus, the

Name a - bove all names. Je - sus, the Lord and King of

Kings. His Name is Life, His Name is health For bod - y, mind and

soul. Je - sus the Name we're sing - ing, In Je - sus'

Name we're bring-ing All of God's love and heal-ing Here to make you whole.

408 Have Faith in God

Have faith in God. Mark 11:22

1. Have faith in God when your path - way is lone - ly, He sees and
2. Have faith in God when your pray'rs are un - an - swered, Your ear - nest
3. Have faith in God in your pain and your sor - row, His heart is
4. Have faith in God tho all else fail a - bout you; Have faith in

knows all the way you have trod; Nev - er a - lone are the
plea He will nev - er for - get; Wait on the Lord, trust His
touched with your grief and de - spair; Cast all your cares and your
God, He pro - vides for His own; He can - not fail tho all

least of His chil - dren; Have faith in God, have faith in God.
Word and be pa - tient, Have faith in God, He'll an - swer yet.
bur - dens up - on Him, And leave them there, oh, leave them there.
king - doms shall per - ish, He rules, He reigns up - on His throne.

Refrain

Have faith in God, He's on His throne; Have faith in God, He watch-es o'er His own;

He can - not fail, He must pre - vail; Have faith in God, have faith in God.

TEXT and MUSIC: B. B. McKinney

MUSKOGEE
11.10.11.8. with Refrain

I Know Whom I Have Believed 409

I know whom I have believed. 2 Tim. 1:12

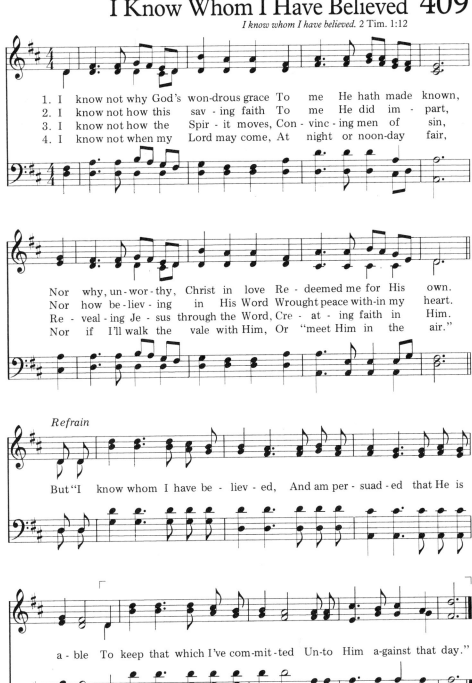

1. I know not why God's won-drous grace To me He hath made known,
2. I know not how this sav - ing faith To me He did im - part,
3. I know not how the Spir - it moves, Con - vinc-ing men of sin,
4. I know not when my Lord may come, At night or noon-day fair,

Nor why, un-wor-thy, Christ in love Re-deemed me for His own.
Nor how be-liev-ing in His Word Wrought peace with-in my heart.
Re-veal-ing Je - sus through the Word, Cre - at-ing faith in Him.
Nor if I'll walk the vale with Him, Or "meet Him in the air."

Refrain

But "I know whom I have be - liev-ed, And am per - suad - ed that He is

a - ble To keep that which I've com-mit-ted Un-to Him a-gainst that day."

TEXT: Daniel W. Whittle; based on 2 Timothy 1:12b
MUSIC: James McGranahan

EL NATHAN
C.M. with Refrain

410 My Faith Looks Up to Thee

In whom we have boldness and access with confidence by the faith of Him. Eph. 3:12

1. My faith looks up to Thee, Thou Lamb of Cal - va - ry,
2. May Thy rich grace im - part Strength to my faint - ing heart,
3. While life's dark maze I tread And griefs a - round me spread,
4. When ends life's pass - ing dream, When death's cold, threat - ening stream

Sav - ior di - vine! Now hear me while I pray, Take all my
My zeal in - spire; As Thou hast died for me, O may my
Be Thou my guide; Bid dark - ness turn to day, Wipe sor - row's
Shall o'er me roll, Blest Sav - ior, then, in love, Fear and dis -

guilt a - way, O let me from this day Be whol - ly Thine!
love to Thee Pure, warm, and change - less be, A liv - ing fire!
tears a - way, Nor let me ev - er stray From Thee a - side.
trust re - move; O lift me safe a - bove, A ran - somed soul! A - men.

TEXT: Ray Palmer
MUSIC: Lowell Mason

OLIVET
6.6.4.6.6.6.4.

411 The Joy of the Lord

The joy of the Lord is your strength. Neh. 8:10

1. The joy of the Lord is my strength, The
2. He heals the bro - ken heart - ed and they cry no more, He
3. He gives me liv - ing wa - ter and I thirst no more, He

TEXT and MUSIC: Alliene G. Vale; based on Nehemiah 8:10

THE JOY OF THE LORD
8.8.7.7.8.

joy of the Lord is my strength, The joy of the
heals the bro-ken heart-ed and they cry no more, He heals the bro-ken
gives me liv-ing wa-ter and I thirst no more, He gives me liv-ing

Lord is my strength, The joy of the Lord is my strength.
heart-ed and they cry no more, The joy of the Lord is my strength.
wa-ter and I thirst no more, The joy of the Lord is my strength.

COMFORT AND ENCOURAGEMENT

Sun of My Soul 412

The Lord God is a sun and shield. Ps. 84:11

1. Sun of my soul, Thou Sav-ior dear, It is not night if Thou be near;
2. When the soft dews of kind-ly sleep My wea-ry eye-lids gen-tly steep,
3. A-bide with me from morn till eve, For with-out Thee I can-not live;
4. Be near to bless me when I wake, Ere thru the world my way I take;

O may no earth-born cloud a-rise To hide Thee from Thy ser-vant's eyes!
Be my last thought, how sweet to rest For-ev-er on my Sav-ior's breast!
A-bide with me when night is nigh, For with-out Thee I dare not die.
A-bide with me till in Thy love I lose my-self in heav'n a-bove.

TEXT: John Keble
MUSIC: *Katholisches Gesangbuch*, Vienna, c. 1774

HURSLEY
L.M.

413 Jesus, Priceless Treasure

Unto you therefore which believe He is precious. 1 Pet. 2:7

1. Je - sus, price - less treas - ure, Source of pur - est pleas - ure, Tru - est friend to me: Long my heart hath pant - ed, 'Til it well - nigh faint - ed, Thirst - ing aft - er Thee. Thine I am, O spot - less Lamb, I will suf - fer nought to hide Thee, Ask for naught be - side Thee.

2. In Thy strength I rest me; Foes who would mo - lest me Can - not reach me here. Though the earth be shak - ing, Ev - ery heart be quak - ing, God dis - pels our fear. Sin and hell in con - flict fell With their heav - iest storms as - sail us: Je - sus will not fail us.

3. Ban - ished is our sad - ness! For the Lord of glad - ness, Je - sus, en - ters in. Those who love the Fa - ther, Tho' the storms may gath - er, Still have peace with - in. Yea, what - e'er we here must bear, Still in Thee lies pur - est pleas - ure, Je - sus, price - less treas - ure! A - men.

TEXT: Johann Franck; translated by Catherine Winkworth
MUSIC: Traditional German melody; adapted by Johann Crüger

JESU, MEINE FREUDE
6.6.5.6.6.5.7.8.6.

I Heard the Voice of Jesus Say 414

Take My yoke upon you . . . and ye shall find rest unto your souls. Matt. 11:29

1. I heard the voice of Je - sus say, "Come un - to Me and rest;
2. I heard the voice of Je - sus say, "Be - hold, I free - ly give
3. I heard the voice of Je - sus say, "I am this dark world's Light;

Lay down, thou wea - ry one, lay down Thy head up - on My breast."
The liv - ing wa - ter; thirst - y one, Stoop down, and drink, and live."
Look un - to Me, thy morn shall rise, And all the day be bright."

I came to Je - sus as I was, Wea - ry, and worn, and sad;
I came to Je - sus, and I drank Of that life - giv - ing stream;
I looked to Je - sus, and I found In Him my Star, my Sun;

I found in Him a rest - ing place, And He has made me glad.
My thirst was quenched, my soul re - vived, And now I live in Him.
And in that Light of life I'll walk, Till trav - 'ling days are done.

TEXT: Horatius Bonar
MUSIC: John B. Dykes

VOX DILECTI
C.M.D.

415 He Giveth More Grace

He giveth more grace. James 4:6

1. He giv-eth more grace when the bur-den grows great-er; He send-eth more strength when the la-bors in-crease. To add-ed af-flic-tion He add-eth His mer-cy; To mul-ti-plied tri-als, His mul-ti-plied peace.

2. When we have ex-haust-ed our store of en-dur-ance, When our strength has failed ere the day is half done, When we reach the end of our hoard-ed re-sourc-es, Our Fa-ther's full giv-ing is on-ly be-gun.

Refrain

His love has no lim-it; His grace has no meas-ure; His pow'r has no bound-a-ry known un-to men. For out of His in-fi-nite

TEXT: Annie Johnson Flint
MUSIC: Hubert Mitchell

HE GIVETH MORE GRACE
Irregular meter

rich-es in Je-sus, He giv-eth, and giv-eth, and giv-eth a-gain!

Come, Ye Disconsolate 416

Let us therefore come boldly unto the throne of grace. Heb. 4:16

1. Come, ye dis-con-so-late, wher-e'er ye lan-guish; Come to the
2. Joy of the des-o-late, Light of the stray-ing, Hope of the
3. Here see the Bread of Life; see wa-ters flow-ing, Forth from the

mer-cy-seat, fer-vent-ly kneel; Here bring your wound-ed hearts, here tell your
pen-i-tent, fade-less and pure, Here speaks the Com-fort-er, ten-der-ly
throne of God, pure from a-bove; Come to the feast of love; come, ev-er

an-guish; Earth has no sor-row that heav'n can-not heal.
say-ing, "Earth has no sor-row that heav'n can-not cure."
know-ing Earth has no sor-row but heav'n can re-move. A-men.

TEXT: Thomas Moore, stanzas 1 and 2;
Thomas Hastings, stanza 3
MUSIC: Samuel Webbe

CONSOLATOR
11.10.11.10.

417 No One Understands Like Jesus

We have not an High Priest which cannot be touched with . . . our infirmities. Heb. 4:15

1. No one un-der-stands like Je - sus, He's a friend be-yond com-pare;
2. No one un-der-stands like Je - sus, Ev - ery woe He sees and feels;
3. No one un-der-stands like Je - sus, When the foes of life as - sail;
4. No one un-der-stands like Je - sus, When you falt-er on the way;

Meet Him at the throne of mer-cy, He is wait-ing for you there.
Ten - der-ly He whis - pers com-fort, And the bro-ken heart He heals.
You should nev-er be dis - cour-aged, Je - sus cares and will not fail.
Tho' you fail Him, sad - ly fail Him, He will par-don you to - day.

Refrain

No one un-der-stands like Je - sus, When the days are dark and grim;

No one is so near, so dear as Je - sus, Cast your ev-ery care on Him.

TEXT and MUSIC: John W. Peterson

NO ONE UNDERSTANDS
8.7.8.7. with Refrain

All Your Anxiety 418

Casting all your care upon Him: for He careth for you. 1 Pet. 5:7

1. Is there a heart o'er-bound by sor-row? Is there a life weighed
2. No oth-er friend so keen to help you, No oth-er friend so
3. Come then at once— de - lay no long-er! Heed His en - treat - y

down by care? Come to the cross—each bur - den bear-ing,
quick to hear; No oth-er place to leave your bur-den,
kind and sweet; You need not fear a dis - ap -point-ment—

Refrain

All your anx - i - e-ty— leave it there. All your anx - i - e-ty,
No oth-er one to hear your prayer.
You shall find peace at the mer - cy seat.

all your care, Bring to the mer - cy seat—leave it there; Nev-er a

bur-den He can - not bear, Nev-er a friend like Je - sus!

TEXT and MUSIC: Edward Henry Joy

ALL YOUR ANXIETY
Irregular meter

419 Abide with Me

The Lord thy God . . . doth go with thee; He will not fail thee, nor forsake thee. Deut. 31:6

1. A - bide with me! Fast falls the e - ven - tide. The dark - ness
2. Swift to its close ebbs out life's lit - tle day. Earth's joys grow
3. I need Thy pres - ence ev - 'ry pass - ing hour. What but Thy
4. I fear no foe, with Thee at hand to bless; Ills have no
5. Hold Thou Thy cross be - fore my clos - ing eyes; Shine thro' the

deep - ens; Lord, with me a - bide! When oth - er help - ers fail and
dim; its glo - ries pass a - way. Change and de - cay in all a -
grace can foil the tempt-er's pow'r? Who, like Thy - self, my guide and
weight, and tears no bit - ter - ness. Where is death's sting? Where, grave, thy
gloom, and point me to the skies. Heav'n's morn-ing breaks, and earth's vain

com - forts flee, Help of the help - less, oh, a - bide with me!
round I see; O Thou who chang-est not, a - bide with me!
stay can be? Thro' clouds and sun-shine, oh, a - bide with me!
vic - to - ry? I tri - umph still if Thou a - bide with me!
shad - ows flee! In life, in death, O Lord, a - bide with me! A - men.

TEXT: Henry F. Lyte
MUSIC: William H. Monk

EVENTIDE
10.10.10.10.

420 Only Believe

All things are possible to him that believeth. Mark 9:23

On - ly be - lieve, on - ly be - lieve; All things are pos-si-ble, on-ly be-lieve;

TEXT and MUSIC: Paul Rader

ONLY BELIEVE
8.10.8.10.

On - ly be-lieve, on - ly be-lieve; All things are pos-si-ble, on-ly be-lieve.

Be Calm My Soul 421

Take heed, and be quiet; fear not, neither be fainthearted. Isa. 7:4

1. Be calm my soul, faint not with care Though bur - dens deep our hearts would tear; He is the Lord, all He com - mands, He hold - eth me Safe in His hands.

2. Be calm my soul, melt not in fear, Though shad-ows dark press in so near, Yet in des - pair I see His light; Lead me, O Lord, with won- d'rous sight.

3. Be calm my soul, rest in Him sure. No wave of doubt His words en - dure; My long - ing soul is sat - is - fied, He now leads forth, my Strength and Guide.

TEXT and MUSIC: Gloria Roe

BE CALM MY SOUL
L.M.

422 No, Not One!

I have called you friends. John 15:15

1. There's not a friend like the low-ly Je-sus— No, not one! no, not one!
2. No friend like Him is so high and ho-ly— No, not one! no, not one!
3. There's not an hour that He is not near us— No, not one! no, not one!
4. Did ev-er saint find this friend for-sake Him? No, not one! no, not one!
5. Was e'er a gift like the Sav-ior giv-en? No, not one! no, not one!

None else could heal all our soul's dis-eas-es— No, not one! no, not one!
And yet no friend is so meek and low-ly— No, not one! no, not one!
No night so dark but His love can cheer us— No, not one! no, not one!
Or sin-ner find that He would not take Him? No, not one! no, not one!
Will He re-fuse us a home in heav-en? No, not one! no, not one!

Refrain

Je-sus knows all a-bout our strug-gles, He will guide till the day is done;

There's not a friend like the low-ly Je-sus— no, not one! no, not one!

TEXT: Johnson Oatman, Jr.
MUSIC: George C. Hugg

NO NOT ONE
10.6.10.6. with Refrain

There Is a Balm in Gilead 423

Is there no balm in Gilead; is there no physician there? Jer. 8:22

There is a balm in Gil-e-ad to make the wound-ed whole;

There is a balm in Gil-e-ad to heal the sin-sick soul.

1. Some - times I feel dis - cour-aged, And think my work's in vain,
2. If you can - not preach like Pe - ter, If you can - not pray like Paul,

But then the Ho - ly Spir - it Re - vives my soul a - gain.
You can tell the love of Je - sus, And say, "He died for all."

TEXT and MUSIC: Traditional Spiritual

BALM IN GILEAD
Irregular meter

424 Tell Me the Old, Old Story

We love Him, because He first loved us. 1 John 4:19

1. Tell me the old, old sto - ry Of un-seen things a - bove, Of Je - sus
2. Tell me the sto - ry slow - ly, That I may take it in— That won - der-
3. Tell me the same old sto - ry When you have cause to fear That this world's

and His glo - ry, Of Je - sus and His love. Tell me the sto - ry
ful re - demp - tion, God's rem-e - dy for sin. Tell me the sto - ry
emp - ty glo - ry Is cost-ing me too dear. Tell me the sto - ry

sim - ply, As to a lit - tle child, For I am weak and wea - ry,
oft - en, For I for - get so soon; The ear - ly dew of morn - ing
al - ways, If you would real - ly be, In an - y time of trou - ble,

Refrain

And help - less and de - filed.
Has passed a - way at noon. Tell me the old, old sto - ry, Tell me the
A com - fort - er to me.

old, old sto - ry, Tell me the old, old sto - ry Of Je - sus and His love.

TEXT: A. Catherine Hankey
MUSIC: William H. Doane

EVANGEL
7.6.7.6.D. with Refrain

In the Garden 425

Then were the disciples glad, when they saw the Lord. John 20:20

1. I come to the gar-den a-lone, While the dew is
2. He speaks, and the sound of His voice Is so sweet the
3. I'd stay in the gar-den with Him Tho the night a-

still on the ros-es; And the voice I hear, fall-ing on my ear,
birds hush their sing-ing; And the mel-o-dy that He gave to me
round me be fall-ing; But He bids me go— thru the voice of woe,

Refrain

The Son of God dis-clos-es.
With-in my heart is ring-ing. And He walks with me, and He
His voice to me is call-ing.

talks with me, And He tells me I am His own; And the joy we

share as we tar-ry there None oth-er has ev-er known.

TEXT and MUSIC: C. Austin Miles

GARDEN
Irregular meter

426 The Lord's Prayer

After this manner therefore pray ye. Matt. 6:9

Our Fa - ther, which art in heav - en, Hal-low-ed

be Thy name. Thy king-dom come,

Thy will be done on earth as it is in heav -

en. Give us this day our dai - ly bread, And for - give us our

TEXT: Matthew 6:9-13
MUSIC: Albert Hay Malotte; arranged by Donald P. Hustad

MALOTTE
Irregular meter

Copyright used by permission of G. Schirmer, Inc.

may be omitted

debts, as we for-give our debt-ors. And

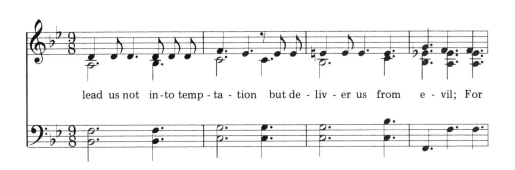

lead us not in-to temp-ta-tion but de-liv-er us from e-vil; For

3 3 3 3 3 3 3 3 3 3 3 3

Thine is the king-dom, and the pow-er, and the glo-ry, For-

3 3 3 3

ev- er, A - men. A - men.

427 Dear Lord and Father of Mankind

Our Father . . . forgive us our sins. Luke 11:2,4

1. Dear Lord and Fa - ther of man - kind, For - give our fool - ish
2. In sim - ple trust like theirs who heard, Be - side the Syr - ian
3. Drop Thy still dews of qui - et - ness, Till all our striv - ings
4. Breathe through the heats of our de - sire Thy cool - ness and Thy

ways! Re - clothe us in our right - ful mind; In pur - er
Sea, The gra - cious call - ing of the Lord, Let us, like
cease; Take from our souls the strain and stress, And let our
balm; Let sense be dumb, let flesh re - tire; Speak through the

lives Thy serv - ice find, In deep - er rev - 'rence, praise.
them, with - out a word, Rise up and fol - low Thee.
or - dered lives con - fess The beau - ty of Thy peace.
earth - quake, wind, and fire, O still small voice of calm! A - men.

TEXT: John G. Whittier
MUSIC: Frederick C. Maker

REST
8.6.8.8.6.

428 I Need Thee Every Hour

O Lord, hear me: for I am poor and needy. Ps. 86:1

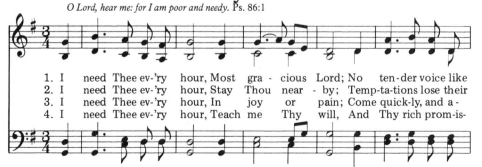

1. I need Thee ev - 'ry hour, Most gra - cious Lord; No ten - der voice like
2. I need Thee ev - 'ry hour, Stay Thou near - by; Temp - ta - tions lose their
3. I need Thee ev - 'ry hour, In joy or pain; Come quick - ly, and a -
4. I need Thee ev - 'ry hour, Teach me Thy will, And Thy rich prom - is -

TEXT: Annie S. Hawks; Robert Lowry, Refrain
MUSIC: Robert Lowry

NEED
6.4.6.4. with Refrain

Thine Can peace af - ford.
pow'r When Thou art nigh.
bide, Or life is vain.
es In me ful - fill.

I need Thee, O I need Thee; Ev - 'ry

hour I need Thee! O bless me now, my Sav-ior, I come to Thee. A - men.

Lord, Listen to Your Children Praying 429

If we ask any thing according to His will, He heareth us. 1 John 5:14

Lord, lis-ten to your chil-dren pray - ing, Lord, send Your Spir-it

in this place; Lord, lis-ten to Your chil-dren pray - ing,

1 *(optional)* D.C. | **Final**

Send us love, send us pow'r, send us grace. grace!

TEXT and MUSIC: Ken Medema   CHILDREN PRAYING
                                                                Irregular meter

430 I Must Tell Jesus

In that He Himself hath suffered . . . He is able to succour them that are tempted. Heb. 2:18

1. I must tell Je - sus all of my tri - als, I can-not bear these
2. I must tell Je - sus all of my trou - bles, He is a kind, com-
3. O how the world to e - vil al - lures me! O how my heart is

bur - dens a - lone; In my dis - tress He kind - ly will help me,
pas - sion-ate friend; If I but ask Him, He will de - liv - er,
tempt-ed to sin! I must tell Je - sus, and He will help me

Refrain

He ev - er loves and cares for His own.
Make of my trou - bles quick - ly an end. I must tell Je - sus!
O - ver the world the vic - t'ry to win.

I must tell Je - sus! I can-not bear my bur-dens a - lone; I must tell

Je - sus! I must tell Je - sus! Je-sus can help me, Je-sus a - lone.

TEXT and MUSIC: Elisha A. Hoffman

ORWIGSBURG
10.9.10.9. with Refrain

I Am Praying for You 431

God our Saviour . . . will have all men to be saved. 1 Tim. 2:3-4

1. I have a Sav - ior, He's plead - ing in glo - ry, A dear, lov - ing
2. I have a Fa - ther; to me He has giv - en A hope for e -
3. I have a robe; 'tis re - splen - dent in white - ness, A wait - ing in
4. When He has found you, tell oth - ers the sto - ry, That my lov - ing

Sav - ior tho' earth - friends be few; And now He is watch - ing in ten - der - ness
ter - ni - ty, bless - ed and true; And soon He will call me to meet Him in
glo - ry my won - der - ing view; Oh, when I re - ceive it all shin - ing in
Sav - ior is your Sav - ior, too; Then pray that your Savior may bring them to

Refrain

o'er me, But oh, that my Sav - ior were your Sav - ior, too!
heav - en, But oh, that He'd let me bring you with me too! For you I am
brightness, Dear friend, could I see you re - ceiv - ing one too!
glo - ry, And prayer will be an - swered, 'twas an - swered for you!

pray - ing, For you I am pray - ing, For you I am pray - ing, I'm pray - ing for you.

TEXT: Samuel Cluff
MUSIC: Ira D. Sankey

PRAYING FOR YOU
9.9.11.11. with Refrain

432 From Every Stormy Wind That Blows

Having . . . boldness to enter into the holiest by the blood of Jesus . . . Heb. 10:19

1. From ev - 'ry storm - y wind that blows, From ev - 'ry swell - ing
2. There is a scene where spir - its blend, Where friend holds fel - low-
3. Ah! whith - er could we flee for aid, When tempt - ed, des - o -
4. Ah! there on ea - gle wings we soar, And sin and sense mo -

tide of woes, There is a calm, a sure re - treat:
ship with friend; Though sun - dered far, by faith they meet
late, dis - mayed: Or how the hosts of hell de - feat,
lest no more: And heav'n comes down our souls to greet,

'Tis found be - neath the mer - cy seat.
A - round one com - mon mer - cy seat.
Had suf - f'ring saints no mer - cy seat.
While glo - ry crowns the mer - cy seat. A - men.

TEXT: Hugh Stowell
MUSIC: Thomas Hastings
Another key and alternate setting may be found at No. 319

RETREAT
L.M.

433 Sweet Hour of Prayer

Peter and John went up together into the temple at the hour of prayer. Acts 3:1

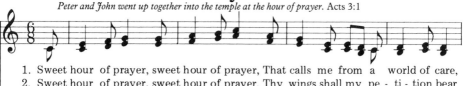

1. Sweet hour of prayer, sweet hour of prayer, That calls me from a world of care,
2. Sweet hour of prayer, sweet hour of prayer, Thy wings shall my pe - ti - tion bear

TEXT: William W. Walford
MUSIC: William B. Bradbury

SWEET HOUR
L.M.D.

And bids me at my Fa-ther's throne Make all my wants and wish-es known:
To Him whose truth and faith-ful - ness En - gage the wait-ing soul to bless:

In sea - sons of dis - tress and grief My soul has of - ten found re-lief,
And since He bids me seek His face, Be - lieve His Word, and trust His grace,

And oft es-caped the tempt-er's snare By thy re-turn, sweet hour of prayer.
I'll cast on Him my ev - 'ry care, And wait for thee, sweet hour of prayer.

Search Me 434

Search me, O God, and know my heart. Ps. 139:23

4 Part Canon

I

Search me, O God, and know my heart to - day! Try me, O

II

III

Fa - ther and know my thoughts I pray. See if there be some

IV

wick-ed way in me; Lead me, O Lord, in Your ev-er-last-ing way!

TEXT and MUSIC: Ken Barker; based on Psalm 139:23, 24

DAVID
10.11.10.10.

435 What a Friend We Have in Jesus

In every thing by prayer . . . let your requests be made known unto God. Phil. 4:6

1. What a Friend we have in Je - sus, All our sins and griefs to bear!
2. Have we tri - als and temp - ta - tions? Is there trou-ble an - y - where?
3. Are we weak and heav - y - la - den, Cum-bered with a load of care?

What a priv - i - lege to car - ry Ev - ery-thing to God in prayer!
We should nev - er be dis - cour-aged, Take it to the Lord in prayer.
Pre - cious Sav - ior, still our Ref - uge— Take it to the Lord in prayer.

O what peace we of - ten for - feit, O what need-less pain we bear,
Can we find a friend so faith - ful Who will all our sor - rows share?
Do thy friends de-spise, for - sake thee? Take it to the Lord in prayer;

All be-cause we do not car - ry Ev - ery-thing to God in prayer!
Je - sus knows our ev - ery weak - ness, Take it to the Lord in prayer.
In His arms He'll take and shield thee, Thou wilt find a sol - ace there.

TEXT: Joseph M. Scriven
MUSIC: Charles C. Converse

CONVERSE
8.7.8.7.D.

Whiter Than Snow 436

Wash me, and I shall be whiter than snow. Ps. 51:7

1. Lord Je - sus, I long to be per - fect - ly whole; I
2. Lord Je - sus, look down from Your throne in the skies And
3. Lord Je - sus, for this I most hum - bly en - treat; I
4. Lord Je - sus, be - fore You I pa - tient - ly wait; Come

want Thee for - ev - er to live in my soul. Break down ev - ery
help me to make a com - plete sac - ri - fice. I give up my-
wait, bless - ed Lord, at Thy cru - ci - fied feet. By faith, for my
now and with- in me a new heart cre - ate. To those who have

i - dol, cast out ev - ery foe— Now wash me and I shall be
self and what - ev - er I know— Now wash me and I shall be
cleans-ing I see Your blood flow— Now wash me and I shall be
sought You, You nev - er said, "No"— Now wash me and I shall be

Refrain

whit - er than snow. Whit - er than snow, yes, whit - er than

snow— Now wash me and I shall be whit - er than snow.

TEXT: James Nicholson
MUSIC: William G. Fischer

FISCHER
11.11.11.11. with Refrain

437 Pure and Holy

Be holy: for I the Lord your God am holy. Lev. 19:2

1. Pure and ho - ly I would be, wor - thy of Your
2. You are great and I am small, You are King and

love for me. Teach me while Your light is clear,
God of all. You are wise in all You do,

Optional descant

Ho - ly, ho - ly

Refrain

change me while my heart is near. Ho - ly, ho - ly,
Lord I put my trust in You. Ho - ly, ho - ly,

1
ho - ly Lord.
ho - ly Lord.

2
ho - ly Lord.
ho - ly Lord.

TEXT and MUSIC: Mike Hudson and Bob Farnsworth;
arranged by David Allen

PURE and HOLY
7.7.7.7. with Refrain

Cleanse Me 438

Search me, O God, and know my heart. Ps. 139:23

1. Search me, O God, and know my heart to-day;
2. I praise Thee, Lord, for cleans-ing me from sin;
3. Lord, take my life, and make it whol-ly Thine;
4. O Ho-ly Ghost, re-viv-al comes from Thee;

Try me, O Sav-ior, know my thoughts, I pray.
Ful-fill Thy Word, and make me pure with-in.
Fill my poor heart with Thy great love di-vine.
Send a re-viv-al, start the work in me.

See if there be some wick-ed way in me;
Fill me with fire, where once I burned with shame;
Take all my will, my pas-sion, self and pride;
Thy Word de-clares Thou wilt sup-ply our need;

Cleanse me from ev-ery sin, and set me free.
Grant my de-sire to mag-ni-fy Thy name.
I now sur-ren-der, Lord—in me a-bide.
For bless-ings now, O Lord, I hum-bly plead.

TEXT: J. Edwin Orr; based on Psalm 139:23
MUSIC: Maori melody; arranged by Robert F. Douglas
Alternate tune: ELLERS at No. 439

MAORI
10.10.10.10.

439 Cleanse Me

Search me, O God, and know my heart. Ps. 139:23

1. Search me, O God, and know my heart to - day; Try me, O
2. I praise Thee, Lord, for cleans-ing me from sin; Ful - fill Thy
3. Lord, take my life and make it whol - ly Thine; Fill my poor
4. O Ho - ly Ghost, re - viv - al comes from Thee; Send a re -

Sav - ior, know my thoughts, I pray. See if there be some wick-ed
Word and make me pure with - in. Fill me with fire where once I
heart with Thy great love di - vine. Take all my will, my pas-sion,
viv - al, start the work in me. Thy Word de - clares Thou wilt sup-

way in me; Cleanse me from ev - 'ry sin and set me free.
burned with shame; Grant my de - sire to mag-ni - fy Thy name.
self, and pride; I now sur - ren - der; Lord, in me a - bide.
ply our need; For bless-ings now, O Lord, I hum-bly plead. A - men.

TEXT: J. Edwin Orr; based on Psalm 139:23
MUSIC: Edward J. Hopkins; arranged by Joseph Barlowe
     Alternate tune: MAORI at No. 438

ELLERS
10.10.10.10.

Arr. © 1986 WORD MUSIC (a div. of WORD, INC.). All Rights Reserved. International Copyright Secured.

440 O for a Heart to Praise My God

Create in me a clean heart, O God. Ps. 51:10

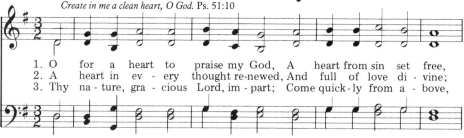

1. O for a heart to praise my God, A heart from sin set free,
2. A heart in ev - ery thought re-newed, And full of love di - vine;
3. Thy na - ture, gra - cious Lord, im - part; Come quick-ly from a - bove,

TEXT: Charles Wesley
MUSIC: Carl G. Gläser; arranged by Lowell Mason
     A higher setting may be found at No. 76

AZMON
C.M.

A heart that al - ways feels Thy blood So free-ly shed for me!
Per - fect and right and pure and good, A cop -y, Lord, of Thine!
Write Thy new name up - on my heart, Thy new, best name of Love. A - men.

Take Time to Be Holy 441

Follow . . . holiness, without which no man shall see the Lord. Heb. 12:14

1. Take time to be ho - ly, Speak oft with thy Lord; A - bide in Him
2. Take time to be ho - ly, The world rush-es on; Much time spend in
3. Take time to be ho - ly, Let Him be thy guide, And run not be -
4. Take time to be ho - ly, Be calm in thy soul; Each thought and each

al - ways, And feed on His Word. Make friends of God's chil - dren; Help
se - cret With Je - sus a - lone; By look-ing to Je - sus, Like
fore Him What - ev - er be - tide; In joy or in sor - row Still
mo - tive Be - neath His con - trol; Thus led by His Spir - it To

those who are weak; For - get - ting in noth-ing His bless-ing to seek.
Him thou shalt be; Thy friends in thy con-duct His like-ness shall see.
fol - low thy Lord, And, look - ing to Je - sus, Still trust in His Word.
foun-tains of love, Thou soon shalt be fit - ted For ser - vice a - bove.

TEXT: William D. Longstaff
MUSIC: George C. Stebbins
　　　Alternate tune: SLANE (altered) at No. 442

HOLINESS
6.5.6.5.D.

442 Take Time to Be Holy

Follow . . . holiness, without which no man shall see the Lord. Heb. 12:14

Unison

1. Take time to be ho - ly, Speak of - ten with God; Find
2. Take time to be ho - ly, The world rush - es on; Much
3. Take time to be ho - ly, Let Him be thy guide, And

rest in Him al - ways And feed on His Word. Make
time spend in se - cret With Je - sus a - lone. By
run not be - fore Him, What - ev - er be - tide. In

friends of God's chil - dren; Help those who are weak, For -
look - ing to Je - sus, Like Him thou shalt be; Thy
joy or in sor - row, Still fol - low thy Lord, And,

get - ting in noth - ing His bless - ing to seek.
friends in thy con - duct His like - ness shall see.
look - ing to Je - sus, Still trust in His Word. A - men.

TEXT: William D. Longstaff
MUSIC: Irish Folk melody; adapted by Ronn Huff; arranged by David Allen
Alternate tune: HOLINESS at No. 441

SLANE (altered)
6.5.6.5.D.

Give Me Jesus 443

What shall it profit a man, if he shall gain the whole world, and lose his own soul? Mark 8:36

1. Take the world, but give me Je - sus, All its joys are but a name;
2. Take the world, but give me Je - sus, Sweet-est com - fort of my soul;
3. Take the world, but give me Je - sus, Let me view His con-stant smile;
4. Take the world, but give me Je - sus, In His cross my trust shall be;

But His love a - bid -eth ev - er, Thru e - ter - nal years the same.
With my Sav - ior watch-ing o'er me, I can sing tho bil -lows roll.
Then thru -out my pil - grim jour - ney Light will cheer me all the while.
Till, with clear - er, bright-er vi - sion, Face to face my Lord I see.

Refrain

O the height and depth of mer -cy! O the length and breadth of love!

O the full - ness of re - demp-tion, Pledge of end - less life a - bove!

TEXT: Fanny J. Crosby
MUSIC: John R. Sweney

GIVE ME JESUS
8.7.8.7. with Refrain

444 I'll Go Where You Want Me to Go

Go to all that I shall send thee, and whatsoever I command thee . . . speak. Jer. 1:7

1. It may not be on the mountain's height Or o-ver the storm-y sea,
2. Per-haps to-day there are lov-ing words Which Je-sus would have me speak,
3. There's sure-ly somewhere a low-ly place In earth's har-vest fields so wide,

It may not be at the bat-tle's front My Lord will have need of me;
There may be now, in the paths of sin, Some wand'rer whom I should seek;
Where I may la-bor thru life's short day For Je-sus the Cru-ci-fied;

But if by a still, small voice He calls To paths I do not know,
O Sav-ior, if Thou wilt be my Guide, Tho dark and rug-ged the way,
So, trust-ing my all un-to Thy care— I know Thou lov-est me—

I'll an-swer, dear Lord, with my hand in Thine, I'll go where You want me to go.
My voice shall ech-o the mes-sage sweet, I'll say what You want me to say.
I'll do Thy will with a heart sin-cere, I'll be what You want me to be.

Refrain

I'll go where You want me to go, dear Lord, O'er mountain or plain or sea;

TEXT: Mary Brown, stanza 1; Charles E. Prior, stanzas 2, 3
MUSIC: Carrie E. Rounsefell

I'LL GO
9.7.9.7.9.8. with Refrain

I'll say what you want me to say, dear Lord, I'll be what You want me to be.

Something for Thee 445

Study to shew thyself approved unto God, a workman. 2 Tim. 2:15

1. Sav - ior, Thy dy - ing love Thou gav - est me, Nor should I
2. At the blest mer - cy seat, Plead - ing for me, My fee - ble
3. Give me a faith - ful heart, Like - ness to Thee, That each de -
4. All that I am and have, Thy gifts so free, In joy, in

aught with-hold, Dear Lord, from Thee: In love my soul would bow, My heart ful-
faith looks up, Je - sus, to Thee: Help me the cross to bear, Thy won-drous
part - ing day Hence-forth may see Some work of love be - gun, Some deed of
grief, thro' life, Dear Lord, for Thee! And when Thy face I see, My ran-som'd

fill its vow, Some of - f'ring bring Thee now, Some - thing for Thee.
love de -clare, Some song to raise, or pray'r, Some - thing for Thee.
kind-ness done, Some wan-d'rer sought and won, Some - thing for Thee.
soul shall be, Thro' all e - ter - ni - ty, Some - thing for Thee. A - men.

TEXT: Sylvanus D. Phelps
MUSIC: Robert Lowry

SOMETHING FOR JESUS
6.4.6.4.6.6.6.4.

446 I Will Serve Thee

Ye serve the Lord Christ. Col. 3:24

I will serve Thee be-cause I love Thee, You have giv - en life to me; I was noth-ing be-fore You found me, You have giv - en life to me. Heart - aches, bro-ken piec - es, Ru -ined lives are why You died on Cal-vary; Your touch was what I longed for, You have giv - en life to me.

TEXT: Gloria Gaither and William J. Gaither
MUSIC: William J. Gaither

SERVING
Irregular meter

Freely, Freely 447

Freely ye have received, freely give. Matt. 10:8

1. God for-gave my sin in Je-sus' name, I've been born a-gain in
2. All pow'r is giv'n in Je-sus' name, In earth and heav'n in

Je-sus' name; And in Je-sus' name I come to you To share
Je-sus' name; And in Je-sus' name I come to you To share

His love as He told me to: He said, "Free-ly, free-ly
His pow'r as He told me to:

Refrain

you have re-ceived—Free-ly, free-ly give; Go in My

name and, be-cause you be-lieve, Oth-ers will know that I live."

TEXT and MUSIC: Carol Owens; based on Matthew 10:8; 28:18

FREELY, FREELY
9.9.9.9. with Refrain

448 A Charge to Keep I Have

It is required in stewards, that a man be found faithful. 1 Cor. 4:2

1. A charge to keep I have, A God to glo - ri - fy, A
2. To serve the pres - ent age, My call - ing to ful - fill; O
3. Arm me with watch - ful care As in Thy sight to live, And
4. Help me to watch and pray, And still on Thee re - ly, O

nev - er - dy - ing soul to save, And fit it for the sky.
may it all my pow'rs en - gage To do my Mas - ter's will!
now Thy serv - ant, Lord, pre - pare A strict ac - count to give!
let me not my trust be - tray, But press to realms on high. A - men.

TEXT: Charles Wesley
MUSIC: Lowell Mason

BOYLSTON
S.M.

449 Must Jesus Bear the Cross Alone?

Whosoever will come after Me, let him . . . take up his cross. Mark 8:34

1. Must Je - sus bear the cross a - lone And all the world go free?
2. The con - se - crat - ed cross I'll bear Till death shall set me free,
3. Up - on the crys - tal pave - ment, down At Je - sus' pierc - ed feet,
4. O pre - cious cross! O glo - rious crown! O res - ur - rec - tion day!

No, there's a cross for ev - 'ry - one, And there's a cross for me.
And then go home my crown to wear, For there's a crown for me.
Joy - ful I'll cast my gold - en crown And His dear name re - peat.
Ye an - gels, from the stars come down And bear my soul a - way.

TEXT: Thomas Shepherd and others
MUSIC: George N. Allen

MAITLAND
C.M.

Lord, Speak to Me 450

The things that thou hast heard of me . . . commit thou to faithful men. 2 Tim. 2:2

1. Lord, speak to me, that I may speak In liv-ing ech-oes of Thy tone;
2. O teach me, Lord, that I may teach The pre-cious things Thou dost im-part;
3. O fill me with Thy full-ness, Lord, Un-til my ver-y heart o'er-flow
4. O use me, Lord, use e-ven me, Just as Thou wilt and when and where;

As Thou hast sought, so let me seek Thy err-ing chil-dren lost and lone.
And wing my words, that they may reach The hid-den depths of many a heart.
In kind-ling thought and glow-ing word Thy love to tell, Thy praise to show.
Un-til Thy bless-ed face I see, Thy rest, Thy joy, Thy glo-ry share. A-men.

TEXT: Frances Ridley Havergal
MUSIC: Robert Schumann

CANONBURY
L.M.

O Master, Let Me Walk with Thee 451

He that saith he abideth in Him ought . . . to walk, even as He walked. 1 John 2:6

1. O Mas-ter, let me walk with Thee In low-ly paths of serv-ice free;
2. Help me the slow of heart to move By some clear, win-ning word of love;
3. Teach me Thy pa-tience! Still with Thee In clos-er, dear-er com-pa-ny,
4. In hope that sends a shin-ing ray Far down the fu-ture's broad-ening way,

Tell me Thy se-cret; help me bear The strain of toil, the fret of care.
Teach me the way-ward feet to stay, And guide them in the home-ward way.
In work that keeps faith sweet and strong, In trust that tri-umphs o-ver wrong;
In peace that on-ly Thou canst give, With Thee, O Mas-ter, let me live. A-men.

TEXT: Washington Gladden
MUSIC: H. Percy Smith
A lower setting may be found at No. 320

MARYTON
L.M.

452 Make Me a Blessing

By the blessing of the upright the city is exalted. Prov. 11:11

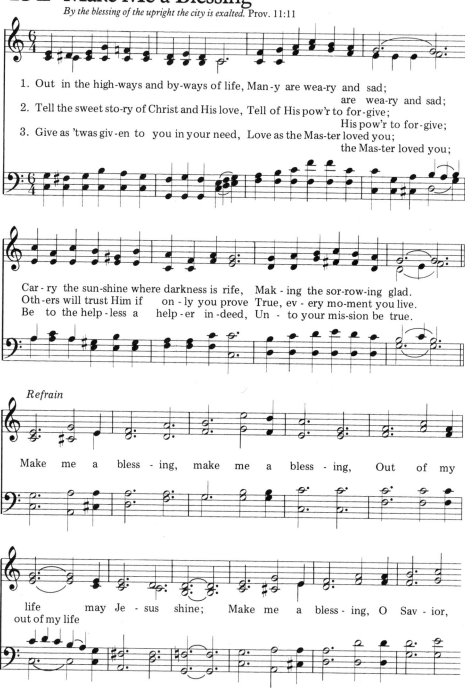

1. Out in the high-ways and by-ways of life, Man-y are wea-ry and sad;
   are wea-ry and sad;
2. Tell the sweet sto-ry of Christ and His love, Tell of His pow'r to for-give;
   His pow'r to for-give;
3. Give as 'twas giv-en to you in your need, Love as the Mas-ter loved you;
   the Mas-ter loved you;

Car-ry the sun-shine where darkness is rife, Mak-ing the sor-row-ing glad.
Oth-ers will trust Him if on-ly you prove True, ev-ery mo-ment you live.
Be to the help-less a help-er in-deed, Un-to your mis-sion be true.

Refrain

Make me a bless-ing, make me a bless-ing, Out of my

life may Je-sus shine; Make me a bless-ing, O Sav-ior,
out of my life

TEXT: Ira B. Wilson
MUSIC: George S. Schuler

SCHULER
10.7.10.7. with Refrain

I pray,
I pray Thee, my Sav-ior, Make me a bless-ing to some-one to-day.

I Gave My Life for Thee 453

Greater love hath no man than this, that a man lay down his life for his friends. John 15:13

1. I gave My life for thee, My pre-cious blood I shed,
2. My Fa-ther's house of light, My glo-ry-cir-cled throne,
3. I suf-fered much for thee, More than the tongue can tell,
4. And I have brought to thee, Down from My home a-bove,

That thou might'st ran-somed be, And quick-ened from the dead;
I left, for earth-ly night, For wan-d'rings sad and lone;
Of bit-t'rest ag-o-ny, To res-cue thee from hell;
Sal-va-tion full and free, My par-don and My love;

I gave, I gave My life for thee, What hast thou given for Me?
I left, I left it all for thee, Hast thou left aught for Me?
I've borne, I've borne it all for thee, What hast thou borne for Me?
I bring, I bring rich gifts to thee, What hast thou brought to Me?

TEXT: Frances Ridley Havergal
MUSIC: Philip P. Bliss

KENOSIS
6.6.6.6.8.8.

454 Glorious Is Thy Name Most Holy

To do good and to communicate, forget not. Heb. 13:16

1. Glo - rious is Thy name, Most Ho - ly, God and Fa - ther of us all;
2. For our world of need and an - guish We would lift to Thee our prayer.
3. In the midst of time we jour - ney, From Thy hand comes each new day;

We Thy ser - vants bow be - fore Thee, Strive to an - swer ev - 'ry call.
Faith-ful stew - ards of Thy boun - ty, May we with our broth-ers share.
We would use it in Thy ser - vice, Hum - bly, wise - ly, while we may.

Thou with life's great good hast blest us, Cared for us from ear - liest years;
In the name of Christ our Sav - ior, Who re - deems and sets us free,
So to Thee, Lord and Cre - a - tor, Praise and hon - or we ac - cord,

Un - to Thee our thanks we ren - der; Thy deep love o'er - comes all fears.
Gifts we bring of heart and trea - sure, That our lives may wor-thier be.
Thine the earth and Thine the heav - ens, Thro' all the E - ter - nal Word.

TEXT: Ruth Elliott
MUSIC: William Moore

HOLY MANNA
8.7.8.7.D.

Come, All Christians, Be Committed 455

. . . fervent in spirit; serving the Lord. Rom. 12:11

1. Come, all Chris - tians, be com - mit - ted To the ser - vice of the
2. Of your time and tal - ents give ye, They are gifts from God a -
3. God's com - mand to love each oth - er Is re - quired of ev - ery
4. Come in praise and ad - o - ra - tion, All who on Christ's name be -

Lord. Make your lives for Him more fit - ted, Tune your hearts with one ac -
bove, To be used by Chris - tians free - ly To pro - claim His won-drous
man. Show-ing mer - cy to a broth - er Mir - rors His re - demp-tive
lieve. Wor - ship Him with con - se - cra - tion, Grace and love will you re -

cord. Come in - to His courts with glad - ness, Each his sa - cred vows re -
love. Come a - gain to serve the Sav - ior, Tithes and off - 'rings with you
plan. In com - pas - sion He has giv - en Of His love that is di -
ceive. For His grace give Him the glo - ry, For the Spir - it and the

new, Turn a - way from sin and sad - ness, Be trans-formed with life a - new.
bring. In your work with Him find fa - vor, And with joy His prais - es sing.
vine; On the cross sins were for - giv - en; Joy and peace are ful - ly thine.
Word, And re - peat the gos - pel sto - ry Till all men His name have heard.

TEXT: Eva B. Lloyd
MUSIC: Traditional American melody; *The Sacred Harp,* 1844;
    harmonized by James H. Wood

BEACH SPRING
8.7.8.7.D.

456 Reaching for Excellence

That ye may approve things that are excellent . . . and without offence. Phil. 1:10

1. Reach for the glor - ious prize, the prize of God's "Well done."
2. So fol - low Je - sus Christ who lived a life un - flawed.
3. Give to the Lord your best, the best that you can do.

Learn to fix your eyes on the long - ings of the Son. Sur -
Think of who it is you now rev - er - ence as Lord. Be -
As you hon - or Him, He will sure - ly hon - or you. So

ren - der all you are, let all be sac - ri - ficed.
cause He gave His all, a crown is His re - ward.
learn to run the race un - til the race is done.

Reach - ing for ex - cel - lence by giv - ing all to Christ,
Reach - ing for ex - cel - lence, our world He will re - store,
Reach - ing for ex - cel - lence un - til the prize is won,

Reach - ing for ex - cel - lence by giv - ing all to Christ.
Reach - ing for ex - cel - lence, our world He will re - store.
Reach - ing for ex - cel - lence un - til the prize is won. A - men.

TEXT: Bryan Jeffery Leech
MUSIC: Kurt Kaiser

EXCELLENCE
Irregular meter

I Will Sing of the Mercies 457

I will sing of the mercies of the Lord for ever. Ps. 89:1

Unison

I will sing of the mer-cies of the Lord for-ev-er, I will

sing, I will sing, I will sing of the mer-cies of the

Fine

Lord. With my mouth will I make known Thy

faith-ful-ness, Thy faith-ful-ness, With my mouth will I make

D.C. al Fine

known Thy faith-ful-ness to all gen-er - a - tions. I will

TEXT: Psalm 89:1
MUSIC: James H. Fillmore; arranged by Lee Herrington

FILLMORE
Irregular meter

458 Gentle Shepherd

He shall feed His flock like a shepherd . . . and shall gently lead. Isa. 40:11

Gen-tle Shep-herd, come and lead us, For we need You to help us find our way. Gen-tle Shep-herd, come and feed us, For we need Your strength from day to day. There's no oth-er we can turn to Who can help us face an-oth-er day; Gen-tle Shep-herd, come and lead us, For we need You to help us find our way.

TEXT: Gloria Gaither and William J. Gaither
MUSIC: William J. Gaither

GENTLE SHEPHERD
Irregular meter

THE LORD IS MY SHEPHERD

A Brief Service in
Recognition of His Leadership

Suggested Hymn Stanzas

To facilitate an uninterrupted flow from stanza to stanza,
the suggested stanzas have been marked with an arrow: ►

All the Way My Savior Leads Me, stanza 1
He Leadeth Me, stanza 1
Savior, Like a Shepherd Lead Us, stanzas 1, 2, 4

WORSHIP LEADER:
I am the good Shepherd: the good Shepherd giveth His life for the sheep.

PEOPLE:
The Lord is my Shepherd; I shall not want. For this God is our God for ever and ever; He will be our guide even unto death. He shall feed His flock like a shepherd: He shall gather the lambs with His arm, and carry them in His bosom, and shall gently lead those that are with young.

WORSHIP LEADER:
I will feed My flock, and I will cause them to lie down, saith the Lord God. I will seek that which was lost, and bring again that which was driven away, and will bind up that which was broken, and will strengthen that which was sick: but I will destroy the fat and the strong; I will feed them with judgment. Now the God of peace, that brought again from the dead our Lord Jesus, that great Shepherd of the sheep, through the blood of the everlasting covenant, make you perfect in every good work to do His will, working in you that which is wellpleasing in His sight, through Jesus Christ; to whom be glory for ever and ever. And when the chief Shepherd shall appear, ye shall receive a crown of glory that fadeth not away.

ALL:
For the Lamb which is in the midst of the throne shall feed them and shall lead them unto living fountains of waters: and God shall wipe away all tears from their eyes.

John 10:11; Ps. 23:1; Ps. 48:14; Isa. 40:11;
Ezek. 34:15-16; Heb. 13:20-21; 1 Pet. 5:4; Rev. 7:17.

Optional introduction to
"All the Way My Savior Leads Me"

mf

460 All the Way My Savior Leads Me

He will be our guide even unto death. Ps. 48:14

1. All the way my Sav-ior leads me; What have I to ask be - side? Can I
2. All the way my Sav-ior leads me; Cheers each wind-ing path I tread, Gives me
3. All the way my Sav-ior leads me; Oh, the full-ness of His love! Per-fect

doubt His ten - der mer - cy, Who thru life has been my guide? Heav'n-ly
grace for ev - 'ry tri - al, Feeds me with the liv - ing bread: Tho my
rest to me is prom-ised In my Fa - ther's house a - bove: When my

peace, di - vin - est com - fort, Here by faith in Him to dwell! For I
wea - ry steps may fal - ter, And my soul a - thirst may be, Gush-ing
spir - it, cloth'd im-mor - tal, Wings its flight to realms of day, This my

know what-e'er be - fall me, Je - sus do - eth all things well; well.
from the Rock be - fore me, Lo! a spring of joy I see; see.
song thru end-less a - ges: Je - sus led me all the way; way.

TEXT: Fanny J. Crosby
MUSIC: Robert Lowry

opt. segue to "He Leadeth Me"
ALL THE WAY
8.7.8.7.D.

He Leadeth Me 461

Thou in Thy mercy hast led forth the people which Thou hast redeemed. Ex. 15:13

1. He lead - eth me! O bless-ed thought! O words with heav'n-ly comfort fraught!
2. Lord, I would clasp Thy hand in mine, Nor ev - er mur - mur nor re - pine,
3. And when my task on earth is done, When, by Thy grace, the vic-t'ry's won,

What - e'er I do, wher-e'er I be, Still 'tis God's hand that lead - eth me!
Con - tent, what-ev - er lot I see, Since 'tis Thy hand that lead - eth me!
E'en death's cold wave I will not flee, Since God thru Jor - dan lead - eth me!

Refrain

He lead-eth me, He lead-eth me, By His own hand He lead-eth me:

His faith-ful fol-l'wer I would be, For by His hand He lead-eth me.

TEXT: Joseph Gilmore
MUSIC: William B. Bradbury

HE LEADETH ME
L.M. with Refrain

Optional transition to
"Savior, Like a Shepherd Lead Us"

462 Savior, Like a Shepherd Lead Us

He calleth His own sheep by name, and leadeth them out. John 10:3

1. Sav-ior, like a shep-herd lead us, Much we need Thy ten-der care;
2. We are Thine; do Thou be-friend us, Be the Guard-ian of our way;
3. Thou hast prom-ised to re-ceive us, Poor and sin-ful though we be;
4. Ear-ly let us seek Thy fa-vor; Ear-ly let us do Thy will;

In Thy pleas-ant pas-tures feed us, For our use Thy folds pre-pare:
Keep Thy flock, from sin de-fend us, Seek us when we go a-stray:
Thou hast mer-cy to re-lieve us, Grace to cleanse, and pow'r to free:
Bless-ed Lord and on-ly Sav-ior, With Thy love our bos-oms fill:

Bless-ed Je-sus, bless-ed Je-sus, Thou hast bought us, Thine we are;
Bless-ed Je-sus, bless-ed Je-sus, Hear, O hear us when we pray;
Bless-ed Je-sus, bless-ed Je-sus, Ear-ly let us turn to Thee;
Bless-ed Je-sus, bless-ed Je-sus, Thou hast loved us, love us still;

Bless-ed Je-sus, bless-ed Je-sus, Thou hast bought us, Thine we are.
Bless-ed Je-sus, bless-ed Je-sus, Hear, O hear us when we pray.
Bless-ed Je-sus, bless-ed Je-sus, Ear-ly let us turn to Thee.
Bless-ed Je-sus, bless-ed Je-sus, Thou hast loved us, love us still.

TEXT: *Hymns for the Young,* 1836; attributed to Dorothy A. Thrupp
MUSIC: William B. Bradbury

BRADBURY
8.7.8.7.D.

Optional choral ending

still. Bless-ed Je-sus, bless-ed Je-sus, Thou hast loved

Sop. or ten. solo: Sav-ior, like a shep-herd lead us.

us, love us still.

The end of "THE LORD IS MY SHEPHERD—A Brief Service in Recognition of His Leadership"

Precious Lord, Take My Hand 463

I the Lord thy God will hold thy right hand. Isa. 41:13

1. Pre-cious Lord, take my hand, Lead me on, help me stand— I am
2. When my way grows drear, Pre-cious Lord, lin-ger near— When my

tired, I am weak, I am worn; Thro' the storm, thro' the night, Lead me
life is al-most gone; Hear my cry, hear my call, Hold my

on to the light— Take my hand, pre-cious Lord, lead me home.
hand lest I fall— Take my hand, pre-cious Lord, lead me home.

TEXT: Thomas A. Dorsey
MUSIC: George N. Allen; adapted by Thomas A. Dorsey

PRECIOUS LORD
6.6.9.6.6.9.

464 Shepherd of Love

What man . . . doth not . . . go after that which is lost, until he find it? Luke 15:4

1. Shep-herd of love, You knew I had lost my way; Shep-herd of
2. Shep-herd of love, Con-tent-ment at last is mine; Deep in my

love, You cared that I'd gone a - stray. You sought and found me,
heart There's peace and a joy di - vine. The fu - ture's bright-er,

placed a - round me Strong arms that car-ried me home; No foe can
bur - den's light - er, My cup runs o - ver each day; Your grace sup-

harm me or a - larm me— Nev - er a - gain will I roam!
plied me now pro-vides me All that I need for the way.

Shep - herd of love, Sav - ior and Lord and Guide,
Shep - herd of love, Sav - ior and Lord and Guide,

TEXT and MUSIC: John W. Peterson

SHEPHERD OF LOVE
Irregular meter

Shep - herd of love, For - ev - er I'll stay by Your side.
Shep - herd of love, For - ev - er I'll stay by Your side.

In His Time 465

He hath made every thing beautiful in His time. Eccl. 3:11

1. In His time (in His time), in His time (in His time);
2. In Your time (in Your time), in Your time (in Your time);

He makes all things beau - ti - ful in His time (in His time).
You make all things beau - ti - ful in Your time (in Your time).

Lord, please show me ev - 'ry day As You're teach-ing me Your way,
Lord, my life to You I bring; May each song I have to sing

That You do just what You say in Your time (in Your time).
Be to You a love - ly thing in Your time (in Your time).

TEXT and MUSIC: Diane Ball

IN HIS TIME
Irregular meter

466 Jesus, Lover of My Soul

Thou hast been . . . a refuge from the storm. Isa. 25:4

1. Je - sus, Lov - er of my soul, Let me to Thy bos - om fly,
2. Oth - er ref - uge have I none; Hangs my help - less soul on Thee;
3. Thou, O Christ, art all I want; More than all in Thee I find;
4. Plen-teous grace with Thee is found, Grace to cov - er all my sin;

While the near - er wa - ters roll, While the tem - pest still is high;
Leave, ah! leave me not a - lone, Still sup - port and com - fort me.
Raise the fall - en, cheer the faint, Heal the sick and lead the blind.
Let the heal - ing streams a - bound; Make and keep me pure with - in.

Hide me, O my Sav - ior, hide, Till the storm of life is past;
All my trust on Thee is stayed, All my help from Thee I bring;
Just and ho - ly is Thy name, I am all un - right-eous - ness;
Thou of life the foun-tain art, Free - ly let me take of Thee;

Safe in - to the ha - ven guide; O re - ceive my soul at last!
Cov - er my de - fense-less head With the shad-ow of Thy wing.
False and full of sin I am, Thou art full of truth and grace.
Spring Thou up with - in my heart, Rise to all e - ter - ni - ty. A - men.

TEXT: Charles Wesley
MUSIC: Joseph Parry

ABERYSTWYTH
7.7.7.7.D.

Anywhere with Jesus 467

I will never leave thee, nor forsake thee. Heb. 13:5

1. An - y - where with Je - sus I can safe - ly go; An - y - where He
2. An - y - where with Je - sus I am not a - lone, Oth - er friends may
3. An - y - where with Je - sus o - ver land and sea, Tell - ing souls in

leads me in this world be - low; An - y - where with - out Him dear - est
fail me, He is still my own; Though His hand may lead me o - ver
dark - ness of sal - va - tion free; Read - y as He sum - mons me to

joys would fade; An - y - where with Je - sus I am not a - fraid.
drear - y ways, An - y - where with Je - sus is a house of praise.
go or stay, An - y - where with Je - sus when He points the way.

Refrain

An - y - where! an - y - where! Fear I can - not know;

An - y - where with Je - sus I can safe - ly go.

TEXT: Jessie Pounds, stanzas 1, 2; Helen C. Dixon, stanza 3
MUSIC: Kurt Kaiser

I CAN SAFELY GO
11.11.11.11. with Refrain

468 The King of Love My Shepherd Is

I am the Good Shepherd . . . I lay down My life for the sheep. John 10:14-15

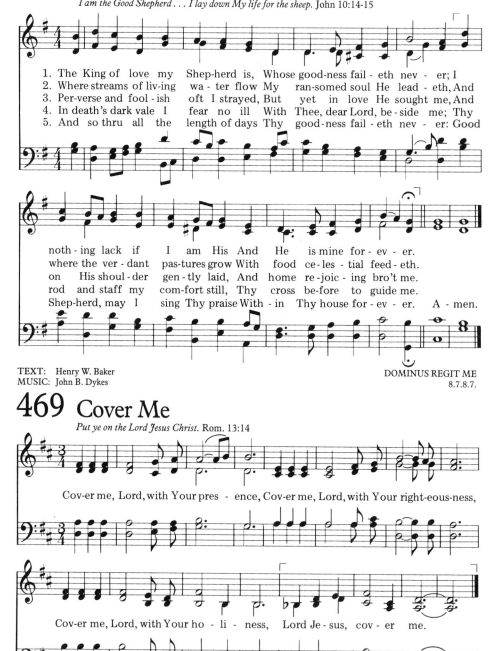

1. The King of love my Shep-herd is, Whose good-ness fail-eth nev-er; I
2. Where streams of liv-ing wa-ter flow My ran-somed soul He lead-eth, And
3. Per-verse and fool-ish oft I strayed, But yet in love He sought me, And
4. In death's dark vale I fear no ill With Thee, dear Lord, be-side me; Thy
5. And so thru all the length of days Thy good-ness fail-eth nev-er: Good

noth-ing lack if I am His And He is mine for-ev-er.
where the ver-dant pas-tures grow With food ce-les-tial feed-eth.
on His shoul-der gen-tly laid, And home re-joic-ing bro't me.
rod and staff my com-fort still, Thy cross be-fore to guide me.
Shep-herd, may I sing Thy praise With-in Thy house for-ev-er. A-men.

TEXT: Henry W. Baker
MUSIC: John B. Dykes

DOMINUS REGIT ME
8.7.8.7.

469 Cover Me

Put ye on the Lord Jesus Christ. Rom. 13:14

Cov-er me, Lord, with Your pres - ence, Cov-er me, Lord, with Your right-eous-ness,

Cov-er me, Lord, with Your ho - li - ness, Lord Je - sus, cov - er me.

TEXT and MUSIC: Andrew Culverwell

COVER ME
Irregular meter

Footsteps of Jesus 470

They forsook all, and followed Him. Luke 5:11

1. Sweet-ly, Lord, have we heard Thee call - ing, "Come, fol - low Me!"
2. Tho they lead o'er the cold, dark moun-tains, Seek - ing His sheep,
3. If they lead thro' the tem - ple ho - ly, Preach-ing the Word,
4. Then at last, when on high He sees us, Our jour - ney done,

And we see where Thy foot-prints fall - ing, Lead us to Thee.
Or a - long by *Si - lo - am's foun-tains, Help - ing the weak.
Or in homes of the poor and low - ly, Serv - ing the Lord.
We will rest where the steps of Je - sus End at His throne.

Refrain

Foot - prints of Je - sus that make the path - way glow;

We will fol - low the steps of Je - sus wher - e'er they go.

*John 9:1-11

TEXT: Mary B. C. Slade
MUSIC: Asa B. Everett

FOOTSTEPS
9.4.9.4. with Refrain

471 The Way of the Cross Leads Home

There is . . . one Mediator between God and men, the Man Christ Jesus. 1 Tim. 2:5

1. I must needs go home by the way of the cross,
2. I must needs go on in the blood-sprin-kled way,
3. Then I bid fare-well to the way of the world,

There's no oth-er way but this; I shall ne'er get sight
The path that the Sav-ior trod, If I ev-er climb
To walk in it nev-er-more; For my Lord says, "Come,"

of the gates of light, If the way of the cross I miss.
to the heights sub-lime, Where the soul is at home with God.
and I seek my home, Where He waits at the o-pen door.

Refrain

The way of the cross leads home, The way of the cross leads home;
leads home, leads home;

It is sweet to know as I on-ward go, The way of the cross leads home.

TEXT: Jessie B. Pounds
MUSIC: Charles H. Gabriel

WAY OF THE CROSS
Irregular meter

The Battle Is the Lord's 472

The battle is the Lord's. 1 Sam. 17:47

1. The bat-tle is the Lord's! The har-vest fields are white:
2. The bat-tle is the Lord's! Not ours in strength or skill,
3. The bat-tle is the Lord's! The Vic-tor cru-ci-fied
4. The bat-tle is the Lord's! Stand still, my soul, and view

How few the reap-ing hands ap-pear, Their strength how slight!
But His a-lone, in sov-ereign grace, To work His will.
Must with the tra-vail of His soul Be sat-is-fied.
The great sal-va-tion God has wrought Re-vealed for you.

Yet vic-to-ry is sure— We face a van-quished foe;
Ours, count-ing not the cost, Un-flinch-ing, to o-bey;
The pow'rs of hell shall fail, And all God's will be done,
Then, rest-ing in His might, Lift high His tri-umph song,

Then for-ward with the ris-en Christ To bat-tle go!
And in His time His ho-ly arm Shall win the day.
Till ev-ery soul whom He has giv'n To Christ be won.
For pow'r, do-min-ion, king-dom, strength To Christ be-long! A-men.

TEXT: Margaret Clarkson
MUSIC: Traditional Hebrew melody; adapted by Meyer Lyon
A higher setting may be found at No. 34

LEONI
6.6.8.4.D.

473 Victory in Jesus

God . . . giveth us the victory through our Lord Jesus Christ. 1 Cor. 15:57

1. I heard an old, old story, how a Savior came from glory,
2. I heard about His healing, of His cleansing pow'r revealing,
3. I heard about a mansion He has built for me in glory,

How He gave His life on Calvary to save a wretch like me:
How He made the lame to walk again and caused the blind to see;
And I heard about the streets of gold beyond the crystal sea;

I heard about His groaning, of His precious blood's atoning,
And then I cried, "Dear Jesus, come and heal my broken spirit,"
About the angels singing, and the old redemption story,

Then I repented of my sins and won the victory.
And somehow Jesus came and bro't to me the victory.
And some sweet day I'll sing up there the song of victory.

Refrain

O victory in Jesus, my Savior, forever, He sought me and

TEXT and MUSIC: Eugene M. Bartlett, Sr.

HARTFORD
Irregular meter

bo't me with His re-deem-ing blood; He loved me ere I knew Him, and all my

love is due Him, He plunged me to vic-to-ry be-neath the cleans-ing flood.

We Will Stand 474

Stand therefore. Eph. 6:14

Unison

You're my broth-er, you're my sis - ter, so take me by the hand. To-geth-er

we will work un-til He comes. There's no foe that can de-feat us when we're

walk-ing side by side; As long as there is love, we will stand.

TEXT: Russ Taff and Tori Taff
MUSIC: James Hollihan

WE WILL STAND
Irregular meter

475 Once to Every Man and Nation

If the Lord be God, follow Him. 1 Kings 18:21

1. Once to ev - ery man and na - tion Comes the mo - ment to de - cide,
2. Then to side with truth is no - ble, When we share her wretch-ed crust,
3. Though the cause of e - vil pros - per, Yet the truth a - lone is strong;

In the strife of truth with false - hood, For the good or e - vil side;
Ere her cause bring fame and prof - it, And 'tis pros-p'rous to be just;
Though her por - tion be the scaf - fold, And up - on the throne be wrong,

Some great cause, some great de - ci - sion, Of - f'ring each the bloom or blight,
Then it is the brave man choos-es While the cow - ard stands a - side,
Yet that scaf - fold sways the fu - ture, And, be - hind the dim un - known,

And the choice goes by for - ev - er 'Twixt that dark -ness and that light.
Till the mul - ti - tude make vir - tue Of the faith they had de -nied.
Stand-eth God with - in the shad - ow, Keep -ing watch a -bove His own. A-men.

TEXT: James Russel Lowell
MUSIC: Thomas J. Williams
A lower setting may be found at No. 211

EBENEZER
8.7.8.7.D.

Music used by permission of Eluned Crump and Dilys Evans.

SOLDIERS OF CHRIST, ARISE

A Brief Service of
Challenge and Victory

Suggested Hymn Stanzas

To facilitate an uninterrupted flow from stanza to stanza,
the suggested stanzas have been marked with an arrow: ▶

Stand Up, Stand Up for Jesus, stanzas 1, 2
Soldiers of Christ, Arise, stanzas 1, 3
Onward, Christian Soldiers, stanzas 1, 4

WORSHIP LEADER:

. . . Be strong in the Lord, and in the power of His might. Put on the whole armour of God, that ye may be able to stand against the wiles of the devil. For we wrestle not against flesh and blood, but against principalities, against powers, against the rulers of the darkness of this world, against spiritual wickedness in high places. Wherefore take unto you the whole armour of God, that ye may be able to withstand in the evil day, and having done all, to stand. Stand therefore, having your loins girt about with truth, and having on the breastplate of righteousness; and your feet shod with the preparation of the gospel of peace; above all, taking the shield of faith, wherewith ye shall be able to quench all the fiery darts of the wicked. And take the helmet of salvation, and the sword of the Spirit, which is the word of God.

Ephesians 6:10-17.

Optional introduction to "Stand Up, Stand Up for Jesus"

477 Stand Up, Stand Up for Jesus

Stand fast in the faith, quit you like men, be strong. 1 Cor. 16:13

1. Stand up, stand up for Je - sus, Ye sol - diers of the cross, Lift high His roy-al
2. Stand up, stand up for Je - sus, The trum-pet call o - bey; Forth to the might-y
3. Stand up, stand up for Je - sus, Stand in His strength a-lone; The arm of flesh will
4. Stand up, stand up for Je - sus, The strife will not be long; This day the noise of

ban - ner, It must not suf - fer loss; From vic-tory un-to vic-tory His ar - my
con-flict In this His glo - rious day, Ye that are men, now serve Him A-gainst un-
fail you—Ye dare not trust your own; Put on the gos-pel ar-mor, Each piece put
bat - tle, The next, the vic-tor's song; To him who o - ver - com-eth A crown of

shall He lead, Till ev - ery foe is van-quished And Christ is Lord in - deed.
num-bered foes; Let cour-age rise with dan - ger, And strength to strength oppose.
on with prayer; Where du -ty calls, or dan - ger, Be nev - er want-ing there.
life shall be; He with the King of glo - ry Shall reign e - ter - nal - ly.

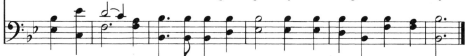

TEXT: George Duffield, Jr.
MUSIC: George J. Webb
Alternate tune: GEIBEL at No. 481

WEBB
7.6.7.6.D.

Optional transition to "Soldiers of Christ, Arise"

f

slight rit.

Soldiers of Christ, Arise 478

Be strong in the Lord . . . Put on the whole armour of God. Eph. 6:10-11

1. Sol - diers of Christ, a - rise And put your ar - mor on, Strong in the strength which God sup-plies Through His e - ter - nal Son; Strong in the Lord of hosts, And in His might - y pow'r, Who in the strength of Je - sus trusts Is more than con - quer - or.

2. Stand then in His great might, With all His strength en - dued, And take, to arm you for the fight, The *pan - o - ply of God; From strength to strength go on, Wres - tle and fight and pray; Tread all the pow'rs of dark - ness down, And win the well-fought day.

3. Leave no un-guard - ed place, No weak-ness of the soul; Take ev - ery vir - tue, ev - 'ry grace, And for - ti - fy the whole. That hav - ing all things done, And all your con - flicts past, Ye may o'er-come through Christ a-lone, And stand com-plete at last. A - men.

*"panoply"—anything protecting completely or forming a magnificent covering; esp. a full suit of armor; see Eph. 6:10-18.

TEXT: Charles Wesley
MUSIC: George J. Elvey
A lower setting may be found at No. 234.

DIADEMATA
S.M.D.

Optional introduction (or transition from "Soldiers of Christ, Arise")

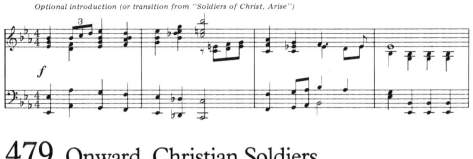

479 Onward, Christian Soldiers

God . . . always causeth us to triumph in Christ. 2 Cor. 2:14

1. On-ward, Chris-tian sol - diers, March-ing as to war, With the cross of
2. At the sign of tri - umph Sa - tan's host doth flee; On, then, Chris-tian
3. Like a might-y ar - my Moves the Church of God; Broth-ers, we are
4. On-ward, then, ye peo - ple, Join our hap-py throng; Blend with ours your

Je - sus Go - ing on be - fore! Christ, the roy-al Mas - ter, Leads a -
sol - diers, On to vic - to - ry! Hell's foun-da-tions quiv - er At the
tread - ing Where the saints have trod. We are not di - vid - ed, All one
voic - es In the tri - umph song. Glo - ry, laud and hon - or Un - to

gainst the foe; For - ward in - to bat - tle See His ban-ners go!
shout of praise; Broth-ers, lift your voic - es, Loud your an-thems raise!
bod - y we— One in hope and doc - trine, One in char - i - ty.
Christ the King— This thru count-less a - ges Men and an - gels sing.

TEXT: Sabine Baring-Gould
MUSIC: Arthur S. Sullivan; Descant by David Allen

ST. GERTRUDE
6.5.6.5.D. with Refrain

Optional descant - final refrain

On - ward, ye sol - diers, march-ing as to war, With the

Refrain

On - ward, Chris-tian sol - diers, march-ing as to war, With the

cross of Je - sus go - ing on be - fore. A - men.

cross of Je - sus go - ing on be - fore. A - men.

The end of "SOLDIERS OF CHRIST, ARISE—A Brief Service of Challenge and Victory"

I Am a Soldier of the Cross! 480

4 Part Canon . . . *that he may please him who hath chosen him to be a soldier.* 2 Tim. 2:4

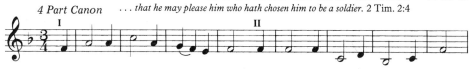

I am a sol-dier of the cross! A fol - l'wer of the pre-cious Lamb.

I will not fear to own His cause Or blush to speak His glo-rious name.

TEXT: Isaac Watts and Gerald S. Henderson
MUSIC: William Billings; adapted by Gerald S. Henderson

AFFIRMATIVE
L.M.

481 Stand Up, Stand Up for Jesus

Stand fast in the faith, quit you like men, be strong. 1 Cor. 16:13

Unison

1. Stand up, stand up for Je - sus, Ye sol - diers of the cross;
2. Stand up, stand up for Je - sus, The trum - pet call o - bey;
3. Stand up, stand up for Je - sus, Stand in His strength a - lone;
4. Stand up, stand up for Je - sus, The strife will not be long.

Lift high His roy - al ban - ner, It must not suf - fer loss:
Forth to the might - y con - flict In this His glo - rious day:
The arm of flesh will fail you; Ye dare not trust your own.
This day the noise of bat - tle; The next, the vic - tor's song.

From vic - t'ry un - to vic - t'ry His ar - my shall He lead,
Ye that are men, now serve Him A - gainst un - num - bered foes;
Put on the gos - pel ar - mor; Each piece put on with prayer.
To him that o - ver - com - eth, A crown of life shall be;

Till ev - ery foe is van - quished And Christ is Lord in - deed.
Let cour - age rise with dan - ger, And strength to strength op - pose.
Where du - ty calls, or dan - ger, Be nev - er want - ing there.
He with the King of Glo - ry Shall reign e - ter - nal - ly.

TEXT: George Duffield, Jr.
MUSIC: Adam Geibel
        Alternate tune: WEBB at No. 477

GEIBEL
7.6.7.6.D. with Refrain

Refrain
In parts

Stand up for Je - sus, Ye sol - diers of the cross;
Stand up, stand up for Je - sus,

Lift high His roy - al ban - ner, It must not, it must not suf - fer loss.

Am I a Soldier of the Cross? 482

Endure hardness, as a good soldier of Jesus Christ. 2 Tim. 2:3

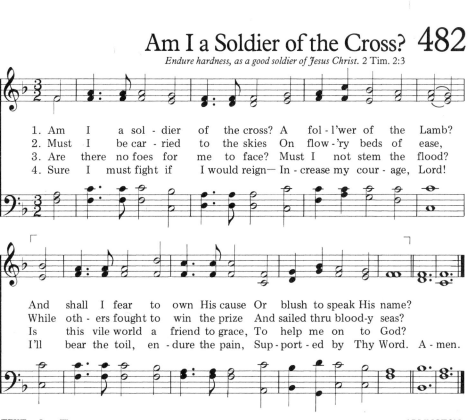

1. Am I a sol - dier of the cross? A fol - l'wer of the Lamb?
2. Must I be car - ried to the skies On flow - 'ry beds of ease,
3. Are there no foes for me to face? Must I not stem the flood?
4. Sure I must fight if I would reign— In - crease my cour - age, Lord!

And shall I fear to own His cause Or blush to speak His name?
While oth - ers fought to win the prize And sailed thru blood - y seas?
Is this vile world a friend to grace, To help me on to God?
I'll bear the toil, en - dure the pain, Sup - port - ed by Thy Word. A - men.

TEXT: Isaac Watts
MUSIC: Thomas A. Arne

ARLINGTON
C.M.

483 Lead On, O King Eternal

So didst Thou lead Thy people, to make Thyself a glorious name. Isa. 63:14

1. Lead on, O King E - ter - nal, The day of march has come;
2. Lead on, O King E - ter - nal, Till sin's fierce war shall cease,
3. Lead on, O King E - ter - nal, We fol - low, not with fears;

Hence-forth in fields of con - quest Your tents shall be our home.
And ho - li - ness shall whis - per The sweet A - men of peace;
For glad - ness breaks like morn - ing Wher - e'er Your face ap - pears;

Through days of prep - a - ra - tion Your grace has made us strong,
For not with swords loud clash - ing, Nor roll of stir - ring drums,
Your cross is lift - ed o'er us; We jour - ney in its light:

And now, O King E - ter - nal, We lift our bat - tle song.
With deeds of love and mer - cy The heav'n-ly king - dom comes.
The crown a - waits the con - quest; Lead on, O God of might. A - men.

TEXT: Ernest W. Shurtleff
MUSIC: Henry T. Smart; Last stanza harmonization by Bruce Greer
A higher setting may be found at No. 226

LANCASHIRE
7.6.7.6.D.

Optional last stanza harmonization
Unison - Broader

comes.   3. Lead   on, O King E - ter - nal, We

fol - low, not with fears;   For glad - ness breaks like morn - ing Where-

e'er Your face ap - pears;   Your cross is lift - ed o'er   us; We

jour - ney in its   light: The crown a - waits the con - quest; Lead

Optional choral ending - sing parts
cresc.   *rit.* *ff*

on, O God of   might.   Lead   on, O   King,   Lead   on!

484 Who Is on the Lord's Side?

Take . . . the whole armour of God, that ye may be able . . . to stand. Eph. 6:13

1. Who is on the Lord's side? Who will serve the King? Who will be His help-ers, Oth-er lives to bring? Who will leave the world's side? Who will face the foe? Who is on the Lord's side? Who for Him will go? By Thy call of mer-cy,

2. Not for weight of glo-ry, Not for crown and palm, En-ter we the ar-my, Raise the war-rior psalm; But for love that claim-eth Lives for whom He died; He whom Je-sus nam-eth Must be on His side. By Thy love con-strain-ing,

3. Je-sus, Thou hast bought us, Not with gold or gem, But with Thine own life-blood, For Thy di-a-dem. With Thy bless-ing fill-ing Each who comes to Thee, Thou hast made us will-ing, Thou hast made us free. By Thy grand re-demp-tion,

4. Fierce may be the con-flict, Strong may be the foe, But the King's own ar-my None can o-ver-throw. Round His stand-ard rang-ing; Vic-t'ry is se-cure; For His truth un-chang-ing Makes the tri-umph sure. Joy-ful-ly en-list-ing

TEXT: Frances Ridley Havergal
MUSIC: C. Luise Reichardt; arranged by John Goss

ARMAGEDDON
6.5.6.5.D. with Refrain

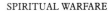

By Thy grace di - vine, We are on the Lord's side, Sav-ior, we are Thine.
By Thy grace di - vine, We are on the Lord's side, Sav-ior, we are Thine.
By Thy grace di - vine, We are on the Lord's side, Sav-ior, we are Thine.
By Thy grace di - vine, We are on the Lord's side, Sav-ior, we are Thine.

The Battle Belongs to the Lord 485

The battle is not yours, but God's. 2 Chr. 20:15

Unison

1. In heav-en-ly ar - mor we'll en - ter the land, the battle belongs to the Lord!
2. When the pow-er of dark-ness comes in like a flood, the battle belongs to the Lord!

No wea-pon that's fashioned against us will stand, the bat-tle be-longs
He's raised up a stan - dard, the pow'r of His blood, the bat-tle be-longs

Refrain

to the Lord! We sing glo - ry, hon - or, pow-er and strength
to the Lord!

to the Lord. We sing glo - ry, hon - or, power and strength to the Lord!

TEXT and MUSIC: Jamie Owens-Collins; arranged by Robert F. Douglas
THE BATTLE
11.8.11.8. with Refrain

486 Faith Is the Victory

This is the victory that overcometh the world, even our faith. 1 John 5:4

1. En - camped a - long the hills of light, Ye Chris - tian sol - diers, rise,
2. His ban - ner o - ver us is love, Our sword the Word of God;
3. On ev - ery hand the foe we find Drawn up in dread ar - ray;
4. To him that o - ver - comes the foe, White rai - ment shall be giv'n;

And press the bat - tle ere the night Shall veil the glow - ing skies.
We tread the road the saints a - bove With shouts of tri - umph trod.
Let tents of ease be left be - hind, And on - ward to the fray;
Be - fore the an - gels he shall know His name con - fessed in heav'n.

A - gainst the foe in vales be - low Let all our strength be hurled;
By faith they, like a whirl-wind's breath, Swept on o'er ev - 'ry field;
Sal - va - tion's hel - met on each head, With truth all girt a - bout,
Then on - ward from the hills of light, Our hearts with love a - flame,

Faith is the vic - to - ry, we know, That o - ver-comes the world.
The faith by which they con-quered death Is still our shin - ing shield.
The earth shall trem-ble 'neath our tread, And ech - o with our shout.
We'll van - quish all the hosts of night, In Je - sus' con - quering name.

TEXT: John H. Yates
MUSIC: Ira D. Sankey

SANKEY
C.M.D. with Refrain

Refrain

Faith is the vic - to - ry! Faith is the vic - to - ry!

O, glo - ri - ous vic - to - ry, That o - ver-comes the world.

Peace, Perfect Peace 487

My peace I give unto you: not as the world giveth. John 14:27

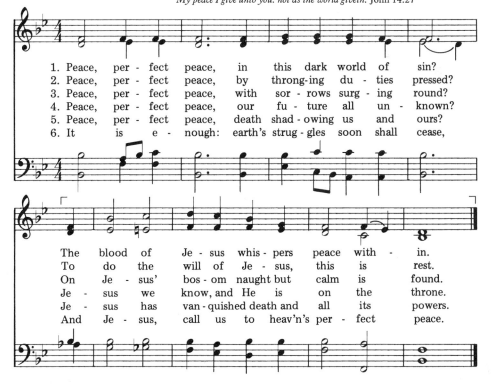

1. Peace, per - fect peace, in this dark world of sin?
2. Peace, per - fect peace, by throng-ing du - ties pressed?
3. Peace, per - fect peace, with sor - rows surg - ing round?
4. Peace, per - fect peace, our fu - ture all un - known?
5. Peace, per - fect peace, death shad - ow-ing us and ours?
6. It is e - nough: earth's strug - gles soon shall cease,

The blood of Je - sus whis - pers peace with - in.
To do the will of Je - sus, this is rest.
On Je - sus' bos - om naught but calm is found.
Je - sus we know, and He is on the throne.
Je - sus has van - quished death and all its powers.
And Je - sus, call us to heav'n's per - fect peace.

TEXT: Edward H. Bickersteth
MUSIC: George T. Caldbeck; arranged by Charles J. Vincent

PAX TECUM
Irregular meter

488 He Keeps Me Singing

Sing unto the Lord; for He hath done excellent things. Isa. 12:5

1. There's with-in my heart a mel - o - dy— Je - sus whis-pers sweet and low,
2. All my life was wrecked by sin and strife, Dis-cord filled my heart with pain;
3. Feast-ing on the rich - es of His grace, Rest-ing 'neath His shel-t'ring wing,
4. Tho sometimes He leads thru wa - ters deep, Tri - als fall a - cross the way,
5. Soon He's com-ing back to wel-come me Far be - yond the star - ry sky;

"Fear not, I am with thee— peace, be still," In all of life's ebb and flow.
Je - sus swept a - cross the bro - ken strings, Stirr'd the slumb'ring chords a-gain.
Al - ways look-ing on His smil-ing face— That is why I shout and sing.
Tho sometimes the path seems rough and steep, See His foot-prints all the way.
I shall wing my flight to worlds un-known, I shall reign with Him on high.

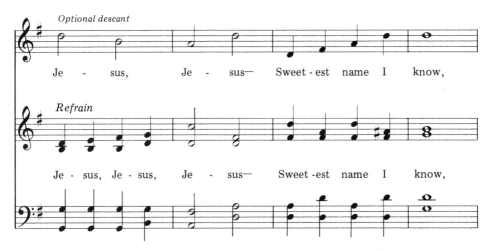

Optional descant

Je - sus, Je - sus— Sweet-est name I know,

Refrain

Je - sus, Je - sus, Je - sus— Sweet-est name I know,

TEXT and MUSIC: Luther B. Bridgers
Descant by Eugene Thomas

SWEETEST NAME
9.7.9.7. with Refrain

Fills my long - ing, Keeps me sing-ing as I go.

Fills my ev - 'ry long - ing, Keeps me sing-ing as I go.

Rejoice in the Lord Always 489

Rejoice in the Lord! Phil. 3:1

4 Part Canon (optional)

Re - joice in the Lord al - ways, a - gain I say, re - joice! Re-

joice in the Lord al - ways, a - gain I say, re - joice! Re - joice, re - joice, a -

gain I say, re - joice! Re - joice, re - joice, a - gain I say, re - joice!

TEXT: Philippians 4:4
MUSIC: Traditional

REJOICE
Irregular meter

490 I Am His, and He Is Mine

Your life is hid with Christ in God. Col. 3:3

1. Loved with ev - er - last - ing love, Led by grace that love to know;
2. Heav'n a - bove is soft - er blue, Earth a - round is sweet-er green!
3. Things that once were wild a - larms Can - not now dis - turb my rest;
4. His for - ev - er, on - ly His; Who the Lord and me shall part?

Gra - cious Spir - it from a - bove, Thou hast taught me it is so!
Some-thing lives in ev - ery hue Christ - less eyes have nev - er seen:
Closed in ev - er - last - ing arms, Pil - lowed on the lov - ing breast.
Ah, with what a rest of bliss Christ can fill the lov - ing heart!

O, this full and per - fect peace! O, this trans - port all di - vine!
Birds with glad - der songs o'er - flow, Flow'rs with deep - er beau - ties shine,
O, to lie for - ev - er here, Doubt and care and self re - sign,
Heav'n and earth may fade and flee, First - born light in gloom de - cline;

In a love which can - not cease, I am His, and He is mine. mine.
Since I know, as now I know, I am His, and He is mine. mine.
While He whis - pers in my ear, I am His, and He is mine. mine.
But while God and I shall be, I am His, and He is mine. mine.

TEXT: George W. Robinson
MUSIC: James Mountain

EVERLASTING LOVE
7.7.7.7.D.

PERFECT PEACE

A Brief Service in
Recognition of His Provision

Suggested Hymn Stanzas

To facilitate an uninterrupted flow from stanza to stanza,
the suggested stanzas have been marked with an arrow: ►

Thou Wilt Keep Him in Perfect Peace, complete
It Is Well with My Soul, stanzas 1, 3
Like a River Glorious, complete

WORSHIP LEADER: These things I have spoken unto you, that in Me ye might have peace. In the world ye shall have tribulation: but be of good cheer; I have overcome the world.

PEOPLE: Therefore being justified by faith, we have peace with God through our Lord Jesus Christ.

WORSHIP LEADER: He came and preached peace to you which were afar off, and to them that were nigh.

PEOPLE: Be careful for nothing; but in every thing by prayer and supplication with thanksgiving let your requests be made known unto God. And the peace of God, which passeth all understanding, shall keep your hearts and minds through Christ Jesus.

WORSHIP LEADER: Finally, brethren, whatsoever things are true, whatsoever things are honest, whatsoever things are just, whatsoever things are pure, whatsoever things are lovely, whatsoever things are of good report; if there be any virtue, and if there be any praise, think on these things. Those things, which ye have both learned, and received, and heard, and seen in Me, do: and the God of peace shall be with you.

PEOPLE: For it pleased the Father that in Him should all fulness dwell; and, having made peace through the blood of His cross, by Him to reconcile all things unto Himself; by Him, I say, whether they be things in earth, or things in heaven.

WORSHIP LEADER: And let the peace of God rule in your hearts, to the which also ye are called in one body; and be ye thankful.

John 16:33; Rom. 5:1; Eph. 2:17;
Phil. 4:6-9; Col. 1:19-20; 3:15.

Optional introduction to
"Thou Wilt Keep Him in Perfect Peace"

mp

492 Thou Wilt Keep Him in Perfect Peace

Thou wilt keep him in perfect peace, whose mind is stayed on Thee. Isa. 26:3

"Thou wilt keep him in per-fect peace whose mind is stayed on Thee."

When the sha-dows come and dark-ness falls, He giv-eth in-ward peace. O He

is the on-ly per-fect rest-ing place, He giv-eth per-fect peace!

"Thou wilt keep him in per-fect peace whose mind is stayed on Thee."

use cued notes with transition to "It Is Well with My Soul"

TEXT and MUSIC: Vivian Kretz; based on Isaiah 26:3

PERFECT PEACE
Irregular meter

Optional transition to
"It Is Well with My Soul"

cresc.

decresc.

It Is Well with My Soul 493

Bless the Lord, O my soul, and forget not all His benefits. Ps. 103:2

1. When peace like a riv-er at-tend-eth my way, When sor-rows like
2. Though Sa-tan should buf-fet, tho' tri-als should come, Let this blest as-
3. My sin— O, the bliss of this glo-ri-ous thought, My sin— not in
4. And, Lord, haste the day when the faith shall be sight, The clouds be rolled

sea-bil-lows roll; What-ev-er my lot, Thou hast taught me to say,
sur-ance con-trol, That Christ has re-gard-ed my help-less es-tate,
part but the whole, Is nailed to the cross and I bear it no more,
back as a scroll, The trump shall re-sound and the Lord shall de-scend,

Refrain

"It is well, it is well with my soul."
And hath shed His own blood for my soul. It is well with my
Praise the Lord, praise the Lord, O my soul! It is well
"E-ven so"— it is well with my soul.

soul, It is well, it is well with my soul.
with my soul,

TEXT: Horatio G. Spafford
MUSIC: Philip P. Bliss

VILLE DU HAVRE
11.8.11.9. with Refrain

Optional transition to
"Like a River Glorious"

faster tempo

494 Like a River Glorious

. . . then had Thy peace been as a river. Isa. 48:18

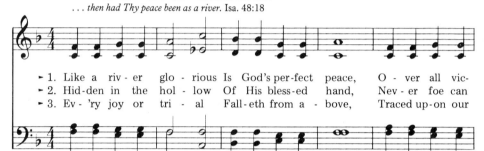

1. Like a riv-er glo-rious Is God's per-fect peace, O-ver all vic-
2. Hid-den in the hol-low Of His bless-ed hand, Nev-er foe can
3. Ev-'ry joy or tri-al Fall-eth from a-bove, Traced up-on our

to-rious In its bright in-crease; Per-fect, yet it flow-eth Full-er
fol-low, Nev-er trai-tor stand; Not a surge of wor-ry, Not a
di-al By the sun of love; We may trust Him ful-ly All for

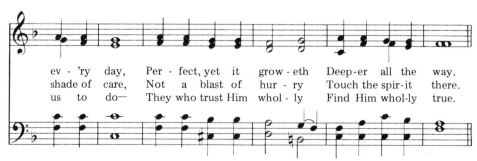

ev-'ry day, Per-fect, yet it grow-eth Deep-er all the way.
shade of care, Not a blast of hur-ry Touch the spir-it there.
us to do— They who trust Him whol-ly Find Him whol-ly true.

TEXT: Frances Ridley Havergal
MUSIC: James Mountain; Descant and choral ending by James C. Gibson

WYE VALLEY
6.5.6.5.D. with Refrain

Descant and choral ending © 1986 WORD MUSIC (a div. of WORD, INC.). All Rights Reserved. International Copyright Secured.

Descant

Stayed up - on Je - ho - vah, Hearts are ful - ly blest—

Refrain

Stayed up - on Je - ho - vah, Hearts are ful - ly blest—

Find - ing as He prom - ised, Per - fect peace and rest.

Find - ing as He prom - ised, Per - fect peace and rest.

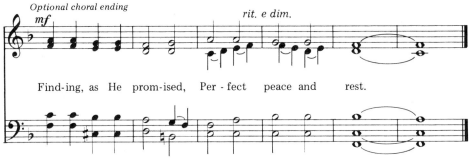

Optional choral ending

mf

rit. e dim.

Find-ing, as He prom-ised, Per - fect peace and rest.

The End of "PERFECT PEACE—A Brief Service in Recognition of His Provision"

495 Heaven Came Down

In Christ Jesus . . . a new creature. Gal. 6:15

1. O what a won-der-ful, won-der-ful day—
2. Born of the Spir-it with life from a-bove
3. Now I've a hope that will sure-ly en-dure

Day I will nev-er for-get;
In-to God's fam-ily di-vine,
Aft-er the pass-ing of time;

Aft-er I'd wan-dered in dark-ness a-way,
Jus-ti-fied ful-ly thro' Cal-va-ry's love,
I have a fu-ture in heav-en for sure,

Je-sus my Sav-ior I met.
O what a stand-ing is mine!
There in those man-sions sub-lime.

O what a ten-der, com-pas-sion-ate friend—
And the trans-ac-tion so quick-ly was made
And it's be-cause of that won-der-ful day

He met the need of my heart;
When as a sin-ner I came,
When at the cross I be-lieved;

Shad-ows dis-pel-ling, With
Took of the of-fer Of
Rich-es e-ter-nal And

TEXT and MUSIC: John W. Peterson

HEAVEN CAME DOWN
Irregular meter

joy I am tell - ing, He made all the dark-ness de - part!
grace He did prof - fer— He saved me, O praise His dear name!
bless-ings su - per - nal From His pre-cious hand I re - ceived.

Refrain

Heav - en came down and glo - ry filled my soul, (filled my soul,)

When at the cross the Sav-ior made me whole; (made me whole;) My

sins were washed a - way And my night was turned to day—

Heav - en came down and glo - ry filled my soul! (filled my soul!)

496 He Hideth My Soul

He shall hide me . . . He shall set me up upon a rock. Ps. 27:5

1. A won-der-ful Sav-ior is Je-sus my Lord, A won-der-ful
2. A won-der-ful Sav-ior is Je-sus my Lord— He tak-eth my
3. With num-ber-less bless-ings each mo-ment He crowns, And, filled with His
4. When clothed in His bright-ness trans-port-ed I rise, To meet Him in

Sav-ior to me; He hid-eth my soul in the cleft of the
bur-den a-way; He hold-eth me up and I shall not be
full-ness di-vine, I sing in my rap-ture, "O glo-ry to
clouds of the sky, His per-fect sal-va-tion, His won-der-ful

Refrain

rock, Where riv-ers of pleas-ure I see.
moved, He giv-eth me strength as my day.   He hid-eth my soul
God For such a Re-deem-er as mine!"
love, I'll shout with the mil-lions on high.

in the cleft of the rock That shad-ows a dry, thirst-y land;

He hid-eth my life in the depths of His love, And cov-ers me

TEXT: Fanny J. Crosby
MUSIC: William J. Kirkpatrick

KIRKPATRICK
11.8.11.8. with Refrain

there with His hand, And cov-ers me there with His hand.

Near to the Heart of God 497

It is good for me to draw near to God. Ps. 73:28

1. There is a place of qui - et rest Near to the heart of God,
2. There is a place of com-fort sweet Near to the heart of God,
3. There is a place of full re - lease Near to the heart of God,

A place where sin can - not mo-lest, Near to the heart of God.
A place where we our Sav - ior meet, Near to the heart of God.
A place where all is joy and peace, Near to the heart of God.

Refrain

O Je - sus, blest Re - deem - er, Sent from the heart of God,

Hold us who wait be - fore Thee Near to the heart of God.

TEXT and MUSIC: Cleland B. McAfee

McAFEE
C.M. with Refrain

498 Peace Like a River

The peace of God . . . shall keep your hearts and minds through Christ Jesus. Phil. 4:7

1. I've got peace like a riv-er, I've got peace like a riv-er, I've got peace like a riv-er in my soul, I've got peace like a riv-er, I've got peace like a riv-er, I've got peace like a riv-er in my soul. (my soul.)
2. I've got love like an o-cean, I've got love like an o-cean, I've got love like an o-cean in my soul, I've got love like an o-cean, I've got love like an o-cean, I've got love like an o-cean in my soul. (my soul.)
3. I've got joy like a foun-tain, I've got joy like a foun-tain, I've got joy like a foun-tain in my soul, I've got joy like a foun-tain, I've got joy like a foun-tain, I've got joy like a foun-tain in my soul. (my soul.)

TEXT and MUSIC: Traditional

PEACE LIKE A RIVER
7.7.10.D.

Sunshine in My Soul 499

God . . . hath shined in our hearts. 2 Cor. 4:6

1. There is sun-shine in my soul to-day, More glo-ri-ous and bright
2. There is mu-sic in my soul to-day, A car-ol to my King,
3. There is spring-time in my soul to-day, For when the Lord is near
4. There is glad-ness in my soul to-day, And hope and love and praise,

Than glows in an-y earth-ly sky, For Je-sus is my light.
And Je-sus, lis-ten-ing can hear The songs I can-not sing.
The dove of peace sings in my heart, The flow'rs of grace ap-pear.
For bless-ings which He gives me now, For joys in fu-ture days.

Refrain

O there's sun-shine, bless-ed sun-shine, When the peace-ful, hap-py mo-ments roll; When Je-sus shows His smil-ing face, There is sun-shine in my soul.

TEXT: Eliza E. Hewitt
MUSIC: John R. Sweney

SUNSHINE
9.6.8.6. with Refrain

500 Wonderful Peace

The Lord of peace Himself give you peace always. 2 Thess. 3:16

1. Far a - way in the depths of my spir - it to - night Rolls a
2. What a treas - ure I have in this won - der - ful peace, Bur - ied
3. I am rest - ing to - night in this won - der - ful peace, Rest - ing
4. And I think when I rise to that Cit - y of peace, Where the
5. O my soul, are you here with - out com - fort or rest, March - ing

mel - o - dy sweet - er than psalm; In ce - les - tial - like strains it un -
deep in the heart of my soul; So se - cure that no pow - er can
sweet - ly in Je - sus' con - trol; For I'm kept from all dan - ger by
Au - thor of peace I shall see, That one strain of the song which the
down the rough path - way of time? Make the Sav - ior your friend when the

Refrain

ceas - ing - ly falls O'er my soul like an in - fi - nite calm.
mine it a - way, While the years of e - ter - ni - ty roll.
night and by day, And His glo - ry is flood - ing my soul. Peace! peace!
ran - somed will sing, In that heav - en - ly king - dom shall be:
shad - ows grow dark; Oh, ac - cept this sweet peace so sub - lime.

won-der-ful peace, Com-ing down from the Fa-ther a - bove; Sweep o - ver my

TEXT: W. D. Cornell, altered
MUSIC: W. G. Cooper

WONDERFUL PEACE
12.9.12.9. with Refrain

spir-it for-ev-er, I pray, In fath-om-less bil-lows of love.

Jesus, Thou Joy of Loving Hearts 501

These things have I spoken unto you, that My joy might remain in you. John 15:11

1. Je - sus, Thou Joy of lov - ing hearts, Thou Fount of
2. Thy truth un - changed hath ev - er stood, Thou sav - est
3. We taste Thee, O Thou liv - ing Bread, And long to
4. Our rest - less spir - its yearn for Thee, Wher - e'er our
5. O Je - sus, ev - er with us stay, Make all our

life, Thou Light of men, From the best bliss that earth im -
those that on Thee call; To them that seek Thee, Thou art
feast up - on Thee still; We drink of Thee, the Foun-tain-
change - ful lot is cast: Glad when Thy gra - cious smile we
mo - ments calm and bright; Chase the dark night of sin a -

parts, We turn un - filled to Thee a - gain.
good, To them that find Thee, all in all.
head, And thirst our souls from Thee to fill.
see, Blest when our faith can hold Thee fast.
way, Shed o'er the world Thy ho - ly light. A - men.

TEXT: Attributed to Bernard of Clairvaux; translated by Ray Palmer
MUSIC: Henry Baker

QUEBEC
L.M.

502 In Heavenly Love Abiding

If ye keep My commandments, ye shall abide in My love. John 15:10

1. In heav'n-ly love a - bid - ing, No change my heart shall fear;
2. Wher - ev - er He may guide me, No want shall turn me back;
3. Green pas - tures are be - fore me, Which yet I have not seen;

And safe is such con - fid - ing, For noth - ing chan - ges here.
My Shep-herd is be - side me, And noth - ing can I lack.
Bright skies will soon be o'er me, Where dark - est clouds have been.

The storm may roar with - out me, My heart may low be laid,
His wis - dom ev - er wak - eth; His sight is nev - er dim.
My hope I can - not meas - ure; My path to life is free;

But God is round a - bout me, And can I be dis - mayed?
He knows the way He tak - eth, And I will walk with Him.
My Sav - ior has my treas - ure, And He will walk with me.

TEXT: Anna L. Waring
MUSIC: Felix Mendelssohn

SEASONS
7.6.7.6.D.

Jesus, I Am Resting, Resting 503

There remaineth therefore a rest to the people of God. Heb. 4:9

1. Je - sus, I am rest - ing, rest - ing In the joy of what Thou art;
2. O, how great Thy lov - ing kind - ness, Vast - er, broad-er than the sea!
3. Sim - ply trust - ing Thee, Lord Je - sus, I be-hold Thee as Thou art,
4. Ev - er lift Thy face up - on me As I work and wait for Thee;
(Ref.) Je - sus, I am rest - ing, rest - ing In the joy of what Thou art;

I am find - ing out the great - ness Of Thy lov - ing heart.
O, how mar - vel - ous Thy good - ness, Lav - ished all on me!
And Thy love, so pure, so change-less, Sat - is - fies my heart;
Rest - ing 'neath Thy smile, Lord Je - sus, Earth's dark shad - ows flee.
I am find - ing out the great - ness Of Thy lov - ing heart.

Fine

Thou hast bid me gaze up - on Thee, And Thy beau-ty fills my soul,
Yes, I rest in Thee, Be - lov - ed, Know what wealth of grace is Thine,
Sat - is - fies its deep-est long-ings, Meets, sup-plies its ev - ery need,
Bright-ness of my Fa - ther's glo - ry, Sun - shine of my Fa - ther's face,

D.C. for Refrain

For by Thy trans - form - ing pow - er, Thou hast made me whole.
Know Thy cer - tain - ty of prom - ise, And have made it mine.
Com - pass-eth me round with bless - ings: Thine is love in - deed!
Keep me ev - er trust - ing, rest - ing, Fill me with Thy grace.

TEXT: Jean S. Pigott
MUSIC: James Mountain

TRANQUILITY
8.7.8.5.D. with Refrain

504 He Touched Me

Jesus . . . touched him, saying, "I will; be thou clean." Matt. 8:3

1. Shack - led by a heav - y bur - den, 'Neath a load of
2. Since I met this bless - ed Sav - ior, Since He cleansed and

guilt and shame; Then the hand of Je - sus touched me,
made me whole; I will nev - er cease to praise Him,

And now I am no long - er the same.
I'll shout it while e - ter - ni - ty rolls.

Refrain

He touched me, O, He touched me, And O, the joy that floods my soul; Some-thing hap-pened, and now I know, He touched me and made me whole.

TEXT and MUSIC: William J. Gaither

HE TOUCHED ME
Irregular meter

Love Lifted Me 505

He loved us, and sent His Son to be the propitiation for our sins. 1 John 4:10

1. I was sink-ing deep in sin, Far from the peace-ful shore, Ver-y deep-ly
2. All my heart to Him I give, Ev-er to Him I'll cling, In His bless-ed
3. Souls in dan-ger, look a-bove, Je-sus com-plete-ly saves; He will lift you

stained with-in, Sink-ing to rise no more; But the Mas-ter of the sea
pres-ence live, Ev-er His prais-es sing; Love so might-y and so true
by His love Out of the an-gry waves; He's the Mas-ter of the sea,

Heard my de-spair-ing cry, From the wa-ters lift-ed me, Now safe am I.
Mer-its my soul's best songs; Faith-ful, lov-ing ser-vice, too, To Him be-longs.
Bil-lows His will o-bey; He your Sav-ior wants to be, Be saved to-day.

Refrain

Love lift-ed me! Love lift-ed me! When noth-ing
e-ven me! e-ven me!

1 else could help, Love lift-ed me.

2 Love lift-ed me.

TEXT: James Rowe
MUSIC: Howard E. Smith

SAFETY
7.6.7.6.7.6.7.4. with Refrain

506 I Will Sing of My Redeemer

In whom we have redemption through His blood. Eph. 1:7

1. I will sing of my Re - deem - er And His won - drous love to me;
2. I will tell the won-drous sto - ry, How, my lost es - tate to save,
3. I will praise my dear Re - deem - er, His tri - um - phant pow'r I'll tell,
4. I will sing of my Re - deem - er And His heav'n - ly love to me;

On the cru - el cross He suf - fered, From the curse to set me free.
In His bound-less love and mer - cy, He the ran - som free - ly gave.
How the vic - to - ry He giv - eth O - ver sin and death and hell.
He from death to life hath bro't me, Son of God with Him to be.

Refrain

Sing, O sing of my Re - deem - er,
of my Re-deem-er, Sing, O sing of my Re-deem-er,

With His blood He pur - chased me;
He pur-chased me, With His blood, He pur-chased me;

TEXT: Philip P. Bliss
MUSIC: James McGranahan
Alternate tune: HYFRYDOL at No. 89

MY REDEEMER
8.7.8.7. with Refrain

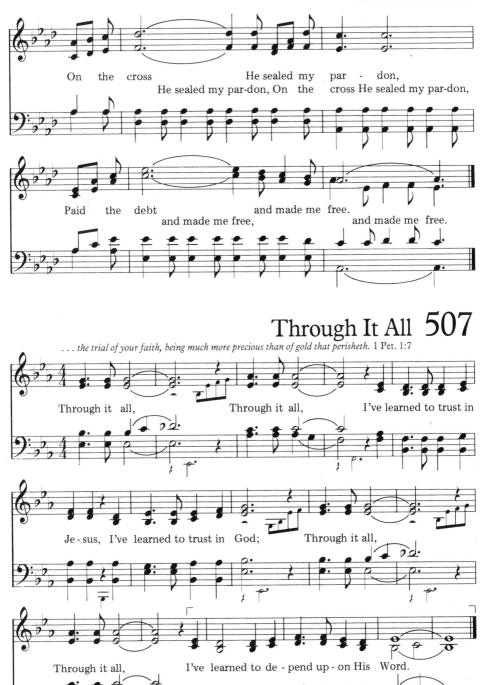

On the cross He sealed my par - don,
He sealed my par-don, On the cross He sealed my par-don,

Paid the debt and made me free.
and made me free, and made me free.

Through It All 507

. . . the trial of your faith, being much more precious than of gold that perisheth. 1 Pet. 1:7

Through it all, Through it all, I've learned to trust in

Je - sus, I've learned to trust in God; Through it all,

Through it all, I've learned to de - pend up - on His Word.

TEXT and MUSIC: Andraé Crouch

THROUGH IT ALL
Irregular meter

508 I Will Sing the Wondrous Story

They sing . . . the song of the Lamb, saying "Great and marvelous are Thy works." Rev. 15:3

1. I will sing the won-drous sto-ry Of the Christ who died for me—
2. I was lost but Je-sus found me—Found the sheep that went a-stray,
3. Days of dark-ness still come o'er me, Sor-row's paths I of-ten tread;
4. He will keep me till the riv-er Rolls its wa-ters at my feet;

How He left His home in glo-ry For the cross of Cal-va-ry.
Threw His lov-ing arms a-round me, Drew me back in-to His way.
But the Sav-ior still is with me—By His hand I'm safe-ly led.
Then He'll bear me safe-ly o-ver, Where the loved ones I shall meet.

Refrain

Yes, I'll sing the won-drous sto-ry Of the Christ who died for me,

Sing it with the saints in glo-ry, Gath-ered by the crys-tal sea.

TEXT: Francis H. Rowley
MUSIC: Peter P. Bilhorn
Alternate tune: HYFRYDOL at No. 89

WONDROUS STORY
8.7.8.7. with Refrain

MY LIFE, MY JOY, MY ALL

A Brief Service of
Testimony and Praise

Suggested Hymn Stanzas

To facilitate an uninterrupted flow from stanza to stanza,
the suggested stanzas have been marked with an arrow: ►

Jesus Is All the World to Me, stanza 1
Now I Belong to Jesus, stanzas 1, 3
My Savior's Love, stanzas 1, 4
O, How He Loves You and Me, complete

WORSHIP LEADER:
I will publish the name of the Lord: ascribe ye greatness unto our God.

PEOPLE:
He is the Rock, His work is perfect: for all His ways are judgment: a God of truth and without iniquity, just and right is He.

WORSHIP LEADER:
The Lord liveth; and blessed be my Rock; and exalted be the God of the rock of my salvation. O Lord, I will praise Thee: though Thou wast angry with me, Thine anger is turned away, and Thou comfortedst me.

PEOPLE:
Behold, God is my salvation; I will trust, and not be afraid: for the Lord JEHOVAH is my strength and my song; He also is become my salvation. Therefore with joy shall ye draw water out of the wells of salvation.

WORSHIP LEADER:
Blessed be the God and Father of our Lord Jesus Christ, which according to His abundant mercy hath begotten us again unto a lively hope by the resurrection of Jesus Christ from the dead, to an inheritance incorruptible, and undefiled, and that fadeth not away, reserved in heaven for you, who are kept by the power of God through faith unto salvation ready to be revealed in the last time.

Deut. 32:3-4; 2 Sam. 22:47;
Isa. 12:1-3; 1 Pet. 1:3-5.

*Optional introduction to
"Jesus Is All the World to Me"*

mf

510 Jesus Is All the World to Me

To me to live is Christ. Phil. 1:21

1. Je - sus is all the world to me, My life, my joy, my all;
2. Je - sus is all the world to me, My Friend in tri - als sore;
3. Je - sus is all the world to me, And true to Him I'll be;
4. Je - sus is all the world to me, I want no bet - ter friend;

He is my strength from day to day, With - out Him I would fall.
I go to Him for bless-ings, and He gives them o'er and o'er.
O, how could I this Friend de - ny, When He's so true to me?
I trust Him now, I'll trust Him when Life's fleet-ing days shall end.

When I am sad to Him I go, No oth - er one can cheer me so;
He sends the sun - shine and the rain, He sends the har - vest's gold - en grain;
Fol - low-ing Him I know I'm right, He watch-es o'er me day and night;
Beau - ti - ful life with such a Friend; Beau - ti - ful life that has no end;

When I am sad He makes me glad, He's my Friend.
Sun - shine and rain, har - vest of grain, He's my Friend.
Fol - low - ing Him by day and night, He's my Friend.
E - ter - nal life, e - ter - nal joy, He's my Friend.

Opt. segue to "Now I Belong to Jesus"

TEXT and MUSIC: Will L. Thompson

ELIZABETH
Irregular meter

Now I Belong to Jesus 511

Whether we live therefore, or die, we are the Lord's. Rom. 14:8

1. Je - sus my Lord will love me for - ev - er, From Him no pow'r of e - vil can
2. Once I was lost in sin's deg - ra - da - tion, Je - sus came down to bring me sal -
3. Joy floods my soul for Je - sus has saved me, Freed me from sin that long had en-

sev - er, He gave His life to ran - som my soul, Now I be - long to Him;
va - tion, Lift - ed me up from sor - row and shame, Now I be - long to Him;
slaved me, His pre - cious blood He gave to re - deem, Now I be - long to Him;

Refrain

Now I be - long to Je - sus, Je - sus be - longs to me,

Not for the years of time a - lone, But for e - ter - ni - ty.

TEXT and MUSIC: Norman J. Clayton

ELLSWORTH
10.10.9.6. with Refrain

*Optional transition to
"My Savior's Love"*

mp accel..e cresc. poco a poco

512 My Savior's Love

The Son of God . . . loved me, and gave Himself for me. Gal. 2:20

1. I stand a-mazed in the pres-ence Of Je-sus the Naz-a-rene,
2. For me it was in the gar-den He prayed, "Not My will, but Thine";
3. In pit-y an-gels be-held Him, And came from the world of light
4. He took my sins and my sor-rows, He made them His ver-y own;
5. When with the ran-somed in glo-ry His face I at last shall see,

And won-der how He could love me, A sin-ner, con-demned, unclean.
He had no tears for His own griefs, But sweat-drops of blood for mine.
To com-fort Him in the sor-rows He bore for my soul that night.
He bore the bur-den to Cal-v'ry, And suf-fered and died a-lone.
'Twill be my joy thru the a-ges To sing of His love for me.

Refrain

How mar-vel-ous! how won-der-ful! And my song shall ev-er be:
O how mar-vel-ous! O how won-der-ful!

How mar-vel-ous! how won-der-ful Is my Sav-ior's love for me!
O how mar-vel-ous! O how won-der-ful

TEXT and MUSIC: Charles H. Gabriel

MY SAVIOR'S LOVE
8.7.8.7. with Refrain

O, How He Loves You and Me 513

As the Father hath loved Me, so have I loved you. John 15:9

1. O, how He loves you and me. O, how He loves you and
2. Je-sus to Cal-v'ry did go, His love for man-kind to

me; He gave His life, what more could He give? O, how He
show; What He did there brought hope from de-spair: O, how He

loves you; O, how He loves me; O, how He loves you and me!
loves you; O, how He loves me; O, how He loves you and me!

TEXT and MUSIC: Kurt Kaiser

PATRICIA
Irregular meter

Optional choral ending - a cappella preferred
very rubato

me.

1. O, how He loves you;
2. O, how He loves me;
O, how He loves you and me, you and me.

me.

The end of "MY LIFE, MY JOY, MY ALL—A Brief Service of Testimony and Praise" me.

514 In My Heart There Rings a Melody

. . . singing with grace in your hearts to the Lord. Col. 3:16

1. I have a song that Je-sus gave me, It was sent from
2. I love the Christ who died on Cal-v'ry, For He washed my
3. 'Twill be my end-less theme in glo-ry, With the an-gels

heav'n a-bove; There nev-er was a sweet-er mel-o-dy,
sins a-way; He put with-in my heart a mel-o-dy,
I will sing; 'Twill be a song with glo-rious har-mo-ny,

Refrain

'Tis a mel-o-dy of love.
And I know it's there to stay. In my heart there rings a mel-o-dy,
When the courts of heav-en ring.

There rings a mel-o-dy with heav-en's har-mo-ny; In my heart

there rings a mel-o-dy, There rings a mel-o-dy of love.

TEXT and MUSIC: Elton M. Roth

HEART MELODY
Irregular meter

Since Jesus Came into My Heart 515

If any man be in Christ, he is a new creature. 2 Cor. 5:17

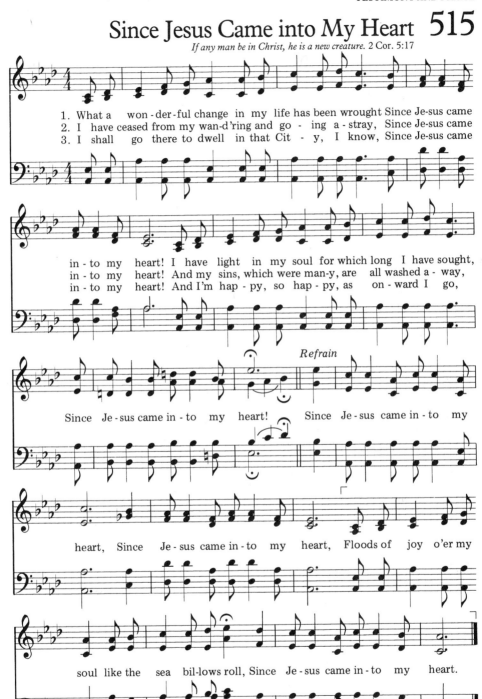

1. What a won-der-ful change in my life has been wrought Since Je-sus came
2. I have ceased from my wan-d'ring and go - ing a-stray, Since Je-sus came
3. I shall go there to dwell in that Cit - y, I know, Since Je-sus came

in - to my heart! I have light in my soul for which long I have sought,
in - to my heart! And my sins, which were man-y, are all washed a - way,
in - to my heart! And I'm hap - py, so hap - py, as on - ward I go,

Refrain

Since Je - sus came in - to my heart! Since Je - sus came in - to my

heart, Since Je - sus came in - to my heart, Floods of joy o'er my

soul like the sea bil - lows roll, Since Je - sus came in - to my heart.

TEXT: Rufus H. McDaniel
MUSIC: Charles H. Gabriel

McDANIEL
12.8.12.8. with Refrain

516 He's Everything to Me

When I consider Thy heavens, . . . What is man, that Thou art mindful of Him? Ps. 8:3-4

In the stars His hand-i - work I see, On the wind He speaks with

maj - es - ty, Tho He rul - eth o - ver land and sea, What is

that to me? I will cel - e - brate Na - tiv - i - ty, for it

has a place in his - to - ry; Sure, He came to set His peo - ple free—

What is that to me? Till by faith I met Him face to face

TEXT and MUSIC: Ralph Carmichael

WOODLAND HILLS
Irregular meter

And I felt the won-der of His grace— Then I knew that He was more than just a God who did-n't care, That lived a-way out there And now He walks be-side me day by day, Ev-er watch-ing o'er me lest I stray, Help-ing me to find that nar-row way—

1 He's ev-'ry-thing to me.

2 He's ev-'ry-thing to me.

517 I'd Rather Have Jesus

I count all things but loss for the excellency of the knowledge of Christ. Phil. 3:8

1. I'd rath-er have Je-sus than sil-ver or gold; I'd rath-er be
2. I'd rath-er have Je-sus than men's ap - plause; I'd rath-er be
3. He's fair-er than lil-ies of rar-est bloom; He's sweet-er than

His than have rich-es un-told; I'd rath-er have Je-sus than
faith-ful to His dear cause; I'd rath-er have Je-sus than
hon-ey from out the comb; He's all that my hun-ger-ing

(small notes, last stanza)

hous-es or lands. I'd rath-er be led by His nail-pierced hand
world-wide fame. I'd rath-er be true to His ho-ly name
spir-it needs. I'd rath-er have Je-sus and let Him lead

Refrain

Than to be the king of a vast do-main Or be held in sin's dread sway.

I'd rath-er have Je-sus than an-y-thing This world af-fords to-day.

TEXT: Rhea F. Miller
MUSIC: George Beverly Shea

I'D RATHER HAVE JESUS
Irregular meter

The Longer I Serve Him 518

God . . . I serve with my spirit in the gospel of His Son. Rom. 1:9

1. Since I start-ed for the King-dom, Since my life He con-trols,
2. Ev - ery need He is sup-ply-ing, Plen-teous grace He be-stows;

Since I gave my heart to Je - sus, The long-er I serve Him, the
Ev - ery day my way gets bright-er, The long-er I serve Him, the

Refrain

sweet-er He grows. The long-er I serve Him the sweet-er He grows,
sweet-er He grows.

The more that I love Him, more love He be-stows; Each day is like heav-en, my

heart o-ver-flows, The long-er I serve Him the sweet-er He grows.

TEXT and MUSIC: William J. Gaither

THE SWEETER HE GROWS
8.6.8.11. with Refrain

519 Something Beautiful

This my son was dead, and is alive again; he was lost, and is found. Luke 15:24

Some-thing beau-ti-ful, some-thing good; All my con - fu - sion

He un-der - stood; All I had to of - fer Him was bro-ken - ness and

strife, But He made some - thing beau-ti - ful of my life.

TEXT: Gloria Gaither
MUSIC: William J. Gaither

SOMETHING BEAUTIFUL
Irregular meter

520 Redeemed

Ye were . . . redeemed . . . with the precious blood of Christ, as of a lamb. 1 Pet. 1:18-19

Unison

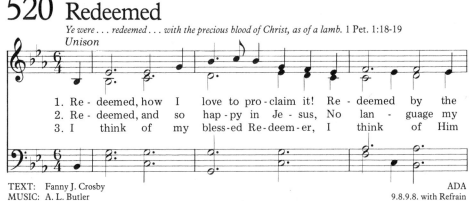

1. Re - deemed, how I love to pro - claim it! Re - deemed by the
2. Re - deemed, and so hap - py in Je - sus, No lan - guage my
3. I think of my bless-ed Re-deem - er, I think of Him

TEXT: Fanny J. Crosby
MUSIC: A. L. Butler

ADA
9.8.9.8. with Refrain

This tune and *Redeemed* by Kirkpatrick, No. 521, may be sung as a medley

521 Redeemed

Ye were . . . redeemed . . . with the precious blood of Christ, as of a lamb. 1 Pet. 1:18-19

1. Re-deemed, how I love to pro-claim it! Re-deemed by the blood of the Lamb;
2. Re-deemed and so hap-py in Je - sus, No lan-guage my rap-ture can tell;
3. I think of my bless-ed Re-deem - er, I think of Him all the day long;
4. I know I shall see in His beau - ty The King in whose law I de - light;

Re-deemed through His in-fi-nite mer - cy, His child, and for-ev - er I am.
I know that the light of His pres-ence With me doth con-tin-ual-ly dwell.
I sing, for I can-not be si - lent; His love is the theme of my song.
Who lov - ing - ly guard-eth my foot-steps, And giv-eth me songs in the night.

Refrain

Re - deemed, re - deemed, Re - deemed by the blood of the Lamb;
re-deemed, re-deemed,

Re - deemed, re - deemed, His child, and for-ev - er, I am.
re-deemed, re-deemed,

TEXT: Fanny J. Crosby
MUSIC: William J. Kirkpatrick

REDEEMED
9.8.9.8. with Refrain

He Lifted Me 522

He brought me up also out of an horrible pit . . . and set my feet upon a rock. Ps. 40:2

1. In lov-ing kind-ness Je-sus came My soul in mer-cy to re-claim,
2. He called me long be-fore I heard, Be-fore my sin-ful heart was stirred,
3. His brow was pierced with man-y a thorn, His hands by cru-el nails were torn,
4. Now on a high-er plane I dwell, And with my soul I know 'tis well;

And from the depths of sin and shame Thro' grace He lift-ed me.
But when I took Him at His word, For-giv'n He lift-ed me.
When from my guilt and grief, for-lorn, In love He lift-ed me.
Yet how or why, I can-not tell, He should have lift-ed me.

(He lift-ed me.)

Refrain

From sink-ing sand He lift-ed me, With ten-der hand He lift-ed me,

From shades of night to plains of light, O praise His name, He lift-ed me!

TEXT and MUSIC: Charles H. Gabriel

HE LIFTED ME
8.8.8.6. with Refrain

523 Yesterday, Today and Tomorrow

Christ died for our sins . . . He rose again . . . according to the scriptures. 1 Cor. 15:3-4

Unison or 2-part

Introduction

Yes-ter-day He died for me, yes-ter-day,

yes-ter-day, Yes-ter-day He died for me, yes-ter-day, Yes-ter-day He

died for me, died for me— This is his-to - ry. To-day He lives for me,

to-day, to-day, To-day He lives for me, to-day, To-day He

lives for me, lives for me— This is vic-to - ry. To-mor-row He

TEXT: Jack Wyrtzen
MUSIC: Don Wyrtzen

YESTERDAY, TODAY AND TOMORROW
Irregular meter

© *Copyright 1966 by Singspiration, Inc. All Rights Reserved. Used by Permission.*

comes for me, He comes, He comes, To-mor-row He comes for me,

He comes, Tomorrow He comes for me, comes for me—This is mys-ter - y.

O friend, do you know Him? know Him? know Him? O friend, do

you know Him? know Him? O friend, do you know Him? do you know Him? Je-sus

Christ the Lord, Je-sus Christ the Lord, Je - sus Christ the Lord!

524 It Took a Miracle

The grace of God that bringeth salvation hath appeared to all. Titus 2:11

1. My Fa-ther is om-ni-po-tent, And that you can't de-ny;
2. Tho here His glo-ry has been shown, We still can't ful-ly see
3. The Bi-ble tells us of His pow'r And wis-dom all way thru,

A God of might and mir-a-cles— 'Tis writ-ten in the sky.
The won-ders of His might, His throne— 'Twill take e-ter-ni-ty.
And ev-'ry lit-tle bird and flow'r Are tes-ti-mo-nies too.

Refrain

It took a mir-a-cle to put the stars in place, It took a

mir-a-cle to hang the world in space; But when He saved my soul,

Cleansed and made me whole, It took a mir-a-cle of love and grace.

TEXT and MUSIC: John W. Peterson

MONTROSE
C.M. with Refrain

I Will Praise Him 525

Unto Him that . . . washed us from our sins in His own blood. Rev. 1:5

1. When I saw the cleans-ing foun-tain, O - pen wide for all my sin,
2. Tho' the way seems straight and nar-row, All I claimed was swept a - way;
3. Bless - ed be the name of Je - sus! I'm so glad He took me in;
4. Glo - ry, glo - ry to the Fa - ther! Glo - ry, glo - ry to the Son!

I o-beyed the Spir - it's woo - ing When He said, "Wilt thou be clean?"
My am - bi-tions, plans and wish - es At my feet in ash - es lay.
He's for - giv - en my trans - gres - sions, He has cleansed my heart from sin.
Glo - ry, glo - ry to the Spir - it! Glo - ry to the Three in One!

Refrain

I will praise Him! I will praise Him! Praise the Lamb for sin-ners slain;

Give Him glo-ry, all ye peo-ple, For His blood can wash a-way each stain.

TEXT and MUSIC: Margaret J. Harris

I WILL PRAISE HIM
8.7.8.7. with Refrain

526 All That Thrills My Soul

Christ is all, and in all. Col. 3:11

1. Who can cheer the heart like Je - sus, By His pres-ence all di - vine?
2. Love of Christ so free - ly giv - en, Grace of God be - yond de - gree,
3. What a won - der - ful re - demp-tion! Nev - er can a mor - tal know
4. Ev - 'ry need His hand sup - ply - ing, Ev - 'ry good in Him I see;
5. By the crys - tal flow-ing riv - er With the ran-somed I will sing,

True and ten - der, pure and pre - cious, O how blest to call Him mine!
Mer - cy high - er than the heav - en, Deep - er than the deep-est sea!
How my sin, tho red like crim - son, Can be whit-er than the snow.
On His strength di - vine re - ly - ing, He is all in all to me.
And for - ev - er and for - ev - er Praise and glo - ri - fy the King.

Refrain

All that thrills my soul is Je - sus, He is more than life to me; to me;

And the fair - est of ten thou - sand In my bless-ed Lord I see.

TEXT and MUSIC: Thoro Harris

HARRIS
8.7.8.7.D.

Glory to His Name 527

Without shedding of blood is no remission. Heb. 9:22

1. Down at the cross where my Sav-ior died, Down where for cleans-ing from
2. I am so won-drous-ly saved from sin, Je-sus so sweet-ly a-
3. O pre-cious foun-tain that saves from sin, I am so glad I have
4. Come to this foun-tain so rich and sweet; Cast your poor soul at the

sin I cried, There to my heart was the blood ap-plied; Glo-ry to His name!
bides with-in, There at the cross where He took me in; Glo-ry to His name!
en-tered in; There Je-sus saves me and keeps me clean; Glo-ry to His name!
Sav-ior's feet; Plunge in to-day and be made com-plete; Glo-ry to His name!

Refrain

Glo-ry to His name, Glo-ry to His name;

There to my heart was the blood ap-plied; Glo-ry to His name!

TEXT: Elisha A. Hoffman
MUSIC: John H. Stockton

GLORY TO HIS NAME
9.9.9.5. with Refrain

528 No One Ever Cared for Me Like Jesus

What is man, that Thou takest knowledge of him! Ps. 144:3

1. I would love to tell you what I think of Je - sus
2. All my life was full of sin when Je - sus found me,
3. Ev - 'ry day He comes to me with new as - sur - ance,

Since I found in Him a friend so strong and true; I would
All my heart was full of mis - er - y and woe; Je - sus
More and more I un - der - stand His words of love; But I'll

tell you how He chang'd my life com - plete - ly— He did some-thing
placed His strong and lov - ing arms a - round me, And He led me
nev - er know just why He came to save me, Till some day I

Refrain

that no oth - er friend could do.
in the way I ought to go. No one ev - er cared for me like
see His bless-ed face a - bove.

Je - sus, There's no oth-er friend so kind as He; No one else could

TEXT and MUSIC: Charles F. Weigle

WEIGLE
12.11.12.11. with Refrain

take the sin and dark-ness from me— O how much He cared for me!

O, How I Love Jesus 529

Whom having not seen, ye love. 1 Pet. 1:8

1. There is a name I love to hear, I love to sing its worth;
2. It tells me of a Sav-ior's love, who died to set me free;
3. It tells me what my Fa-ther hath In store for ev-'ry day,
4. It tells of One whose lov-ing heart Can feel my deep-est woe,

It sounds like mu - sic in my ear, The sweet-est name on earth.
It tells me of His pre-cious blood, The sin - ner's per-fect plea.
And, tho I tread a dark-some path, Yields sun-shine all the way.
Who in each sor - row bears a part That none can bear be - low.

Refrain

O, how I love Je - sus, O, how I love Je - sus,

O, how I love Je - sus— Be - cause He first loved me!

TEXT: Frederick Whitfield
MUSIC: Traditional American melody

O, HOW I LOVE JESUS
C.M. with Refrain

530 Saved, Saved!

According to His mercy He saved us. Titus 3:5

Unison

1. I've found a Friend who is all to me, His
2. He saves me from ev-ery sin and harm, Se-
3. When poor and need-y and all a - lone, In

love is ev - er true; I love to tell how He
cures my soul each day; I'm lean - ing strong on His
love He said to me, "Come un - to Me and I'll

lift - ed me, And what His grace can do for you.
might - y arm; I know He'll guide me all the way.
lead you home, To live with Me e - ter - nal - ly."

Refrain (parts optional)

Saved by His pow'r di-vine, Saved to new life sub-lime!
Saved by His pow'r, Saved to new life,

TEXT and MUSIC: Jack P. Scholfield

SCHOLFIELD
8.6.8.8. with Refrain

Life now is sweet and my joy is com-plete, For I'm saved, saved, saved!

Satisfied 531

He satisfieth the longing soul, and filleth the hungry soul with goodness. Ps. 107:9

1. All my life long I had pant - ed For a drink, from some clear spring,
2. Feed-ing on the husks a - round me, Till my strength was al - most gone,
3. Well of wa - ter ev - er spring-ing, Bread of life so rich and free,

That I hoped would quench the burn-ing Of the thirst I felt with - in.
Longed my soul for some-thing bet - ter, On-ly still to hun-ger on.
Un - told wealth that nev - er fail - eth, My Re - deem-er is to me.

Refrain

Hal - le - lu - jah! I have found Him Whom my soul so long has craved!

Je - sus sat - is - fies my long - ings— Thru His blood I now am saved.

TEXT: Clara T. Williams
MUSIC: Ralph E. Hudson

SATISFIED
8.7.8.7. with Refrain

532 O Happy Day!

We will be glad and rejoice in His salvation. Isa. 25:9

1. O hap-py day that fixed my choice On Thee, my Sav - ior and my God!
2. O hap-py bond that seals my vows To Him who mer - its all my love!
3. 'Tis done, the great trans-ac-tion's done— I am my Lord's and He is mine;
4. Now rest, my long-di-vid-ed heart, Fixed on this bliss-ful cen-ter, rest,

Well may this glow - ing heart re - joice And tell its rap-tures all a - broad.
Let cheer-ful an - thems fill His house, While to that sa - cred shrine I move.
He drew me, and I fol-lowed on, Charmed to con-fess the voice di - vine.
Nor ev - er from my Lord de - part, With Him of ev - 'ry good pos-sessed.

Refrain

Hap - py day, hap - py day, When Je - sus washed my sins a - way!

He taught me how to watch and pray And live re - joic - ing ev - ery day;

Hap - py day, hap - py day, When Je - sus washed my sins a - way!

TEXT: Philip Doddridge
MUSIC: Edward F. Rimbault

HAPPY DAY
L.M. with Refrain

O Perfect Love 533

Husbands, love your wives. Col. 3:19   *Women . . . love their husbands.* Titus 2:4

1. O   per - fect   love,   all   hu - man thought tran - scend - ing,
2. O   per - fect   Life,   be   Thou their   full   as - sur - ance
3. Grant   them the   joy   which   bright-ens earth - ly   sor - row;
4. Hear   us,   O   Fa - ther,   gra - cious and   for - giv - ing,

Low - ly   we   kneel   in   prayer be - fore Thy   throne,
Of   ten - der   char - i - ty   and   stead - fast   faith,
Grant   them the   peace   which   calms all   earth - ly   strife,
Through Je - sus   Christ, Thy   co - e - ter - nal   Word,

That   theirs may   be   the   love which knows no   end - ing,
Of   pa - tient   hope, and   qui - et,   brave en - dur - ance,
And   to   life's   day   the   glo - rious, un - known mor - row
Who,   with the   Ho - ly   Ghost, by   all   things   liv - ing

Whom Thou for - ev - er - more dost   join   in   one.
With   child - like   trust that fears not   pain   nor   death.
That   dawns up - on   e - ter - nal   love and   life.
Now   and to   end - less   a - ges   art a - dored.   A - men.

TEXT: Dorothy F. Gurney, stanzas 1, 2, 3; John Ellerton, stanza 4
MUSIC: Joseph Barnby

SANDRINGHAM
11.10.11.10.

534 She Will Be Called Blessed

Her children . . . call her blessed; her husband . . . praiseth her. Prov. 31:28

Stanza 1, Spoken

Worship Leader: Her strength and her dignity clothe her with beauty;
In works of her hands she excells.
A heart of compassion she turns to the needy;
In service to others, she gives of herself.

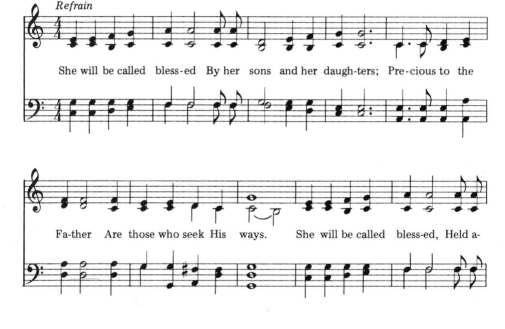

She will be called bless-ed By her sons and her daugh-ters; Pre-cious to the Fa-ther Are those who seek His ways. She will be called bless-ed, Held a-bove ev-'ry oth-er; Bless-ed is the moth-er Who turns to God in praise.

Optional: instruments may play the final 8 bars of the Refrain while worship leader recites stanza 2.

Stanza 2, Spoken

Worship Leader: She rises each morning to see her household;
She looks toward the future with joy.
She teaches her children true lessons of kindness;
And shares with them wisdom the world can't destroy.

Repeat the Refrain

TEXT: Elizabeth de Gravelles; based on Proverbs 31:10-31
MUSIC: Joseph Barlowe

IRENE
13.12.13.12.

A Christian Home 535

From a child thou hast known the holy Scriptures. 2 Tim. 3:15

1. O give us homes built firm up-on the Sav-ior, Where Christ is
2. O give us homes with god-ly fa-thers, moth-ers, Who al-ways
3. O Lord, our God, our homes are Thine for-ev-er! We trust to

Head and Coun-sel-lor and Guide; Where ev-ery child is
place their hope and trust in Him; Whose ten-der pa-tience
Thee their prob-lems, toil, and care; Their bonds of love no

taught His love and fa-vor And gives His heart to Christ, the cru-ci-
tur-moil nev-er both-ers, Whose calm and cour-age trou-ble can-not
en-e-my can sev-er If Thou art al-ways Lord and Mas-ter

fied: How sweet to know that though his foot-steps wa-ver
dim; A home where each finds joy in serv-ing oth-ers,
there: Be Thou the cen-ter of our least en-deav-or—

His faith-ful Lord is walk-ing by his side!
And love still shines, tho days be dark and grim.
Be Thou our Guest, our hearts and homes to share. A-men.

TEXT: Barbara B. Hart
MUSIC: Jean Sibelius
A higher setting may be found at No. 347

FINLANDIA (altered)
11.10.11.10.11.10.

536 Happy the Home When God Is There

As for me and my house, we will serve the Lord. Josh. 24:15

1. Hap-py the home when God is there And love fills ev-ery-one,
2. Hap-py the home where God's strong love Is start-ing to ap-pear,
3. Hap-py the home where prayer is heard And praise is ev-ery-where,
4. Lord, let us in our homes a-gree This bless-ed peace to gain;

When with u-ni-ted work and prayer The Mas-ter's will is done.
Where all the chil-dren hear His fame And par-ents hold Him dear.
Where par-ents love the sa-cred Word And its true wis-dom share.
U-nite our hearts in love to Thee, And love to all will reign. A-men.

TEXT: Henry Ware, Jr.; altered by Bryan Jeffery Leech
MUSIC: John B. Dykes
A higher setting may be found at No. 79

ST. AGNES
C.M.

Text revision © Copyright 1976 by Fred Bock Music Company. All Rights Reserved. Used by Permission.

537 As for Me and My House

Except the Lord build the house, they labour in vain that build it. Ps. 127:1

As for me and my house, we will serve the Lord; As for me and my

house, we will praise His name. For un-less He builds the house we have

TEXT: Elizabeth de Gravelles; based on Joshua 24:15
MUSIC: Kurt Kaiser

WE WILL SERVE
Irregular meter

© Copyright 1986 WORD MUSIC (a div. of WORD, INC.). All Rights Reserved. International Copyright Secured.

worked in vain; As for me and my house we will serve the Lord.

When I Can Read My Title Clear 538

I go to prepare a place for you. John 14:2

1. When I can read my ti - tle clear To man - sions in the skies,
2. Should earth a - gainst my soul en - gage And fier - y darts be hurled,
3. Let cares like a wild del - uge come And storms of sor - row fall!

D.S. I'll bid fare - well to ev - ery fear And wipe my weep-ing eyes.
D.S. Then I can smile at Sa - tan's rage And face a frown-ing world.
D.S. May I but safe - ly reach my home, My God, my heaven, my all.

Fine

And wipe my weep-ing eyes, And wipe my weep-ing eyes,
And face a frown-ing world, And face a frown-ing world,
My God, my heaven, my all, My God, my heaven, my all,

D.S.

TEXT: Isaac Watts
MUSIC: Traditional American melody; from *Kentucky Harmony*, 1816

PISGAH
8.6.8.6.6.6.8.6.

539 O That Will Be Glory

The sufferings of this present time are not worthy to be compared with the glory. Rom. 8:18

1. When all my la - bors and tri - als are o'er, And I am safe on that
2. When by the gift of His in - fi - nite grace, I am ac - cord - ed in
3. Friends will be there I have loved long a - go; Joy like a riv - er a -

beau - ti - ful shore, Just to be near the dear Lord I a - dore
heav - en a place, Just to be there and to look on His face
round me will flow; Yet, just a smile from my Sav - ior, I know,

Refrain

Will through the a - ges be glo - ry for me. O that will be

O that will

glo-ry for me, Glo-ry for me, glo-ry for me; When by His grace
be glo-ry for me, Glo-ry for me, glo-ry for me;

rit.

I shall look on His face, That will be glo - ry, be glo - ry for me.

TEXT and MUSIC: Charles H. Gabriel

GLORY SONG
10.10.10.10. with Refrain

AN UPWARD LOOK

A Brief Service of Joyful Anticipation

Suggested Hymn Stanzas

To facilitate an uninterrupted flow from stanza to stanza,
the suggested stanzas have been marked with an arrow: ►

He the Pearly Gates Will Open, stanzas 1, 3
When We All Get to Heaven, stanzas 1, 3, 4
When the Roll Is Called Up Yonder, stanzas 1, 3

WORSHIP LEADER:
And I saw a new heaven and a new earth: for the first heaven and the
first earth were passed away; and there was no more sea. And I John
saw the Holy City, New Jerusalem, coming down from God out of
heaven, prepared as a bride adorned for her husband. And I heard a
great voice out of heaven saying, Behold, the tabernacle of God is
with men, and He will dwell with them, and they shall be His people,
and God Himself shall be with them, and be their God. And God
shall wipe away all tears from their eyes; and there shall be no more
death, neither sorrow, nor crying, neither shall there be any more
pain: for the former things are passed away.

And I saw no temple therein: for the Lord God Almighty and the
Lamb are the temple of it. And the city had no need of the sun, neither of the moon, to shine in it: for the glory of God did lighten it,
and the Lamb is the light thereof. And the gates of it shall not be shut
at all by day: for there shall be no night there. And there shall in
no wise enter into it any thing that defileth, neither whatsoever
worketh abomination, or maketh a lie: but they which are written in
the Lamb's Book of Life.

Revelation 21:1-4, 22-23, 25, 27.

*Optional introduction to
"He the Pearly Gates Will Open"*

541 He the Pearly Gates Will Open

They that do His commandments . . . may enter in through the gates into the city. Rev. 22:14

1. Love di-vine, so great and won-drous, Deep and might-y, pure, sub - lime;
2. Like a dove when hunt-ed, fright-ened, As a wound-ed fawn was I,
3. Love di-vine, so great and won-drous—All my sins He then for - gave,
4. In life's e - ven-tide, at twi - light, At His door I'll knock and wait;

Com - ing from the heart of Je - sus—Just the same thru tests of time.
Bro - ken heart-ed, yet He healed me—He will heed the sin - ner's cry.
I will sing His praise for - ev - er, For His blood, His pow'r to save.
By the pre - cious love of Je - sus, I shall en - ter heav - en's gate.

Refrain

He the pearl - y gates will o - pen, So that I may en - ter in;

For He pur-chased my re - demp-tion, And for - gave me all my sin.

TEXT: Frederick A. Blom; translated by Nathaniel Carlson
MUSIC: Elsie Ahlwén

PEARLY GATES
8.7.8.7. with Refrain

Optional transition to
"When We All Get to Heaven"

faster tempo
f
accented

When We All Get to Heaven 542

We . . . shall be caught up . . . to . . . ever be with the Lord. 1 Thess. 4:17

1. Sing the won-drous love of Je - sus, Sing His mer - cy and His grace;
2. While we walk the pil - grim path-way Clouds will o - ver - spread the sky;
3. Let us then be true and faith - ful, Trust - ing, serv - ing ev - ery day;
4. On - ward to the prize be - fore us! Soon His beau - ty we'll be - hold;

In the man - sions bright and bless - ed He'll pre - pare for us a place.
But when trav - 'ling days are o - ver, Not a shad-ow, not a sigh.
Just one glimpse of Him in glo - ry Will the toils of life re - pay.
Soon the pearl - y gates will o - pen, We shall tread the streets of gold.

Refrain

When we all get to heav - en, What a day of re-
When we all What a

joic - ing that will be! When we all see
day of re - joic - ing that will be! When we all

Je - sus, We'll sing and shout the vic - to - ry.
and shout the vic - to - ry.

TEXT: Eliza E. Hewitt
MUSIC: Emily D. Wilson

HEAVEN
8.7.8.7. with Refrain

Optional transition to
"When the Roll Is Called Up Yonder"

543 When the Roll Is Called Up Yonder

The Lord Himself shall descend . . . with the trump of God. 1 Thess. 4:16

1. When the trum-pet of the Lord shall sound and time shall be no more
2. On that bright and cloud-less morning when the dead in Christ shall rise
3. Let us la - bor for the Mas - ter from the dawn till set - ting sun,

And the morn-ing breaks e - ter - nal, bright and fair— When the
And the glo - ry of His res - ur - rec - tion share— When His
Let us talk of all His won-drous love and care; Then when

saved of earth shall gath - er o - ver on the oth - er shore
cho - sen ones shall gath - er to their home be - yond the skies
all of life is o - ver and our work on earth is done

And the roll is called up yon - der, I'll be there!
And the roll is called up yon - der, I'll be there!
And the roll is called up yon - der, I'll be there!

TEXT and MUSIC: James M. Black

ROLL CALL
Irregular meter

The end of "AN UPWARD LOOK—A Brief Service of Joyful Anticipation"

544 We'll Understand It Better By and By

Faith is the substance of things hoped for, the evidence of things not seen. Heb. 11:1

1. Tri - als dark on ev - 'ry hand, And we can - not un - der - stand
2. Oft our cher-ished plans have failed, Dis - ap - point-ments have pre -vailed,
3. Temp - ta - tions, hid - den snares Of - ten take us un - a - wares,

All the ways that God would lead us to that bless-ed Prom-ised Land;
And we've wan - dered in the dark-ness, heav-y - heart-ed and a - lone;
And our hearts are made to bleed for some tho't-less word or deed,

But He'll guide us with His eye, And we'll fol - low till we die; We will
But we're trust-ing in the Lord, And, ac - cord-ing to His Word, We will
And we won - der why the test When we try to do our best, But we'll

Refrain

un - der-stand it bet-ter by and by. By and by, when the morn-ing

comes, When the saints of God are gath-ered home, We will tell the sto - ry

TEXT and MUSIC: Charles A. Tindley; arranged by B. B. McKinney

BY AND BY
Irregular meter

How we've o-ver-come; We will un-der-stand it bet-ter by and by.

We Shall See His Lovely Face 545

They shall see His face. Rev. 22:4

1. We shall see His love-ly face Some bright, gold-en morn-ing, When the
2. God shall wipe a-way all tears Some bright, gold-en morn-ing, When the
3. We shall meet to part no more, Some bright, gold-en morn-ing, At the

clouds have rift-ed, And the shades have flown; Sor-row will be turned to joy,
jour-ney's end-ed, And the course is run; No more cry-ing, pain or death
gates of glo-ry Where our loved ones stand; Songs of vic-t'ry fill the skies

Heart-aches gone for-ev-er; No more night, on-ly light, When we see His face.
In that hour of glad-ness, Tri-als cease, all is peace, When we see His face.
In that hour of greet-ing, End-less days, end-less praise, When we see His face.

TEXT and MUSIC: Norman J. Clayton

CLAYTON
6.6.6.5.D.

546 For All the Saints

. . . that they may rest from their labours; and their works do follow them. Rev. 14:13

1. For all the saints who from their la - bors rest, Who
2. Thou wast their rock, their for - tress, and their might,
3. O may Thy sol - diers, faith - ful, true, and bold,
4. O blest com - mu - nion, fel - low - ship di - vine!
5. But lo! there breaks a yet more glo - rious day: The
6. From earth's wide bounds, from o - cean's far - thest coast, Thru

Thee by faith be - fore the world con - fessed, Thy
Thou, Lord, their cap - tain in the well - fought fight;
Fight as the saints who no - bly fought of old, And
We fee - bly strug - gle, they in glo - ry shine; Yet
saints tri - um - phant rise in bright ar - ray; The
gates of pearl streams in the count - less host,

name, O Je - sus, be for - ev - er blest:
Thou, in the dark - ness drear, their one true Light:
win with them the vic - tor's crown of gold:
all are one in Thee, for all are Thine:
King of glo - ry pass - es on His way:
Sing - ing to Fa - ther, Son, and Ho - ly Ghost:

TEXT: William W. How
MUSIC: Ralph Vaughan Williams

SINE NOMINE
10.10.10. with Alleluias

Music from the English Hymnal by permission of Oxford University Press London.

Al - le - lu - ia! Al - le - lu - ia!

The Kingdom of God 547

I saw a new heaven and a new earth. Rev. 21:1

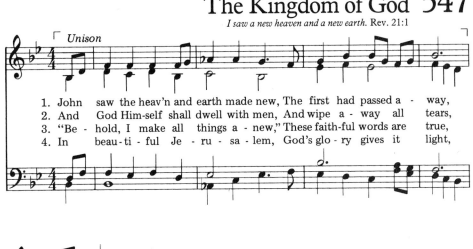

Unison

1. John saw the heav'n and earth made new, The first had passed a - way,
2. And God Him-self shall dwell with men, And wipe a - way all tears,
3. "Be - hold, I make all things a - new," These faith-ful words are true,
4. In beau-ti - ful Je - ru - sa - lem, God's glo - ry gives it light,

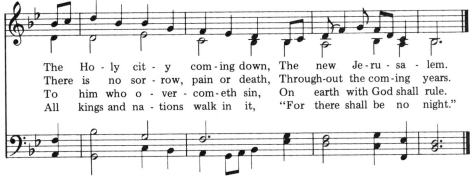

The Ho - ly cit - y com - ing down, The new Je - ru - sa - lem.
There is no sor - row, pain or death, Through-out the com - ing years.
To him who o - ver - com - eth sin, On earth with God shall rule.
All kings and na - tions walk in it, "For there shall be no night."

TEXT: Louise Lapp; based on Revelation 21
MUSIC: Traditional Spiritual melody; arranged by H.T. Burleigh

McKEE
C.M.

548 Beyond the Sunset

There shall be no more death, . . . sorrow, nor crying, neither . . . any more pain. Rev. 21:4

1. Be - yond the sun - set, O bliss - ful morn - ing, When with our
2. Be - yond the sun - set no clouds will gath - er, No storms will
3. Be - yond the sun - set, O glad re - un - ion, With our dear

Sav - ior heaven is be - gun; Earth's toil-ing end - ed, O glo - rious
threat-en, no fears an - noy; O day of glad - ness, O day un -
loved ones who've gone be - fore; In that fair home - land we'll know no

dawn - ing, Be - yond the sun - set, when day is done.
end - ing, Be - yond the sun - set, e - ter - nal joy!
part - ing, Be - yond the sun - set, for - ev - er - more!

TEXT: Virgil P. Brock
MUSIC: Blanche Kerr Brock

SUNSET
10.9.10.9.

549 Face to Face

Now we see through a glass, darkly; but then face to face. 1 Cor. 13:12

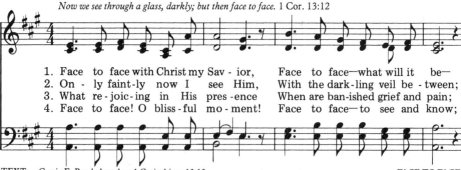

1. Face to face with Christ my Sav - ior, Face to face—what will it be—
2. On - ly faint-ly now I see Him, With the dark-ling veil be - tween;
3. What re - joic-ing in His pres - ence When are ban-ished grief and pain;
4. Face to face! O bliss - ful mo - ment! Face to face—to see and know;

TEXT: Carrie E. Breck; based on 1 Corinthians 13:12
MUSIC: Grant C. Tullar
This tune and *Saved by Grace*, No. 550, may be sung as a medley.

FACE TO FACE
8.7.8.7. with Refrain

When with rap-ture I be - hold Him, Je - sus Christ who died for me?
But a bless-ed day is com - ing When His glo - ry shall be seen.
When the crook-ed ways are straight-ened And the dark things shall be plain.
Face to face with my Re - deem - er, Je - sus Christ who loves me so.

Refrain

Face to face I shall be-hold Him, Far be-yond the star-ry sky; Face to

Optional transition to
"Saved by Grace"

face in all His glo-ry, I shall see Him by and by. by.

Saved by Grace 550

For by grace are ye saved through faith. Eph. 2:8

And I shall see Him face to face, And tell the sto-ry—Saved by
shall see to face,

grace; And I shall see Him face to face, And tell the sto-ry—Saved by grace.
shall see to face,

TEXT: Fanny J. Crosby
MUSIC: George C. Stebbins; arranged by Robert F. Douglas
This tune and *Face to Face*, No. 549, may be sung as a medley.

SAVED BY GRACE
L.M.

551 Soon and Very Soon

"Surely I come quickly." Amen. Even so, come, Lord Jesus. Rev. 22:20

1., 4. Soon and ver-y soon, We are going to see the King;
2. No more cry-ing there, We are going to see the King;
3. No more dy-ing there, We are going to see the King;

Soon and ver - y soon, We are going to see the King;
No more cry - ing there, We are going to see the King;
No more dy - ing there, We are going to see the King;

Soon and ver - y soon, We are going to see the King;
No more cry -ing there, We are going to see the King;
No more dy - ing there, We are going to see the King; Hal-le-

1,3

lu - jah! Hal-le - lu - jah! We're going to see the King.

2,4

going to see the King. Hal - le - lu - jah! Hal-le - lu - jah!

TEXT and MUSIC: Andraé Crouch

SOON AND VERY SOON
Irregular meter

On Jordan's Stormy Banks 552

Let us labour therefore to enter into that rest. Heb. 4:11

1. On Jor-dan's storm-y banks I stand, And cast a wish-ful eye
2. All o'er those wide ex-tend-ed plains Shines one e-ter-nal day;
3. No chill-ing winds nor pois'nous breath Can reach that health-ful shore;
4. When shall I reach that hap-py place, And be for-ev-er blest?

To Ca-naan's fair and hap-py land, Where my pos-ses-sions lie.
There God the Son for-ev-er reigns And scat-ters night a-way.
Sick-ness and sor-row, pain and death Are felt and feared no more.
When shall I see my Fa-ther's face, And in His bos-om rest?

Refrain

I am bound for the prom-ised land, I am bound for the prom-ised land;

O who will come and go with me? I am bound for the prom-ised land.

TEXT: Samuel Stennett
MUSIC: Traditional American melody; arranged by Rigdon M. McIntosh

PROMISED LAND
C.M. with Refrain

553 Sweet By and By

Here have we no continuing city, but we seek one to come. Heb. 13:14

1. There's a land that is fair - er than day, And by faith we can
2. We shall sing on that beau - ti - ful shore The me - lo - di - ous
3. To our boun - ti - ful Fa - ther a - bove We will of - fer our

see it a - far, For the Fa - ther waits o - ver the way To pre-
songs of the blest; And our spir - its shall sor - row no more— Not a
trib - ute of praise, For the glo - ri - ous gift of His love And the

Refrain

pare us a dwell - ing place there. In the sweet by and
sigh for the bless - ing of rest. In the sweet
bless - ings that hal - low our days.

by, We shall meet on that beau - ti - ful shore; In the
by and by, by and by,

sweet by and by, We shall meet on that beau - ti - ful shore.
In the sweet by and by,

TEXT: Sanford F. Bennett
MUSIC: Joseph P. Webster

SWEET BY AND BY
9.9.9.9. with Refrain

I'll Fly Away 554

We are . . . willing . . . to be absent from the body, and to be present with the Lord. 2 Cor. 5:8

1. Some glad morn-ing when this life is o'er, I'll fly a-
2. When the shad-ows of this life have gone, fly a-way,
3. Just a few more wea-ry days and then,

way; To a home on God's ce-les-tial shore, I'll
fly a-way; Like a bird from pris-on bars has flown, fly a-way,
To a land where joys shall nev-er end,

Refrain

fly a-way. I'll fly a-way, O glo-ry, I'll
fly a-way. fly a-way, fly a-way,

fly a-way; When I die, hal-le-lu-jah, by and by,
in the morn-ing;

Optional choral ending
ff

I'll fly a-way. I'll fly a-way.
fly a-way, fly a-way.
ff

TEXT and MUSIC: Albert E. Brumley

I'LL FLY AWAY
9.4.9.4. with Refrain

555 We're Marching to Zion

Ye are come unto Mount Sion . . . the city of the living God. Heb. 12:22

1. Come, we that love the Lord, And let our joys be known,
2. Let those re - fuse to sing Who nev - er knew our God,
3. The hill of Zi - on yields A thou - sand sa - cred sweets
4. Then let our songs a - bound And ev - ery tear be dry;

Join in a song with sweet ac-cord, Join in a song with sweet ac-cord
But chil-dren of the heav'n-ly King, But chil-dren of the heav'n-ly King
Be - fore we reach the heav'n-ly fields, Be - fore we reach the heav'n-ly fields
We're march-ing thro' Im-manuel's ground, We're march-ing thro' Im-man-uel's ground

And thus sur - round the throne, And thus sur-round the throne.
May speak their joys a - broad, May speak their joys a - broad.
Or walk the gold - en streets, Or walk the gold - en streets.
To fair - er worlds on high, To fair - er worlds on high.

Refrain

We're march-ing to *Zi - on, Beau-ti - ful, beau-ti - ful Zi - on;

We're march-ing up-ward to Zi - on, The beau-ti - ful cit - y of God.

TEXT: Isaac Watts; Robert Lowry, Refrain
MUSIC: Robert Lowry

MARCHING TO ZION
6.6.8.8.6.6. with Refrain

*Psalm 2:6. By extension this refers to the New Jerusalem.

Now Thank We All Our God 556

Praise the Lord . . . declare His doings. Isa. 12:4

1. Now thank we all our God With heart and hands and voic - es,
2. O may this boun - teous God Thro' all our life be near us,
3. All praise and thanks to God The Fa - ther now be giv - en,

Who won - drous things hath done, In whom His world re - joic - es;
With ev - er joy - ful hearts And bless - ed peace to cheer us;
The Son, and Him who reigns With them in high - est heav - en,

Who, from our moth - er's arms, Hath blest us on our way
And keep us in His grace, And guide us when per - plexed,
The one e - ter - nal God, Whom earth and heav'n a - dore;

With count - less gifts of love, And still is ours to - day.
And free us from all ills In this world and the next.
For thus it was, is now, And shall be ev - er - more. A - men.

TEXT: Martin Rinkart; translated by Catherine Winkworth
MUSIC: Johann Crüger; harmonized by Felix Mendelssohn

NUN DANKET
6.7.6.7.6.6.6.6.

557 In Thanksgiving Let Us Praise Him

They sang . . . in praising and giving thanks unto the Lord. Ezra 3:11

1. From the first bright light of morn-ing, To the last warm glow of dusk;
2. In the sea-son of our plen-ty, In the sea-son of our need;
3. Safe with-in His hand that guides us, Hid-den in His heal-ing wings;

Ev - 'ry breath we take is sa-cred, For it is God's gift to us.
We will find His grace suf - fi -cient, We will find His love com-plete.
Day by day His love pro-vides us Ev - 'ry good and per - fect thing.

In thanks-giv-ing, let us praise Him; In thanks-giv-ing, let us sing

Songs of praise and ad - o - ra - tion To our gra-cious Lord, and King. A-men.

TEXT: Claire Cloninger
MUSIC: Franz Joseph Haydn
A higher setting may be found at No. 278; Alternate tune: BEECHER at No. 92

AUSTRIAN HYMN
8.7.8.7.D.

WITH A SONG OF THANKSGIVING 558

A Brief Service of
Praise to God, the Creator
Suggested Hymn Stanzas

To facilitate an uninterrupted flow from stanza to stanza,
the suggested stanzas have been marked with an arrow: ▶

Come, Ye Thankful People, Come, stanza 1
For the Beauty of the Earth, stanzas 1, 3, 5
We Gather Together, complete

WORSHIP LEADER:
God saw every thing that He had made, and, behold, it was very good.

PEOPLE:
Thou visitest the earth, and waterest it: Thou greatly enrichest it with the river of God, which is full of water: Thou preparest them corn, when Thou hast so provided for it.

WORSHIP LEADER:
Thou crownest the year with Thy goodness; and Thy paths drop fatness. They drop upon the pastures of the wilderness: and the little hills rejoice on every side.

PEOPLE:
The pastures are clothed with flocks; the valleys also are covered over with corn; they shout for joy, they also sing.

WORSHIP LEADER:
He causeth the grass to grow for the cattle, and herb for the service of man: that He may bring forth good out of the earth. O Lord, how manifold are Thy works! In wisdom hast Thou made them all: the earth is full of Thy riches.

PEOPLE:
Oh that men would praise the Lord for His goodness, and for His wonderful works to the children of men! For He satisfieth the longing soul, and filleth the hungry soul with goodness.

ALL:
But I will sacrifice unto Thee with the voice of thanksgiving; I will pay that that I have vowed. Salvation is of the Lord.

Gen. 1:31; Ps. 65:9, 11-13;
104:14, 24; 107:8-9;
Jonah 2:9.

Optional introduction to
"Come, Ye Thankful People, Come"

mf

559 Come, Ye Thankful People, Come

Thou crownest the year with Thy goodness. Ps. 65:11

1. Come, ye thank-ful peo-ple, come— Raise the song of har-vest-home:
2. All the world is God's own field, Fruit un-to His praise to yield;
3. For the Lord our God shall come And shall take His har-vest home;
4. E-ven so, Lord, quick-ly come To Thy fi-nal har-vest-home;

All is safe-ly gath-ered in Ere the win-ter storms be-gin.
Wheat and tares to-geth-er sown, Un-to joy or sor-row grown.
From His field shall in that day All of-fens-es purge a-way;
Gath-er Thou Thy peo-ple in, Free from sor-row, free from sin;

God, our Mak-er, doth pro-vide For our wants to be sup-plied:
First the blade and then the ear, Then the full corn shall ap-pear:
Give His an-gels charge at last In the fire the tares to cast,
There, for-ev-er pu-ri-fied, In Thy pres-ence to a-bide:

Come to God's own tem-ple, come—Raise the song of har-vest-home.
Lord of har-vest, grant that we Wholesome grain and pure may be.
But the fruit-ful ears to store In His gar-ner ev-er-more.
Come, with all Thine an-gels, come— Raise the glo-rious har-vest-home. A - men.

TEXT: Henry Alford
MUSIC: George J. Elvey

ST. GEORGE'S, WINDSOR
7.7.7.7.D.

Optional transition to
"For the Beauty of the Earth"

For the Beauty of the Earth 560

Praise the Lord for His goodness, and for His wonderful works. Ps. 107:8

1. For the beau-ty of the earth, For the glo-ry of the skies,
2. For the won-der of each hour Of the day and of the night,
3. For the joy of hu-man love, Broth-er, sis-ter, par-ent, child;
4. For Thy Church that ev-er-more Lift-eth ho-ly hands a-bove,
5. For Thy-self, best gift di-vine, To our race so free-ly given;

For the love which from our birth O-ver and a-round us lies;
Hill and vale and tree and flower, Sun and moon and stars of light:
Friends on earth and friends a-bove; For all gen-tle thoughts and mild:
Off-ering up on ev-ery shore Her pure sac-ri-fice of love:
For that great, great love of Thine, Peace on earth and joy in heaven:

Lord of all, to Thee we raise This our hymn of grate-ful praise. A - men.

TEXT: Folliott S. Pierpoint, altered
MUSIC: Conrad Kocher; arranged by William H. Monk

DIX
7.7.7.7.7.7.

Optional transition to
"We Gather Together"

mf *f*

561 We Gather Together

God be merciful unto us, and bless us. Ps. 67:1

1. We gath-er to-geth-er to ask the Lord's bless-ing;
2. Be-side us to guide us, our God with us join-ing,
3. We all do ex-tol Thee, Thou Lead-er tri-um-phant,

He chas-tens and has-tens His will to make known;
Or-dain-ing, main-tain-ing His king-dom di-vine;
And pray that Thou still our De-fend-er wilt be.

The wick-ed op-press-ing now cease from dis-tress-ing,
So from the be-gin-ning the fight we were win-ning:
Let Thy con-gre-ga-tion es-cape trib-u-la-tion:

Sing prais-es to His name: He for-gets not His own.
Thou, Lord, wast at our side, all glo-ry be Thine!
Thy name be ev-er praised! O Lord, make us free! A-men.

TEXT: Netherlands Folk hymn; translated by Theodore Baker
MUSIC: Netherlands Folk song; arranged by Edward Kremser
Last stanza harmonization by Dick Bolks

KREMSER
12.11.12.11.

562 Rejoice, Ye Pure in Heart

Be glad in the Lord, and rejoice, ye righteous: and shout for joy. Ps. 32:11

1. Re - joice, ye pure in heart, Re - joice, give thanks, and sing.
2. With all the an - gel choirs, With all the saints on earth,
3. Yes, on through life's long path, Still chant - ing as we go;
4. Still lift your stan - dard high, Still march in firm ar - ray;

Your fes - tal ban - ner wave on high, The cross of Christ your King.
Pour out the strains of joy and bliss, True rap - ture, no - blest mirth!
From youth to age, by night and day, In glad - ness and in woe.
As war - riors through the dark - ness toil Till dawns the gold - en day.

Refrain

Re - joice, re - joice, Re - joice, give thanks, and sing! A - men.
Re - joice, re - joice,

TEXT: Edward H. Plumptre
MUSIC: Arthur H. Messiter

MARION
S.M. with Refrain

563 Count Your Blessings

Many, O Lord my God, are Thy wonderful works which Thou hast done. Ps. 40:5

1. When up - on life's bil - lows you are tem - pest tossed, When you are dis -
2. Are you ev - er bur - dened with a load of care? Does the cross seem
3. When you look at oth - ers with their lands and gold, Think that Christ has
4. So, a - mid the con - flict, wheth - er great or small, Do not be dis-

TEXT: Johnson Oatman, Jr.
MUSIC: Edwin O. Excell

BLESSINGS
11.11.11.11. with Refrain

564 We Are So Blessed

God . . . hath blessed us with all spiritual blessings . . . in Christ. Eph. 1:3

We are so blessed by the gifts from Your hand, I just
so blessed, we just can't find a way or the

can't un-der-stand Why You've loved us so much. We are Lord, for Your
words that can say, Thank You

touch. When we're emp-ty You fill us 'Til we o-ver-

flow, When we're hun-gry You feed us and cause us to

know; We are so blessed, Take what we have to

TEXT and MUSIC: William J. Gaither, Gloria Gaither, Greg Nelson;
arranged by Keith Phillips

SO BLESSED
Irregular meter

bring; Take it all, ev-'ry-thing, Lord, we love You so much.

We Thank You, Lord 565

Unto Thee, O God, do we give thanks . . . for . . . Thy name is near. Ps. 75:1

4 Part Canon

1. We thank You for Your love, We thank You for Your care,
2. We thank You for Your Son, We thank You for Your Word,

We thank You for Your faith-ful-ness, We thank You, Lord.
We thank You for e-ter-nal life, We thank You, Lord.

TEXT and MUSIC: Gerald S. Henderson

COLIN
6.6.8.4.

© *Copyright 1986 WORD MUSIC (a div. of WORD, INC.). All Rights Reserved. International Copyright Secured.*

For Health and Strength 566

God . . . giveth us richly all things to enjoy. 1 Tim. 6:17

4 Part Canon

For health and strength, and dai-ly food, We praise Thy Name, O Lord.

TEXT and MUSIC: Traditional Dutch Folk song

GRACE
Irregular meter

567 Another Year Is Dawning

So teach us to number our days, that we may apply our hearts unto wisdom. Ps. 90:12

1. An - oth - er year is dawn - ing: Dear Fa - ther, let it be,
2. An - oth - er year of mer - cies, Of faith - ful - ness and grace;
3. An - oth - er year of serv - ice, Of wit - ness for Thy love;

In work - ing or in wait - ing, An - oth - er year with Thee;
An - oth - er year of glad - ness In the shin - ing of Thy face;
An - oth - er year of train - ing For ho - lier work a - bove.

An - oth - er year of prog - ress, An - oth - er year of praise,
An - oth - er year of lean - ing Up - on Thy lov - ing breast;
An - oth - er year is dawn - ing: Dear Fa - ther, let it be,

An - oth - er year of prov - ing Thy pres - ence all the days.
An - oth - er year of trust - ing, Of qui - et, hap - py rest.
On earth or else in heav - en, An - oth - er year for Thee. A - men.

TEXT: Frances Ridley Havergal
MUSIC: Samuel S. Wesley
A higher setting may be found at No. 277

AURELIA
7.6.7.6.D.

God of the Ages 568

From everlasting to everlasting, Thou art God. Ps. 90:2

Unison

1. God of the a - ges, His - to - ry's Mak - er,
2. God of this morn - ing, Glad-ly Your chil - dren
3. God of to - mor - row, Strong O-ver - com - er,
4. Lord of past a - ges, Lord of this morn - ing,

Plan-ning our path - way, Hold - ing us fast,
Wor-ship be - fore You, Trust-ing-ly bow:
Princ-es of dark - ness Own Your com-mand:
Lord of the fu - ture, Help us, we pray:

Shap-ing in mer - cy All that con - cerns us:
Teach us to know You Al - ways a - mong us,
What then can harm us? We are Your peo - ple,
Teach us to trust You, Love and o - bey You,

Fa - ther, we praise You, Lord of the past.
Qui-et - ly sov - 'reign— Lord of our now.
Now and for - ev - er Kept by Your hand.
Crown You each mo - ment Lord of to - day.

TEXT: Margaret Clarkson
MUSIC: Traditional Gaelic melody; arranged by Tom Fettke

BUNESSAN
5.5.5.4.D.

569 Battle Hymn of the Republic

We are more than conquerors through Him that loved us. Rom. 8:37

1. Mine eyes have seen the glo - ry of the com - ing of the Lord,
2. I have seen Him in the watch-fires of a hun-dred cir-cling camps,
3. He has sound - ed forth the trum - pet that shall nev - er sound re-treat,
4. In the beau - ty of the lil - ies Christ was born a - cross the sea,

He is tramp-ling out the vin - tage where the grapes of wrath are stored;
They have build - ed Him an al - tar in the eve - ning dews and damps;
He is sift - ing out the hearts of men be - fore His judg-ment seat;
With a glo - ry in His bos - om that trans - fig - ures you and me;

He hath loosed the fate - ful light-ning of His ter - ri - ble swift sword—
I can read His right-eous sen - tence by the dim and flar - ing lamps—
O be swift, my soul, to an - swer Him! be ju - bi - lant, my feet!
As He died to make men ho - ly, let us live to make men free,

Refrain

His truth is march-ing on.
His day is march-ing on.
Our God is march-ing on.
While God is march-ing on.

Glo - ry! glo-ry, hal - le - lu - jah! Glo - ry!

TEXT: Julia Ward Howe
MUSIC: Traditional American melody;
Descant and arrangement of last Refrain by Eugene Thomas

BATTLE HYMN
15.15.15.6. with Refrain

570

ONE NATION, UNDER GOD
A Medley

Suggested Hymn Stanzas

To facilitate an uninterrupted flow from stanza to stanza,
the suggested stanzas have been marked with an arrow: ▶
My Country, 'Tis of Thee, stanzas 1, 4
America, the Beautiful, stanza 1
God of Our Fathers, stanzas 1, 2, 4

WORSHIP LEADER: Righteousness exalteth a nation; but sin is a reproach to any people.
PEOPLE: Blessed is the nation whose God is the Lord.

Prov. 14:34; Ps. 33:12.

571 My Country, 'Tis of Thee

Righteousness exalteth a nation: but sin is a reproach to any people. Prov. 14:34

1. My coun-try, 'tis of thee, Sweet land of lib-er-ty, Of thee I sing: Land where my fa-thers died, Land of the pil-grim's pride, From ev-'ry moun-tain side Let free-dom ring!
2. My na-tive coun-try, thee, Land of the no-ble free, Thy name I love: I love thy rocks and rills, Thy woods and tem-pled hills; My heart with rap-ture thrills Like that a-bove.
3. Let mu-sic swell the breeze, And ring from all the trees Sweet free-dom's song: Let mor-tal tongues a-wake, Let all that breathe par-take; Let rocks their si-lence break, The sound pro-long.
4. Our fa-thers' God, to Thee, Au-thor of lib-er-ty, To Thee we sing: Long may our land be bright With free-dom's ho-ly light; Pro-tect us by Thy might, Great God, our King!

Opt. segue to "America, the Beautiful"

TEXT: Samuel F. Smith
MUSIC: *Thesaurus Musicus*, c. 1745

AMERICA
6.6.4.6.6.6.6.4.

America, the Beautiful 572

Honour all men . . . Fear God. 1 Pet. 2:17

1. O beau-ti-ful for spa-cious skies, For am-ber waves of grain,
2. O beau-ti-ful for pil-grim feet, Whose stern im-pas-sioned stress
3. O beau-ti-ful for he-roes proved In lib-er-at-ing strife,
4. O beau-ti-ful for pa-triot dream That sees be-yond the years

For pur-ple moun-tain maj-es-ties A-bove the fruit-ed plain!
A thor-ough-fare for free-dom beat A-cross the wil-der-ness!
Who more than self their coun-try loved, And mer-cy more than life!
Thine al-a-bas-ter cit-ies gleam, Un-dimmed by hu-man tears!

A-mer-i-ca! A-mer-i-ca! God shed His grace on thee,
A-mer-i-ca! A-mer-i-ca! God mend thine ev-ery flaw,
A-mer-i-ca! A-mer-i-ca! May God thy gold re-fine,
A-mer-i-ca! A-mer-i-ca! God shed His grace on thee,

And crown thy good with broth-er-hood From sea to shin-ing sea! *sea!
Con-firm thy soul in self-con-trol, Thy lib-er-ty in law!
Till all suc-cess be no-ble-ness, And ev-ery gain di-vine!
And crown thy good with broth-er-hood From sea to shin-ing sea!

*Opt. segue to "God of Our Fathers"

TEXT: Katharine Lee Bates
MUSIC: Samuel A. Ward

MATERNA
C.M.D.

573 God of Our Fathers

Our fathers trusted in Thee . . . and Thou didst deliver them. Ps. 22:4

Trumpets
before each stanza

1. God of our fa - thers, whose al-might-y hand
2. Thy love di - vine hath led us in the past,
3. From war's a - larms, from dead-ly pes - ti - lence,
4. Re - fresh Thy peo - ple on their toil-some way,

Leads forth in beau - ty all the star - ry band
In this free land by Thee our lot is cast;
Be Thy strong arm our ev - er - sure de - fense;
Lead us from night to nev - er - end - ing day;

Of shin - ing worlds in splen - dor thru the skies,
Be Thou our Rul - er, Guard - ian, Guide, and Stay,
Thy true re - li - gion in our hearts in - crease,
Fill all our lives with love and grace di - vine,

Our grate - ful songs be - fore Thy throne a - rise.
Thy Word our law, Thy paths our cho - sen way.
Thy boun - teous good - ness nour - ish us in peace.
And glo - ry, laud, and praise be ev - er Thine! A - men.

TEXT: Daniel C. Roberts
MUSIC: George W. Warren
Last stanza harmonization by Kurt Kaiser

NATIONAL HYMN
10.10.10.10.

Optional last stanza harmonization   Unison

4. Re - fresh Thy peo - ple on their toil-some way, Lead us from night to nev - er - end - ing day; Fill all our lives with love and grace di - vine, And glo - ry, laud, and praise be ev - er Thine!

A - men, A - men.

The end of "ONE NATION, UNDER GOD—A Medley"

574 If My People's Hearts Are Humbled

If My people . . . shall humble themselves . . . then will I . . . heal their land. 2 Chr. 7:14

1. If My peo-ple's hearts are hum-bled, If they pray and seek My face;
2. Then My eyes will see their sor - row, Then My ears will hear their plea.

If they turn a - way from e - vil, I will not with - hold My grace.
If My peo - ple's hearts are hum-bled I will set their na - tion free.

I will hear their prayers from heav - en; I will par - don ev - 'ry sin.
If My peo - ple's hearts are hum-bled, If they pray and seek My face;

If My peo - ple's hearts are hum-bled, I will sure - ly heal their land.
If they turn a - way from e - vil, I will not with - hold My grace.

TEXT: Claire Cloninger; based on 2 Chronicles 7:14
MUSIC: John Zundel
A higher setting may be found at No. 268; Alternate tune: AUSTRIAN HYMN at No. 278

BEECHER
8.7.8.7.D.

Eternal Father, Strong to Save 575

He bringeth them unto their desired haven. Oh that men would praise the Lord. Ps. 107:30-31

1. E - ter - nal Fa - ther, strong to save, Whose arm hath bound the
2. O Christ, the Lord of hill and plain O'er which our traf - fic
3. O Spir - it, whom the Fa - ther sent To spread a - broad the
4. O Trin - i - ty of love and power, Our breth-ren shield in

rest - less wave, Who bids the might - y o - cean deep Its
runs a - main By moun - tain pass or val - ley low: Wher-
fir - ma - ment: O Wind of heav - en, by Thy might Save
dan - ger's hour; From rock and tem - pest, fire and foe, Pro -

own ap - point - ed lim - its keep: O hear us when we
ev - er, Lord, our breth - ren go, Pro - tect them by Thy
all who dare the ea - gle's flight, And keep them by Thy
tect them where - so - e'er they go; Thus ev - er - more shall

cry to Thee For those in per - il on the sea.
guard - ing hand From ev - ery per - il on the land.
watch - ful care From ev - ery per - il in the air.
rise to Thee Glad praise from air and land and sea. A - men.

TEXT: William Whiting, stanzas 1, 4; Robert Nelson Spencer, stanzas 2, 3
MUSIC: John Bacchus Dykes

MELITA
8.8.8.8.8.8.

Stanzas 2 and 3 from The Hymnal 1940, Copyright The Church Pension Fund. Used by Permission.

576 The Star-Spangled Banner

As free . . . but as the servants of God. 1 Pet. 2:16

1. O say, can you see, by the dawn's ear-ly light, What so
2. O thus be it ev - er, when free men shall stand Be -

proud - ly we hailed at the twi - light's last gleam - ing, Whose broad
tween their loved homes and the war's des - o - la - tion! Blest with

stripes and bright stars, thro' the per - il - ous fight, O'er the ram-parts we
vic - t'ry and peace, may the heav'n-res - cued land Praise the Pow'r that hath

watched, were so gal-lant-ly stream-ing? And the rock-ets' red glare, the bombs
made and pre-served us a na - tion! Then con-quer we must, when our

burst-ing in air, Gave proof thro' the night that our flag was still
cause it is just; And this be our mot - to: "In God is our

TEXT: Francis Scott Key
MUSIC: Attributed to John Stafford Smith

NATIONAL ANTHEM
Irregular meter

there. O say, does that star span-gled ban-ner yet wave
trust!" And the star-span-gled ban-ner in tri-umph shall wave

O'er the land of the free and the home of the brave?
O'er the land of the free and the home of the brave!

Blessed the Nation 577

Happy is that people, whose God is the Lord. Ps. 144:15

1. Bless-ed the na-tion whose God is the Lord; Bless-ed the
2. He is a lov-ing and mer-ci-ful God; We are but
3. Bless-ed the na-tion whose God is the Lord; Bless-ed the

land where He reigns. Bless-ed the peo-ple who
chil-dren of dust. He is our Re-fuge, our
land where He reigns. Bless-ed the peo-ple who

trust in His Word, And wor-ship His glo-ri-ous name.
Strength and our Shield; And He is the Lord that we trust.
trust in His Word, And wor-ship His glo-ri-ous name.

TEXT: Elizabeth de Gravelles; based on Psalm 144:15
MUSIC: Joseph Barlowe

CARMEL
10.7.10.8.

578 All Things Bright and Beautiful

God saw every thing that He had made, and, behold, it was very good. Gen. 1:31

Refrain: All things bright and beau-ti-ful, All crea-tures great and small, And

all things wise and won-der-ful; The Lord God made them all. *rit. last time* *Fine*

1. Each lit-tle flow'r that o-pens up, Each lit-tle bird that sings, He
2. The cold wind in the win-ter-time, The pleas-ant sum-mer sun, The

made their glow-ing col-ors and He made their ti-ny wings. The
ripe fruits in the gar-den now, He made them ev-'ry-one; He

pur-ple head-ed moun-tain, The riv-er run-ning by, The
gave us eyes to see them all, And lips that we might tell How

TEXT: Cecil F. Alexander, altered
MUSIC: Sonny Salsbury; arranged by Lee Herrington

SALSBURY
Irregular meter

D.C. for Refrain

sun - set and the morn-ing light That bright-ens up the sky.
great is the Al - might-y God Who has made all things well.

Jesus Loves Me 579

Christ also hath loved us, and hath given Himself for us. Eph. 5:2

1. Je - sus loves me! this I know, For the Bi - ble tells me so; Lit - tle
2. Je - sus loves me! He who died Heav-en's gate to o - pen wide; He will
3. Je - sus loves me! He will stay Close be-side me all the way; He's pre-

Refrain

ones to Him be-long, They are weak but He is strong. Yes, Je-sus loves me!
wash a - way my sin, Let His lit - tle child come in.
pared a home for me, And some day His face I'll see.

Yes, Je - sus loves me! Yes, Je - sus loves me! The Bi - ble tells me so.

TEXT: Anna B. Warner, altered
MUSIC: William B. Bradbury

JESUS LOVES ME
7.7.7.7. with Refrain

580 Jesus Loves the Little Children

Suffer little children, and forbid them not, to come unto Me. Matt. 19:14

Je - sus loves the lit - tle chil - dren, All the chil-dren of the

world. Red and yel-low, black and white, They are pre-cious in His sight—

Je - sus loves the lit - tle chil - dren of the world.

TEXT: Reverend C. H. Woolston
MUSIC: George F. Root

CHILDREN
8.7.7.7.11.

581 Commit Thy Way

Commit thy way unto the Lord; trust also in Him; and He shall bring it to pass. Ps. 37:5

Unison

Com - mit thy way un - to the Lord, trust al - so in Him. Com-mit thy

TEXT: Psalm 37:5
MUSIC: Kurt Kaiser

COMMIT THY WAY
Irregular meter

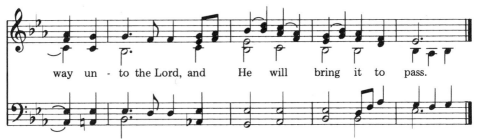

Reach Your Hand 582

Love one another with a pure heart fervently. 1 Pet. 1:22

TEXT: Gerald DiPego, stanzas 1, 2; Kurt Kaiser, stanza 3
MUSIC: Kurt Kaiser

REACH YOUR HAND
L.M.

583 The Wise May Bring Their Learning

God is not unrighteous to forget your work and labour of love . . . toward His name. Heb. 6:10

1. The wise may bring their learn - ing, The rich may bring their wealth,
2. We'll bring Him hearts that love Him; We'll bring Him thank-ful praise,
3. We'll bring the lit - tle du - ties We have to do each day;

And some may bring their great - ness, And some bring strength and health;
And young souls meek - ly striv - ing To walk in ho - ly ways:
We'll try our best to please Him, At home, at school, at play:

We, too, would bring our treas - ures To of - fer to the King;
And these shall be the treas - ures We of - fer to the King,
And bet - ter are these treas - ures To of - fer to our King,

We have no wealth or learn - ing: What shall we chil - dren bring?
And these are gifts that e - ven The poor - est child may bring.
Than rich - est gifts with - out them; Yet these a child may bring.

TEXT: Anonymous; from *The Book of Praise for Children*, 1881
MUSIC: Joe E. Parks

ELDER MOUNTAIN
7.6.7.6.D.

It Is Good to Sing Thy Praises 584

It is a good thing to give thanks unto the Lord. Ps. 92:1

1. It   is good to   sing Thy prais-es And   to thank Thee, O   Most High,
2. Thou has filled my heart with glad-ness Thro the works Thy hands have wrought;
3. But the good shall live   be-fore Thee, Plant-ed in   Thy dwell-ing place,

Show-ing forth Thy lov-ing-kind-ness When the morn-ing   lights the sky.
Thou hast made my life vic-to-rious, Great Thy works and deep Thy thought.
Fruit-ful trees and   ev-er ver-dant, Nour-ished by Thy   bound-less grace.

It   is good when night is fall-ing   Of Thy faith-ful-ness to tell,
Thou, O Lord, on high ex-alt-ed,   Reign-est ev-er-more in might;
In   His good-ness   to the right-eous God His right-eous-ness dis-plays;

While with sweet, me-lo-dious prais-es Songs of ad-o-ra-tion swell.
All   Thy en-e-mies shall per-ish, Sin   be ban-ished from Thy sight.
God   my Rock, my Strength, my Ref-uge, Just and true are   all His ways. A-men.

TEXT: *The Psalter;* based on Psalm 92
MUSIC: Leavitt's *The Christian Lyre,* 1831; attributed to Wolfgang A. Mozart;
        arranged by Hubert P. Main
        A lower setting may be found at No. 377

ELLESDIE
8.7.8.7.D.

585 Brethren, We Have Met to Worship

Worship the Lord in the beauty of holiness. 1 Chr. 16:29

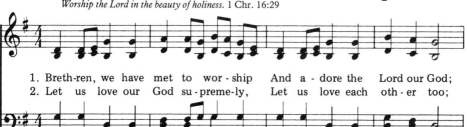

1. Breth-ren, we have met to wor-ship And a-dore the Lord our God;
2. Let us love our God su-preme-ly, Let us love each oth-er too;

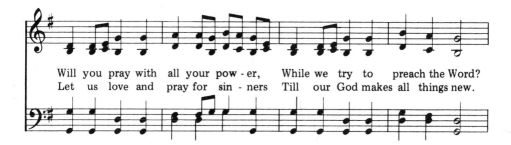

Will you pray with all your pow-er, While we try to preach the Word?
Let us love and pray for sin-ners Till our God makes all things new.

All is vain un-less the Spir-it Of the Ho-ly One comes down;
Then He'll call us home to heav-en, At His ta-ble we'll sit down;

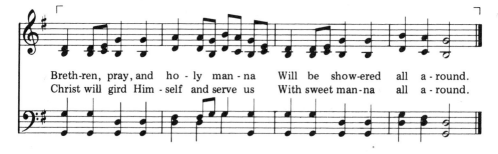

Breth-ren, pray, and ho-ly man-na Will be show-ered all a-round.
Christ will gird Him-self and serve us With sweet man-na all a-round.

TEXT: George Atkins
MUSIC: William Moore

HOLY MANNA
8.7.8.7.D.

Jesus, Stand Among Us 586

Jesus . . . stood in the midst, and saith . . . "Peace be unto you." John 20:19

1. Je - sus, stand a - mong us In Thy ris - en power;
2. Breathe the Ho - ly Spir - it In - to ev - ery heart;

Let this time of wor - ship Be a hal-lowed hour.
Bid the fears and sor - rows From each soul de - part. A - men.

TEXT: William Pennefather
MUSIC: Friedrich Filitz

BEMERTON
6.5.6.5.

All Praise to Our Redeeming Lord 587

The whole body . . . joined together . . . maketh increase . . . unto . . . edifying . . . in love. Eph. 4:16

1. All praise to our re - deem-ing Lord, Who joins us by His grace
2. He bids us build each oth - er up; And gath-ered in - to one,

And bids us, each to each re-stored, To - geth-er seek His face.
To our high call-ing's glo-rious hope, We hand in hand go on. A - men.

TEXT: Charles Wesley
MUSIC: Carl G. Gläser; arranged by Lowell Mason
A higher setting may be found at No. 76

AZMON
C.M.

588 We Have Come into His House

They came and held Him by the feet, and worshipped Him. Matt. 28:9

1. We have come in-to His house and gath-ered in His name to wor - ship Him. We have come in - to His house and gath -ered in His name to wor - ship Him. We have come in-to His house and gath-ered in His name to wor - ship Christ the Lord. Wor - ship Him, Christ the Lord.

2. Let's for - get a - bout our-selves and mag-ni - fy His name and wor - ship Him. Let's for - get a - bout our - selves and mag - ni - fy His name and wor - ship Him. Let's for - get a-bout our-selves and mag - ni - fy His name and wor - ship Christ the Lord. Wor - ship Him, Christ the Lord.

TEXT and MUSIC: Bruce Ballinger

WORSHIP HIM
Irregular meter

Come into His Presence 589

Come before His presence with singing. Ps. 100:2

4 Part Canon

1. Come in-to His pres-ence sing-ing Al - le-lu-ia,   al - le-lu-ia,   al - le-lu-ia.
2. Come in-to His pres-ence sing-ing Je - sus is Lord, Je - sus is Lord, Je - sus is Lord.
3. Praise the Lord together singing Worthy the Lamb, worthy the Lamb, worthy the Lamb.
4. Praise the Lord to-geth-er sing-ing Glo - ry to God, glo - ry to God, glo - ry to God.

TEXT and MUSIC: Source unknown

HIS PRESENCE
8.4.4.4.

This Is the Day 590

This is the day which the Lord hath made; we will rejoice and be glad in it. Ps. 118:24

This is the day, this is the day that the Lord hath made, that the Lord hath made.

We will re-joice, we will re-joice and be glad in it, and be glad in it.

This is the day that the Lord hath made; We will re-joice and be glad in it.

This is the day, this is the day that the Lord hath made.

TEXT and MUSIC: Les Garrett; adapted from Psalm 118:24

THIS IS THE DAY
Irregular meter

591 Come Let Us Reason

Though your sins be as scarlet, they shall be as white as snow. Isa. 1:18

"Come, let us rea - son to - geth-er," that's what God says. "Come, let us rea - son to - geth - er," says the Lord. Lord. "Tho' your sins be as scar - let, they shall be as white as snow; Tho' they be red as crim - son, they shall be as wool."

D.C. al Fine

TEXT and MUSIC: Ken Medema; arranged by David Allen

COME LET US REASON
Irregular meter

In This Quiet Moment 592

In quietness and in confidence shall be your strength. Isa. 30:15

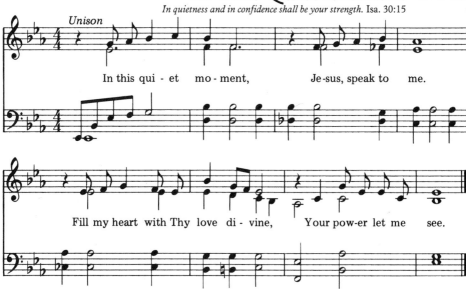

In this qui-et mo-ment, Je-sus, speak to me.

Fill my heart with Thy love di-vine, Your pow-er let me see.

TEXT and MUSIC: Larry Mayfield

QUIET MOMENT
Irregular meter

O Worship the Lord 593

O worship the Lord in the beauty of holiness. Ps. 96:9

O wor-ship the Lord in the beau-ty of ho-li-ness;

Serve Him with glad - ness, all the earth. A - men.

TEXT: Psalm 96:9
MUSIC: Robert G. McCutchan

McCUTCHAN
Irregular meter

594 The Lord Is in His Holy Temple

In Thy fear will I worship toward Thy holy temple. Ps. 5:7

The Lord is in His ho-ly tem - ple, The Lord is in His ho-ly
tem - ple; Let all the earth keep si-lence, Let all the earth keep si - lence be-
fore Him, Keep si-lence, keep si-lence be - fore Him. A - men.

TEXT: Habakkuk 2:20
MUSIC: George F. Root

QUAM DILECTA
Irregular meter

595 Now to the King of Heaven

To God only wise, be glory through Jesus Christ for ever. Rom. 16:27

Now to the King of heav'n Your cheer - ful voic - es raise; To
Him be glo - ry giv'n, Pow'r, maj - es - ty and praise; Wide as He reigns His

TEXT: Isaac Watts and Philip Doddridge
MUSIC: *The Parish Choir*, 1851

ST. JOHN
6.6.6.6.8.8.

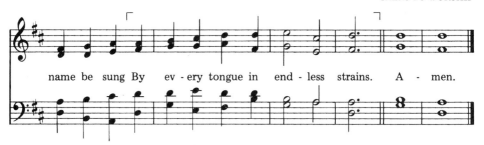

name be sung By ev-ery tongue in end-less strains. A - men.

Praise Ye the Name of the Lord 596

Sing forth the honour of His name: make His praise glorious. Ps. 66:2

Choir Unison

Praise ye the name of the Lord of Hosts. Praise Him,

praise Him, all ye peo - ple. Let all the na - tions

praise the Lord.

keyboard play cued notes only

Sing Parts

ff Praise ye the Lord!

rit. e rall. *fff*

Let all the na - tions praise the Lord!

TEXT and MUSIC: Gordon Young

PRAISE YE
Irregular meter

597 Christ, We Do All Adore Thee

Worthy is the Lamb . . . to receive . . . honour, and glory, and blessing. Rev. 5:12

Christ, we do all a - dore Thee, and we do praise Thee for - ev - er;

Christ, we do all a - dore Thee, and we do praise Thee for - ev - er,

For on the ho - ly cross hast Thou the world from sin re - deem - ed.

Christ, we do all a - dore Thee, and we do praise Thee for - ev - er.

Instruments

Christ, we do all a - dore Thee!

*These 2 measures may be omitted.

TEXT: *Adoramus Te*, English version by Theodore Baker
MUSIC: Theodore Dubois; from *The Seven Last Words of Christ*

ADORE THEE
Irregular meter

Cast Thy Burden upon the Lord 598

Cast thy burden upon the Lord, and He shall sustain thee. Ps. 55:22

Cast thy bur-den up-on the Lord, and He shall sus-tain thee; He nev-er will suf-fer the right-eous to fall: He is at thy right hand.

Optional ending

Thy mer-cy, Lord, is great and far a-bove the heav'ns: Let none be made a-sham-ed that wait up-on Thee. A-men.

TEXT: Based on Psalm 55:22
MUSIC: Felix Mendelssohn; from *Elijah*

CAST THY BURDEN
Irregular meter

599 Spoken Calls to Worship

1 The earth is the Lord's, and the fulness thereof; the world, and they that dwell therein. Lift up your heads, O ye gates; even lift them up, ye everlasting doors; and the King of glory shall come in. Who is this King of glory? The Lord of hosts, He is the King of glory. Ps. 24:1, 9-10

2 O come, let us sing unto the Lord: let us make a joyful noise to the Rock of our salvation. Let us come before His presence with thanksgiving, and make a joyful noise unto Him with psalms. Ps. 95:1-2

3 O come, let us worship and bow down: let us kneel before the Lord our Maker. For He is our God; and we are the people of His pasture, and the sheep of His hand. Ps. 95:6-7

4 Make a joyful noise unto the Lord, all ye lands. Serve the Lord with gladness: come before His presence with singing. Know ye that the Lord He is God: it is He that hath made us, and not we ourselves; we are His people, and the sheep of His pasture. Ps. 100:1-3

5 Enter into His gates with thanksgiving, and into His courts with praise: be thankful unto Him, and bless His name. For the Lord is good: His mercy is everlasting; and His truth endureth to all generations. Ps. 100:4-5

6 Praise ye the Lord. Praise God in His sanctuary: praise Him in the firmament of His power. Praise Him for His mighty acts: praise Him according to His excellent greatness. Let every thing that hath breath praise the Lord. Praise ye the Lord. Ps. 150:1-2, 6

7 Come unto Me, all ye that labour and are heavy laden, and I will give you rest. Take My yoke upon you, and learn of Me; for I am meek and lowly in heart: and ye shall find rest unto your soul. For My yoke is easy, and My burden is light. Matt. 11:28-30

8 Worthy is the Lamb that was slain to receive power, and riches, and wisdom, and strength, and honour, and glory, and blessing. Blessing, and honour, and glory, and power, be unto Him that sitteth upon the throne, and unto the Lamb for ever and ever. Rev. 5:12-13

9 I will sing of the mercies of the Lord for ever: with my mouth will I make known Thy faithfulness to all generations. For I have said, Mercy shall be built up for ever: Thy faithfulness shalt Thou establish in the very heavens. Ps. 89:1-2

10 Be still, and know that I am God: I will be exalted among the heathen. I will be exalted in the earth. Ps. 46:10

11 Give unto the Lord the glory due unto His name; worship the Lord in the beauty of holiness. Ps. 29:2

12 It is a good thing to give thanks unto the Lord, and to sing praises unto Thy name, O most High: to shew forth Thy lovingkindness in the morning, and Thy faithfulness every night. Ps. 92:1-2

13 Thou art my God, and I will praise Thee: Thou art my God, I will exalt Thee. O give thanks unto the Lord; for He is good: for His mercy endureth for ever. Ps. 118:28-29

14 But the hour cometh, and now is, when the true worshippers shall worship the Father in spirit and in truth: for the Father seeketh such to worship Him. God is a Spirit: and they that worship Him must worship Him in spirit and in truth. John 4:23-24

If You Will Only Let God Guide You 600

Our soul waiteth for the Lord: He is our Help and our Shield. Ps. 33:20

1. If you will on - ly let God guide you, And hope in
2. On - ly be still, and wait His lei - sure In cheer - ful
3. Sing, pray, and swerve not from His ways, But do your

Him thru all your ways, What-ev - er comes, He'll stand be - side you,
hope, with heart con - tent To take what - e'er the Fa - ther's plea-sure
part in con-science true; Trust His rich prom - is - es of grace,

To bear you thru the e - vil days; Who trusts in God's un-
And all dis - cern - ing love have sent; Nor doubt our in - most
So shall they be ful - filled in you; God hears the call of

chang - ing love Builds on the rock that can - not move.
wants are known To Him who chose us for His own.
those in need, The souls that trust in Him in - deed.

TEXT: Georg Neumark; translated by Catherine Winkworth, altered
MUSIC: Georg Neumark

NEUMARK
9.8.9.8.8.8.

601 Lord, Dismiss Us with Thy Blessing

Thy blessing is upon Thy people. Ps. 3:8

1. Lord, dis - miss us with Thy bless-ing, Fill our hearts with joy and peace;
2. Thanks we give and ad - o - ra - tion For Thy gos - pel's joy -ful sound;

Let us each, Thy love pos-sess - ing, Tri - umph in re - deem-ing grace.
May the fruits of Thy sal - va - tion In our hearts and lives a - bound.

O re - fresh us, O re - fresh us, Trav-eling through this wil-der-ness.
Ev - er faith-ful, ev - er faith-ful To the truth may we be found. A - men.

TEXT: John Fawcett, altered
MUSIC: Tattersall's *Psalmody*, 1794

SICILIAN MARINERS
8.7.8.7.8.7.

602 God Be with You

The grace of our Lord Jesus Christ be with you. 1 Thess. 5:28

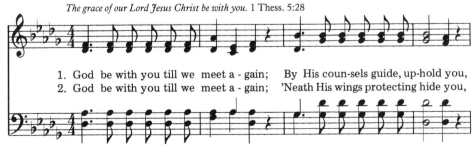

1. God be with you till we meet a - gain; By His coun-sels guide, up-hold you,
2. God be with you till we meet a - gain; 'Neath His wings protecting hide you,

TEXT: Jeremiah E. Rankin
MUSIC: William G. Tomer

GOD BE WITH YOU
Irregular meter

With His sheep se-cure-ly fold you; God be with you till we meet a - gain.
Dai - ly man-na still pro - vide you; God be with you till we meet a - gain.

The Lord Whom We Love 603

. . . For the perfecting of the saints, for the work of the ministry. Eph. 4:12

The Lord whom we love, whom we wor-ship and a - dore, We will serve through-

out this com-ing week. He it is who binds us to - geth-er,

And He it is who sends us a - part, To be God's

peo-ple, be God's peo-ple, A - men, a - men.

TEXT and MUSIC: Kurt Kaiser

BROOKS
Irregular meter

604 Savior, Again to Thy Dear Name

The Lord will bless His people with peace. Ps. 29:11

1. Sav - ior, a - gain to Thy dear name we raise With one ac - cord our
2. Grant us Thy peace up - on our home-ward way; With Thee be - gan, with

part - ing hymn of praise; Once more we bless Thee ere our wor-ship cease;
Thee shall end the day; Guard Thou the lips from sin, the hearts from shame,

With ea - ger hearts we wait Thy word of peace.
That in this house have called up - on Thy name. A - men.

TEXT: John Ellerton
MUSIC: Edward J. Hopkins; arranged by Joseph Barlowe

ELLERS
10.10.10.10.

Arr. © 1986 WORD MUSIC (a div. of WORD, INC.). All Rights Reserved. International Copyright Secured.

605 When This Song of Praise Shall Cease

Mercy unto you, and peace, and love, be multiplied. Jude 2

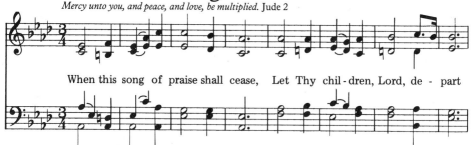

When this song of praise shall cease, Let Thy chil-dren, Lord, de - part

TEXT: William Bradbury, altered
MUSIC: Louis M. Gottschalk

MERCY
7.7.7.7.

With the bless-ing of Thy peace, And Thy love in ev-'ry heart. A - men.

Grace, Love and Fellowship 606

Grace . . . love . . . and . . . communion . . . be with you all. 2 Cor. 13:14

Unison

May the   grace of Christ, our Sav - ior,   and the   love   of   God, our

Fa - ther, and the   fel - low - ship of the   Spir - it   be   with   us.

1

May the   us   for - ev - er,   and

2

ev - er,   for - ev - er-more, A - men.

rit.

TEXT and MUSIC: Tom Fettke; based on 2 Cor. 13:14

CANE PEAK
Irregular meter

607 The Lord Bless You and Keep You

The Lord bless thee, and keep thee . . . and give thee peace. Num. 6:24, 26

TEXT: Numbers 6:24-26
MUSIC: Peter C. Lutkin

BENEDICTION
Irregular meter

*The "Amens" may be used separately. Bass begins with first "Amen" on the downbeat of the measure (cued half-note).

May the Grace of Christ, Our Savior 608

The grace of our Lord Jesus Christ be with you all. Rev. 22:21

1. May the grace of Christ, our Sav - ior, And the Fa - ther's bound-less love,
2. Thus we may a - bide in un - ion With each oth - er and the Lord,

With the Ho - ly Spir - it's fa - vor, Rest up - on us from a - bove.
And pos - sess, in sweet com-mun-ion, Joys which earth can- not af - ford. A - men.

TEXT: John Newton
MUSIC: Ludwig van Beethoven

SARDIS
8.7.8.7.

609 Lord, Let Us Now Depart in Peace

Peace be to thee. 3 John 14

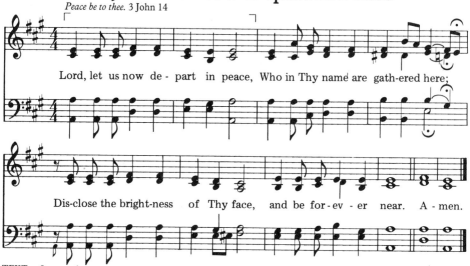

Lord, let us now de-part in peace, Who in Thy name are gath-ered here;

Dis-close the bright-ness of Thy face, and be for-ev-er near. A-men.

TEXT: Source unknown
MUSIC: George Whelpton

DISMISSAL
Irregular meter

610 Go Now and Live for the Savior

Walk worthy of the Lord. Col. 1:10

Go now, and live for the Sav - ior; Go, may this

joy be your joy too. Go, may this pres-ence ev - er

guide you; Go, live this life the whole day through.

TEXT and MUSIC: Kurt Kaiser

GO NOW
8.8.9.8.

Now unto the King 611

Unto the King eternal, immortal, invisible, the only wise God, be honour. 1 Tim. 1:17

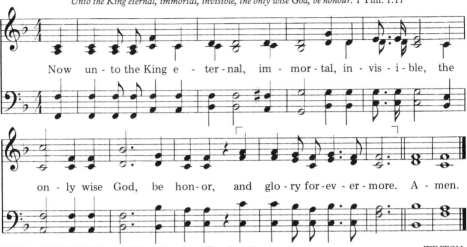

Now un-to the King e-ter-nal, im-mor-tal, in-vis-i-ble, the

on-ly wise God, be hon-or, and glo-ry for-ev-er-more. A-men.

TEXT and MUSIC: William David Young; based on 1 Timothy 1:17

WINTON
Irregular meter

© Copyright 1986 WORD MUSIC (a div. of WORD, INC.). All Rights Reserved. International Copyright Secured.

Benediction 612

The grace of the Lord Jesus Christ . . . be with you all. 2 Cor. 13:14

May the grace of the Lord, may the grace of the Lord Je-sus Christ,

mp — *mf*

and the love of God, and the fel-low-ship of the Ho-ly

the

sub. p   *ten.*

Spir-it, be with you all. A-men.

ten.

TEXT: 2 Corinthians 13:14
MUSIC: Ken Barker

PAUL
Irregular meter

© Copyright 1981 by WORD MUSIC (a div. of WORD, INC.). All Rights Reserved. International Copyright Secured.

613 Spoken Benedictions

1 The Lord bless thee, and keep thee: The Lord make His face shine upon thee, and be gracious unto thee: The Lord lift up His countenance upon thee, and give thee peace. Num. 6:24-26

2 The grace of the Lord Jesus Christ, and the love of God, and the communion of the Holy Ghost, be with you all. Amen. 2 Cor. 13:14

3 Now the God of peace, that brought again from the dead our Lord Jesus, that great Shepherd of the sheep, through the blood of the everlasting covenant, Make you perfect in every good work to do His will, working in you that which is well pleasing in His sight, through Jesus Christ; to whom be glory for ever and ever. Amen. Heb. 13:20-21

4 Now unto Him that is able to keep you from falling, and to present you faultless before the presence of His glory with exceeding joy, To the only wise God our Saviour, be glory and majesty, dominion and power, both now and ever. Amen. Jude 24-25

5 Now our Lord Jesus Christ Himself, and God, even our Father, which hath loved us, and hath given us everlasting consolation and good hope through grace, Comfort your hearts, and stablish you in every good word and work. 2 Thess. 2:16-17

6 But the God of all grace, who hath called us unto His eternal glory by Christ Jesus, after that ye have suffered a while, make you perfect, stablish, strengthen, settle you. To Him be glory and dominion for ever and ever. Amen. 1 Pet. 5:10-11

7 Now unto Him that is able to do exceeding abundantly above all that we ask or think, according to the power that worketh in us, Unto Him be glory in the church by Christ Jesus throughout all ages, world without end. Amen. Eph. 3:20-21

8 The grace of our Lord Jesus Christ be with you. Amen. 1 Thess. 5:28

9 Now unto the King eternal, immortal, invisible, the only wise God, be honour and glory for ever and ever. Amen. 1 Tim. 1:17

10 The grace of our Lord Jesus Christ be with you all. Amen. Rev. 22:21

Hear Our Prayer, O Lord 614

Hear our prayer, O Lord, Hear our prayer, O Lord;

In - cline Thine ear to us, And grant us Thy peace. A - men.

TEXT: Psalm 143:1
MUSIC: George Whelpton

Spirit Divine, Hear Our Prayer 615

Spir - it Di - vine, hear our prayer, And make our

hearts Your home; De - scend with all Your gra - cious

pow'r, Come, Ho - ly Spir - it, come. A - men.

TEXT: Andrew Reed
MUSIC: Bill Wolaver

616 Hear Our Prayer, O Heavenly Father

Hear our prayer, O heav'n-ly Fa-ther, for the dear Re-deem-er's sake. A - men.

TEXT: Traditional
MUSIC: Attributed to Frederic Chopin

617 Thou Wilt Keep Him in Perfect Peace

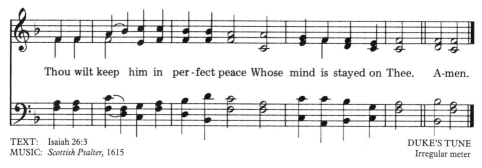

Thou wilt keep him in per-fect peace Whose mind is stayed on Thee. A-men.

TEXT: Isaiah 26:3
MUSIC: *Scottish Psalter*, 1615

DUKE'S TUNE
Irregular meter

618 Let the Words of My Mouth

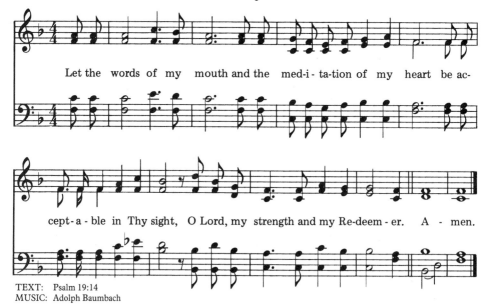

Let the words of my mouth and the med-i-ta-tion of my heart be ac-

cept-a-ble in Thy sight, O Lord, my strength and my Re-deem-er. A - men.

TEXT: Psalm 19:14
MUSIC: Adolph Baumbach

We Give You Thanks 619

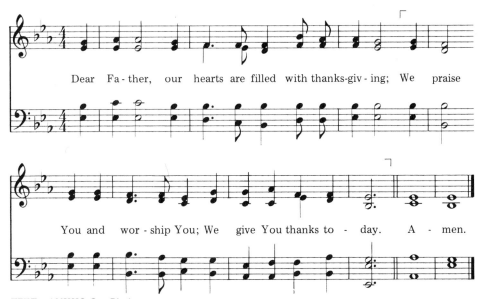

Dear Fa-ther, our hearts are filled with thanks-giv-ing; We praise You and wor-ship You; We give You thanks to-day. A-men.

TEXT and MUSIC: Gary Rhodes

We Give Thee But Thine Own 620

Of Thine own have we given Thee. 1 Chr. 29:14

1. We give Thee but Thine own, What-e'er the gift may be: All
2. May we Thy boun-ties thus As stew-ards true re-ceive, And

that we have is Thine a-lone, A trust, O Lord, from Thee.
glad-ly as Thou bless-est us, To Thee our first-fruits give. A-men.

TEXT: William W. How

MUSIC: Mason and Webb's *Cantica Laudis,* 1850

SCHUMANN
S.M.

621 God's Ways Are Wonderful

He which soweth bountifully shall reap also bountifully. 2 Cor. 9:6

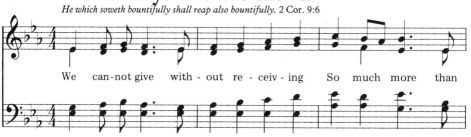

We can-not give with-out re-ceiv-ing So much more than

we have giv-en. God's ways are won-der-ful, God's ways are won-der-ful.

TEXT and MUSIC: Kurt Kaiser

GOD'S WAYS
Irregular meter

622 Gloria Patri

Give unto the Lord the glory due unto His name. Ps. 96:8

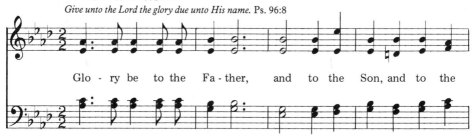

Glo - ry be to the Fa - ther, and to the Son, and to the

Ho - ly Ghost: as it was in the be - gin - ning, is

TEXT: *Gloria Patri;* Traditional, 2nd century
MUSIC: Christoph Meineke

MEINEKE
Irregular meter

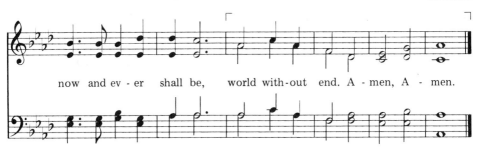

now and ev - er shall be, world with-out end. A - men, A - men.

Gloria Patri 623

Give unto the Lord the glory due unto His name. Ps. 96:8

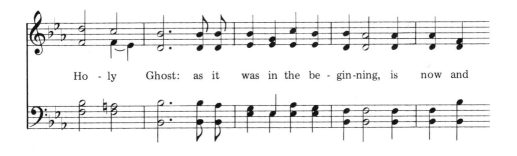

Glo - ry be to the Fa - ther, and to the Son, and to the

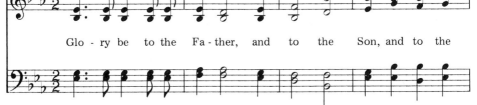

Ho - ly Ghost: as it was in the be - gin-ning, is now and

ev - er shall be, world with-out end. A - men, A - men.

TEXT: *Gloria Patri;* Traditional, 2nd century
MUSIC: Henry W. Greatorex

GREATOREX
Irregular meter

624 Doxology

Blessed be the God and Father of our Lord Jesus Christ, who hath blessed us. Eph. 1:3

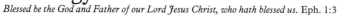

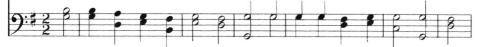

Praise God from whom all bless-ings flow; Praise Him, all crea-tures here be - low;

Praise Him a-bove, ye heav'n-ly host; Praise Fa-ther, Son and Ho-ly Ghost. A - men.

TEXT: Thomas Ken
MUSIC: *Genevan Psalter*, 1551; attributed to Louis Bourgeois

OLD HUNDREDTH
L.M.

625 Doxology

Blessed be the God and Father of our Lord Jesus Christ, who hath blessed us. Eph. 1:3

Praise God from whom all bless-ings flow; Praise Him, all crea - tures here be - low;

Praise Him a-bove, ye heav'n-ly host; Praise Fa-ther, Son and Ho-ly Ghost. A - men.

TEXT: Thomas Ken
MUSIC: *Genevan Psalter*, 1551; attributed to Louis Bourgeois

OLD HUNDREDTH
L.M.

Doxology 626

Blessed be the God and Father of our Lord Jesus Christ, who hath blessed us. Eph. 1:3

Praise God from whom all bless - ings flow; Praise Him all crea - tures here be - low. Praise Him a - bove ye heav-en-ly host; Praise Fa - ther, Son and Ho - ly Ghost. A - men.

TEXT: Thomas Ken
MUSIC: Jimmy Owens

FAIRHILL
L.M.

© *Copyright 1972 by LEXICON MUSIC, INC./ASCAP. All Rights Reserved. International Copyright Secured. Used by Permission.*

A Doxology Canon 627

Let every thing that hath breath praise the Lord. Ps. 150:6

4 Part Canon

Praise God from whom all bless-ings flow; Praise Him, all crea-tures here be - low; Praise

Him a-bove, ye   heav - n'ly   host; Praise Fa-ther, Son and   Ho - ly   Ghost.

TEXT: Thomas Ken
MUSIC: Gerald S. Henderson

PRAISE GOD
L.M.

Music © Copyright 1986 WORD MUSIC (a div. of WORD, INC.). All Rights Reserved. International Copyright Secured.

628 Amens

I. GENEVA — Louis Bourgeois

A — men.

II. TWOFOLD — Dresden

A - men, A — men.

III. TWOFOLD — Greek

A — men, A — men.

IV. THREEFOLD — Denmark

A-men, A-men, A — men.

V. THREEFOLD — Traditional

A — men, A - men, A — men.

VI. FOURFOLD — Ken Barker

A - men, A — men, A — men, A - men.

VII. FOURFOLD — John Stainer

A — men, A — men, A — men, A - men.

VIII. FIVEFOLD

Kurt Kaiser

IX. SEVENFOLD

John Stainer

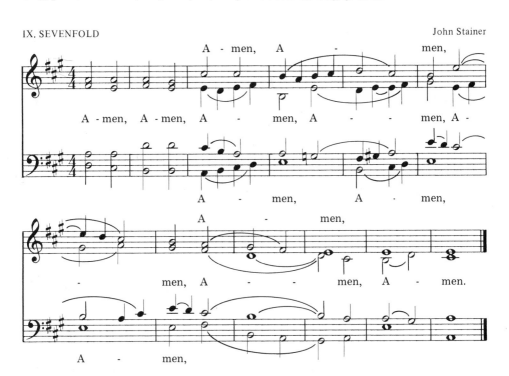

SCRIPTURE RESOURCES

for Worship and Celebration
including
Scriptures for Individual, Unison,
Responsive or Antiphonal Reading
and
Psalms for Unison Reading
or Personal Meditation

---

*O God, whose Word
is quick and powerful, and sharper
than any two-edged sword, grant us grace
to receive Thy truth in
faith and love.*

PREFACE

From time immemorial Scripture has been read to the congregation of God's people. Examples abound in the Bible; here are two:

1. "[Ezra] read [the law] . . . from the morning until midday . . . and the ears of all the people were attentive unto the book of the law." Neh. 8:3

2. "Blessed is he that readeth, and they that hear the words of this prophecy, and keep those things which are written therein." Rev. 1:3

1 Timothy 4:13 is particularly relevant for the Church. Here Paul instructed Timothy: "Give attendance to reading [reference is to the public reading of Scripture], to exhortation, to doctrine." The combining of the public reading of Scripture with exhortation and doctrine (or teaching) in this verse would seem to indicate that the latter are to be based on the text of Scripture itself. In any case, it is clear that Scripture reading is to be a vital part of the Church's worship services.

We have provided a number of Scripture resources that are appropriate for a wide variety of applications. There are sections with:

1. Scripture readings for individual, unison, responsive or antiphonal reading.
2. Psalms for unison reading or personal meditation.

In addition, the body of the hymnal contains:

3. Scripture readings introducing the *Brief Services*.
4. Spoken calls to worship.
5. Spoken benedictions.
6. Scripture verses appearing with hymn titles. (These verses could furnish guidance in the selection of appropriate hymns for certain Biblical texts.)

Now we "commend you to God, and to the word of His grace, which is able to build you up, and to give you an inheritance among all them which are sanctified." Acts 20:32

Dr. Kenneth L. Barker
Scripture Editor and Theological Consultant

Scripture Readings from the
King James Version
of the Holy Bible

The quotation on the facing page is from the *Worship Hymnal*, General Conference of Mennonite Brethren Churches. Used by Permission.

SCRIPTURES FOR INDIVIDUAL, UNISON, RESPONSIVE OR ANTIPHONAL READING

Indexes to Scripture Readings may be found on pages 665 to 673

629 THE TEN COMMANDMENTS

God spake all these words, saying, I am the Lord thy God, which have brought thee out of the land of Egypt, out of the house of bondage.

Thou shalt have no other gods before Me.

Thou shalt not make unto thee any graven image, or any likeness of any thing that is in heaven above, or that is in the earth beneath, or that is in the water under the earth: thou shalt not bow down thyself to them, nor serve them.

For I the Lord thy God am a jealous God, visiting the iniquity of the fathers upon the children unto the third and fourth generation of them that hate Me; and shewing mercy unto thousands of them that love Me, and keep My commandments.

Thou shalt not take the name of the Lord thy God in vain; for the Lord will not hold him guiltless that taketh His name in vain.

Remember the Sabbath day, to keep it holy.

Six days shalt thou labour, and do all thy work; but the seventh day is the sabbath of the Lord thy God.

In it thou shalt not do any work, thou, nor thy son, nor thy daughter, thy manservant, nor thy maidservant, nor thy cattle, nor thy stranger that is within thy gates.

In six days the Lord made heaven and earth, the sea, and all that in them is, and rested the seventh day.

Wherefore the Lord blessed the Sabbath day, and hallowed it.

Honour thy father and thy mother: that thy days may be long upon the land which the Lord thy God giveth thee.

Thou shalt not kill.

Thou shalt not commit adultery.

Thou shalt not steal.

Thou shalt not bear false witness against thy neighbour.

Thou shalt not covet thy neighbour's house, thou shalt not covet thy neighbour's wife, nor his manservant, nor his maidservant, nor his ox, nor his ass, nor any thing that is thy neighbour's.

Ex. 20:1-17

630 TEACHING CHILDREN

Only take heed to thyself, and keep thy soul diligently, lest thou forget the things which thine eyes have seen, and lest they depart from thy heart all the days of thy life: but teach them thy sons, and thy sons' sons.

Now these are the commandments, the statutes, and the judgments, which the Lord your God commanded to teach you, that ye might do them in the land whither ye go to possess it:

That thou mightest fear the Lord thy God, to keep all His statutes and His commandments, which I command thee, thou, and thy son, and thy son's son, all the days of thy life; and that thy days may be prolonged.

Hear therefore, O Israel, and observe to

do it; that it may be well with thee, and that ye may increase mightily, as the Lord God of thy fathers hath promised thee, in the land that floweth with milk and honey.

Hear, O Israel: The Lord our God is one Lord:

And thou shalt love the Lord thy God with all thine heart, and with all thy soul, and with all thy might.

And these words, which I command thee this day, shall be in thine heart:

And thou shalt teach them diligently unto thy children, and shalt talk of them when thou sittest in thine house, and when thou walkest by the way, and when thou liest down, and when thou risest up.

And thou shalt bind them for a sign upon thine hand, and they shall be as frontlets between thine eyes.

And thou shalt write them upon the posts of thy house, and on thy gates.

Train up a child in the way he should go: and when he is old, he will not depart from it.

And, ye fathers, provoke not your children to wrath: but bring them up in the nurture and admonition of the Lord.

Deut. 4:9; 6:1-9; Prov. 22:6; Eph. 6:4

631 OBEDIENCE

Therefore thou shalt love the Lord thy God, and keep His charge, and His statutes, and His judgments, and His commandments, alway.

For this commandment which I command thee this day, it is not hidden from thee, neither is it far off.

It is not in heaven, that thou shouldest

say, Who shall go up for us to heaven, and bring it unto us, that we may hear it, and do it?

Neither is it beyond the sea, that thou shouldest say, Who shall go over the sea for us, and bring it unto us, that we may hear it, and do it?

But the word is very nigh unto thee, in thy mouth, and in thy heart, that thou mayest do it.

This book of the law shall not depart out of thy mouth; but thou shalt meditate therein day and night, that thou mayest observe to do according to all that is written therein: for then thou shalt make thy way prosperous, and then thou shalt have good success.

Hath the Lord as great delight in burnt offerings and sacrifices, as in obeying the voice of the Lord? Behold, to obey is better than sacrifice, and to hearken than the fat of rams.

He that hath My commandments, and keepeth them, he it is that loveth Me: and he that loveth Me shall be loved of My Father, and I will love him, and will manifest Myself to him.

Jesus answered and said unto him, If a man love Me, he will keep My words: and My Father will love him, and We will come unto him, and make Our abode with him.

Though He were a Son, yet learned He obedience by the things which He suffered.

By faith Abraham, when he was called to go out into a place which he should after receive for an inheritance, obeyed; and he went out, not knowing whither he went.

And hereby we do know that we know Him, if we keep His commandments.
Deut. 11:1; 30:11-14; Josh. 1:8; 1 Sam. 15:22; John 14:21, 23; Heb. 5:8; 11:8; 1 John 2:3

632 FORGIVENESS

Come now, and let us reason together, saith the Lord: though your sins be as scarlet, they shall be as white as snow; though they be red like crimson, they shall be as wool.

And they shall teach no more every man his neighbour, and every man his brother, saying, Know the Lord: for they shall all know Me, from the least of them unto the greatest of them, saith the Lord: for I will forgive their iniquity, and I will remember their sin no more.

Who is a God like unto Thee, that pardoneth iniquity, and passeth by the transgression of the remnant of His heritage?

He retaineth not His anger for ever, because He delighteth in mercy.

For if ye forgive men their trespasses, your heavenly Father will also forgive you:

But if ye forgive not men their trespasses, neither will your Father forgive your trespasses.

Then came Peter to Him, and said, Lord, how oft shall my brother sin against me, and I forgive him? till seven times?

Jesus saith unto him, I say not unto thee, Until seven times: but, Until seventy times seven.

And be ye kind one to another, tenderhearted, forgiving one another, even as God for Christ's sake hath forgiven you.

If we say that we have no sin, we deceive ourselves, and the truth is not in us.

If we confess our sins, He is faithful and just to forgive us our sins, and to cleanse us from all unrighteousness.

If we say that we have not sinned, we make Him a liar, and His word is not in us.

My little children, these things write I unto you, that ye sin not. And if any man sin, we have an Advocate with the Father, Jesus Christ the righteous:

And He is the propitiation for our sins: and not for ours only, but also for the sins of the whole world.
Isa. 1:18; Jer. 31:34; Micah 7:18; Matt. 6:14-15; 18:21-22; Eph. 4:32; 1 John 1:8-2:2

633 SCRIPTURE

The grass withereth, the flower fadeth: but the word of our God shall stand for ever. But continue thou in the things which thou hast learned and hast been assured of, knowing of whom thou hast learned them;

And that from a child thou hast known the Holy Scriptures, which are able to make thee wise unto salvation through faith which is in Christ Jesus.

All Scripture is given by inspiration of God, and is profitable for doctrine, for reproof, for correction, for instruction in righteousness:

That the man of God may be perfect, throughly furnished unto all good works.

For the word of God is quick, and powerful, and sharper than any twoedged sword, piercing even to the dividing asunder of soul and spirit, and of the joints and marrow, and is a discerner of the thoughts and intents of the heart.

Neither is there any creature that is not manifest in His sight: but all things are naked and opened unto the eyes of Him with whom we have to do.

For we have not followed cunningly devised fables, when we made known unto you the power and coming of our Lord Jesus Christ, but were eyewitnesses of His majesty.

For He received from God the Father honour and glory, when there came such a voice to Him from the excellent glory, This is My beloved Son, in whom I am well pleased.

And this voice which came from heaven we heard, when we were with Him in the holy mount.

We have also a more sure word of prophecy; whereunto ye do well that ye take heed, as unto a light that shineth in a dark place, until the day dawn, and the day star arise in your hearts:

Knowing this first, that no prophecy of the Scripture is of any private interpretation.

For the prophecy came not in old time by the will of man: but holy men of God spake as they were moved by the Holy Ghost.

Isa. 40:8; 2 Tim. 3:14-17; Heb. 4:12-13; 2 Pet. 1:16-21

634 THE MESSIANIC KING

Nevertheless the dimness shall not be such as was in her vexation, when at the first He lightly afflicted the land of Zebulun and the land of Naphtali, and afterward did more grievously afflict her by the way of the sea, beyond Jordan, in Galilee of the nations.

The people that walked in darkness have seen a great Light: they that dwell in the land of the shadow of death, upon them hath the Light shined.

Thou hast multiplied the nation, and not increased the joy: they joy before Thee according to the joy in harvest, and as men rejoice when they divide the spoil.

For Thou hast broken the yoke of his burden, and the staff of his shoulder, the rod of his oppressor, as in the day of Midian.

For every battle of the warrior is with confused noise, and garments rolled in blood; but this shall be with burning and fuel of fire.

For unto us a Child is born, unto us a Son is given: and the government shall be upon His shoulder: and His name shall be called Wonderful, Counsellor, The Mighty God, The Everlasting Father, The Prince of Peace.

Of the increase of His government and peace there shall be no end, upon the throne of David, and upon his kingdom, to order it, and to establish it with judgment and with justice from henceforth even for ever.

The zeal of the Lord of hosts will perform this.

Isa. 9:1-7

635 CHRIST'S INCARNATION

In the beginning was the Word, and the Word was with God, and the Word was God.

The same was in the beginning with God.

All things were made by Him; and without Him was not any thing made that was made.

In Him was Life; and the Life was the Light of men.

And the Light shineth in darkness; and the darkness comprehended it not.

There was a man sent from God, whose name was John.

The same came for a witness, to bear witness of the Light, that all men through Him might believe.

He was not that Light, but was sent to bear witness of that Light.

That was the true Light, which lighteth every man that cometh into the world.

He was in the world, and the world was made by Him, and the world knew Him not.

He came unto His own, and His own received Him not.

But as many as received Him, to them gave He power to become the sons of God, even to them that believe on His name:

Which were born, not of blood, nor of the will of the flesh, nor of the will of man, but of God.

And the Word was made flesh, and dwelt among us, (and we beheld His glory, the glory as of the only begotten of the Father,) full of grace and truth.

John 1:1-14

636 THE MAGI'S VISIT

Now when Jesus was born in Bethlehem of Judea in the days of Herod the king, behold, there came wise men from the east to Jerusalem, saying,

Where is He that is born King of the Jews? for we have seen His star in the east, and are come to worship Him.

When Herod the king had heard these things, he was troubled, and all Jerusalem with him.

And when he had gathered all the chief priests and scribes of the people together, he demanded of them where Christ should be born.

And they said unto him, In Bethlehem of Judea: for thus it is written by the prophet,

And thou Bethlehem, in the land of Judah, art not the least among the princes of Judah: for out of thee shall come a Governor, that shall rule my people Israel.

Then Herod, when he had privily called the wise men, inquired of them diligently what time the star appeared.

And he sent them to Bethlehem, and said, Go and search diligently for the young Child; and when ye have found Him, bring me word again, that I may come and worship Him also.

When they had heard the king, they departed; and, lo, the star, which they saw in the east, went before them, till it came and stood over where the young Child was.

When they saw the star, they rejoiced with exceeding great joy.

And when they were come into the house, they saw the young Child with Mary His mother, and fell down, and worshipped Him: and when they had opened their treasures, they presented unto Him gifts; gold, and frankincense, and myrrh.

And being warned of God in a dream that they should not return to Herod, they departed into their own country another way.

Matt. 2:1-12

637 CHRIST'S BAPTISM

In those days came John the Baptist, preaching in the wilderness of Judea, and saying, Repent ye: for the kingdom of heaven is at hand.

For this is he that was spoken of by the prophet Esaias, saying, The voice of one crying in the wilderness, Prepare ye the way of the Lord, make His paths straight.

But when he saw many of the Pharisees and Sadducees come to his baptism, he said unto them, O generation of vipers, who hath warned you to flee from the wrath to come?

Bring forth therefore fruits meet for repentance.

I indeed baptize you with water unto repentance: but He that cometh after me is mightier than I, whose shoes I am not worthy to bear:

He shall baptize you with the Holy Ghost, and with fire:

Whose fan is in His hand, and He will throughly purge His floor, and gather His wheat into the garner; but He will burn up the chaff with unquenchable fire.

Then cometh Jesus from Galilee to Jordan unto John, to be baptized of him.

But John forbad Him, saying, I have need to be baptized of Thee, and comest Thou to me?

And Jesus answering said unto him, Suffer it to be so now: for thus it becometh us to fulfil all righteousness. Then he suffered Him.

And Jesus, when He was baptized, went up straightway out of the water: and, lo, the heavens were opened unto Him, and He saw the Spirit of God descending like a dove, and lighting upon Him:

And lo a voice from heaven, saying, This is My beloved Son, in whom I am well pleased.

Matt. 3:1-3, 7-8, 11-17

638 CHRIST'S TRIUMPHAL ENTRY

And when they drew nigh unto Jerusalem, and were come to Bethphage,

unto the Mount of Olives, then sent Jesus two disciples, saying unto them:

Go into the village over against you, and straightway ye shall find an ass tied, and a colt with her: loose them, and bring them unto Me.

And if any man say ought unto you, ye shall say, The Lord hath need of them; and straightway he will send them.

All this was done, that it might be fulfilled which was spoken by the prophet, saying:

Tell ye the daughter of Sion, Behold, thy King cometh unto thee, meek, and sitting upon an ass, and a colt the foal of an ass.

And the disciples went, and did as Jesus commanded them;

And brought the ass, and the colt, and put on them their clothes, and they set Him thereon.

And a very great multitude spread their garments in the way; others cut down branches from the trees, and strawed them in the way.

And the multitudes that went before, and that followed, cried, saying:

Hosanna to the Son of David: Blessed is He that cometh in the name of the Lord; Hosanna in the highest.

And when He was come into Jerusalem all the city was moved, saying, Who is this?

And the multitude said, This is Jesus the prophet of Nazareth of Galilee.

Matt. 21:1-11

639 CHRIST'S SUFFERINGS

Who hath believed our report? and to whom is the arm of the Lord revealed?

For He shall grow up before Him as a tender plant, and as a root out of a dry ground:

He hath no form nor comeliness; and when we shall see Him, there is no beauty that we should desire Him.

He is despised and rejected of men; a Man of sorrows, and acquainted with grief:

And we hid as it were our faces from Him; He was despised, and we esteemed Him not.

Surely He hath borne our griefs, and carried our sorrows: yet we did esteem Him stricken, smitten of God, and afflicted.

But He was wounded for our transgressions, He was bruised for our iniquities: the chastisement of our peace was upon Him; and with His stripes we are healed.

All we like sheep have gone astray; we have turned every one to his own way; and the Lord hath laid on Him the iniquity of us all.

He was oppressed, and He was afflicted, yet He opened not His mouth: He is brought as a lamb to the slaughter, and as a sheep before her shearers is dumb, so He openeth not His mouth.

He was taken from prison and from judgment:

And who shall declare His generation? For He was cut off out of the land of the living: for the transgression of my people was He stricken.

And He made His grave with the wicked, and with the rich in His death; because He had done no violence, neither was any deceit in His mouth.

Isa. 53:1-9

640   CHRIST'S DEATH

Then Pilate therefore took Jesus, and scourged Him.

And the soldiers platted a crown of thorns, and put it on His head, and they put on Him a purple robe,

And said, Hail, King of the Jews! and they smote Him with their hands.

Pilate therefore went forth again, and saith unto them, Behold, I bring Him forth to you, that ye may know that I find no fault in Him.

Then came Jesus forth, wearing the crown of thorns, and the purple robe. And Pilate saith unto them, Behold the Man!

When the chief priests therefore and officers saw Him, they cried out, saying, Crucify Him, crucify Him. Pilate saith unto them, Take ye Him, and crucify Him: for I find no fault in Him.

Then delivered he Him therefore unto them to be crucified. And they took Jesus, and led Him away.

And He bearing His cross went forth into a place called the place of a skull, which is called in the Hebrew Golgotha:

Where they crucified Him, and two other with Him, on either side one, and Jesus in the midst.

And Pilate wrote a title, and put it on the cross. And the writing was, JESUS OF NAZARETH THE KING OF THE JEWS.

John 19:1-6, 16-19

641   CHRIST'S ASCENSION

The former treatise have I made, O Theophilus, of all that Jesus began both to do and teach, until the day in which He was taken up, after that He through the Holy Ghost had given commandments unto the apostles whom He had chosen:

To whom also He shewed Himself alive after His passion by many infallible proofs, being seen of them forty days, and speaking of the things pertaining to the kingdom of God:

And, being assembled together with them, commanded them that they should not depart from Jerusalem, but wait for the promise of the Father, which, saith He, ye have heard of Me.

For John truly baptized with water; but ye shall be baptized with the Holy Ghost not many days hence.

When they therefore were come together, they asked of Him, saying, Lord, wilt Thou at this time restore again the kingdom to Israel?

He said unto them, It is not for you to know the times or the seasons, which the Father hath put in His own power.

But ye shall receive power, after that the Holy Ghost is come upon you: and ye shall be witnesses unto Me both in Jerusalem, and in all Judea, and in Samaria, and unto the uttermost part of the earth.

When He had spoken these things, while they beheld, He was taken up; and a cloud received Him out of their sight.

While they looked stedfastly toward heaven as He went up, behold, two men stood by them in white apparel;

Which also said, Ye men of Galilee, why stand ye gazing up into heaven? this same Jesus, which is taken up from you into heaven, shall so come in like manner as ye have seen Him go into heaven.

Acts 1:1-11

642 CHRIST'S EXALTATION

If there be therefore any consolation in Christ, if any comfort of love,

If any fellowship of the Spirit, if any bowels and mercies,

Fulfil ye my joy, that ye be like-minded, having the same love, being of one accord, of one mind.

Let nothing be done through strife or vainglory; but in lowliness of mind let each esteem other better than them-selves.

Look not every man on his own things, but every man also on the things of others.

Let this mind be in you, which was also in Christ Jesus:

Who, being in the form of God, thought it not robbery to be equal with God:

But made Himself of no reputation, and took upon Him the form of a servant, and was made in the likeness of men:

And being found in fashion as a man, He humbled Himself, and became obedient unto death, even the death of the cross.

Wherefore God also hath highly exalted Him, and given Him a name which is above every name:

That at the name of Jesus every knee should bow, of things in heaven, and things in earth, and things under the earth;

And that every tongue should confess that Jesus Christ is Lord, to the glory of God the Father.

Phil. 2:1-11

643 CHRIST'S RETURN

But I would not have you to be ignorant, brethren, concerning them which are asleep, that ye sorrow not, even as others which have no hope.

For if we believe that Jesus died and rose again, even so them also which sleep in Jesus will God bring with Him.

For this we say unto you by the word of the Lord, that we which are alive and remain unto· the coming of the Lord shall not prevent them which are asleep.

For the Lord Himself shall descend from heaven with a shout, with the voice of the archangel, and with the trump of God: and the dead in Christ shall rise first:

Then we which are alive and remain shall be caught up together with them in the clouds, to meet the Lord in the air: and so shall we ever be with the Lord.

Wherefore comfort one another with these words.

1 Thess. 4:13-18

644 THE HOLY SPIRIT

And I will pray the Father, and He shall give you another Comforter, that He may abide with you for ever;

Even the Spirit of truth; whom the world cannot receive, because it seeth Him not, neither knoweth Him: but ye know Him; for He dwelleth with you, and shall be in you.

I will not leave you comfortless: I will come to you.

But now I go My way to Him that sent Me; and none of you asketh Me, Whither goest Thou?

But because I have said these things unto you, sorrow hath filled your heart.

Nevertheless I tell you the truth; It is expedient for you that I go away: for if I go not away, the Comforter will not come unto you; but if I depart, I will send Him unto you.

And when He is come, He will reprove the world of sin, and of righteousness, and of judgment:

Of sin because they believe not on Me;

Of righteousness, because I go to My Father, and ye see Me no more;

Of judgment, because the prince of this world is judged.

I have yet many things to say unto you, but ye cannot bear them now.

Howbeit when He, the Spirit of truth, is come, He will guide you into all truth: for He shall not speak of Himself; but whatsoever He shall hear, that shall He speak: and He will shew you things to come.

He shall glorify Me: for He shall receive of Mine, and shall shew it unto you.

All things that the Father hath are Mine: therefore said I, that He shall take of Mine, and shall shew it unto you.

John 14:16-18; 16:5-15

645 MISSIONS

Then the eleven disciples went away into Galilee, into a mountain where Jesus had appointed them.

And when they saw Him, they worshipped Him: but some doubted.

And Jesus came and spake unto them, saying, All power is given unto Me in heaven and in earth. Go ye therefore, and teach all nations, baptizing them in the name of the Father, and of the Son, and of the Holy Ghost: Teaching them to observe all things whatsoever I have commanded you: and, lo, I am with you alway, even unto the end of the world. Amen.

Say not ye, There are yet four months, and then cometh harvest? behold, I say unto you, Lift up your eyes, and look on the fields; for they are white already to harvest.

But what saith it? The word is nigh thee, even in thy mouth, and in thy heart: that is, the word of faith, which we preach;

That if thou shalt confess with thy mouth the Lord Jesus, and shalt believe in thine heart that God hath raised Him from the dead, thou shalt be saved.

For with the heart man believeth unto righteousness; and with the mouth confession is made unto salvation.

For the Scripture saith, Whosoever believeth on Him shall not be ashamed.

For there is no difference between the Jew and the Greek: for the same Lord over all is rich unto all that call upon Him.

For whosoever shall call upon the name of the Lord shall be saved.

How then shall they call on Him in whom they have not believed? and how shall they believe in Him of whom they have not heard? and how shall they hear without a preacher?

And how shall they preach, except they be sent? as it is written, How beautiful are the feet of them that preach the gospel of peace, and bring glad tidings of good things!

Matt. 28:16-20; John 4:35; Rom. 10:8-15

646 THE CHURCH

He saith unto them, But whom say ye that I am?

And Simon Peter answered and said, Thou art the Christ, the Son of the living God.

And Jesus answered and said unto him, Blessed art thou, Simon Bar-jona: for flesh and blood hath not revealed it unto thee, but My Father which is in heaven.

And I say also unto thee, That thou art Peter, and upon this rock I will build My church; and the gates of hell shall not prevail against it.

And I will give unto thee the keys of the kingdom of heaven: and whatsoever thou shalt bind on earth shall be bound in heaven: and whatsoever thou shalt loose on earth shall be loosed in heaven.

For as the body is one, and hath many members, and all the members of that one body, being many, are one body: so also is Christ.

For by one Spirit are we all baptized into one body, whether we be Jews or Gentiles, whether we be bond or free; and have been all made to drink into one Spirit.

He hath put all things under His feet, and gave Him to be the head over all things to the church, which is His body, the fulness of Him that filleth all in all.

Now therefore ye are no more strangers and foreigners, but fellow-citizens with the saints, and of the household of God;

And are built upon the foundation of the apostles and prophets, Jesus Christ Himself being the chief corner stone;

In whom all the building fitly framed together groweth unto an holy temple in the Lord:

In whom ye also are builded together for an habitation of God through the Spirit.

Husbands, love your wives, even as Christ also loved the church, and gave Himself for it; that He might sanctify and cleanse it with the washing of water by the word;

That He might present it to Himself a glorious church, not having spot, or wrinkle, or any such thing; but that it should be holy and without blemish.

Matt. 16:15-19; 1 Cor. 12:12-13; Eph. 1:22-23; 2:19-22; 5:25-27

647 THE LORD'S SUPPER

For I have received of the Lord that which also I delivered unto you, That the Lord Jesus the same night in which He was betrayed took bread:

And when He had given thanks, He brake it, and said, Take, eat: this is My body, which is broken for you: this do in remembrance of Me.

After the same manner also He took the cup, when He had supped, saying, This cup is the new testament in My blood: this do ye, as oft as ye drink it, in remembrance of Me.

For as often as ye eat this bread, and drink this cup, ye do shew the Lord's death till He come.

Wherefore whosoever shall eat this bread, and drink this cup of the Lord, unworthily, shall be guilty of the body and blood of the Lord.

But let a man examine himself, and so let him eat of that bread, and drink of that cup.

For he that eateth and drinketh unwor-

thily, eateth and drinketh damnation to himself, not discerning the Lord's body.

For this cause many are weak and sickly among you, and many sleep.

For if we would judge ourselves, we should not be judged.

But when we are judged, we are chastened of the Lord, that we should not be condemned with the world.

1 Cor. 11:23-32

648 THE BEATITUDES

Seeing the multitudes, He went up into a mountain: and when He was set, His disciples came unto Him;

And He opened His mouth, and taught them, saying:

Blessed are the poor in spirit: for theirs is the kingdom of heaven.

Blessed are they that mourn: for they shall be comforted.

Blessed are the meek: for they shall inherit the earth.

Blessed are they which do hunger and thirst after righteousness: for they shall be filled.

Blessed are the merciful: for they shall obtain mercy.

Blessed are the pure in heart: for they shall see God.

Blessed are the peacemakers: for they shall be called the children of God.

Blessed are they which are persecuted for righteousness' sake: for theirs is the kingdom of heaven.

Blessed are ye, when men shall revile you, and persecute you, and shall say all manner of evil against you falsely, for My sake.

Rejoice, and be exceeding glad: for great is your reward in heaven: for so persecuted they the prophets which were before you.

Matt. 5:1-12

649 THE VINE AND THE BRANCHES

I am the true vine, and My Father is the husbandman.

Every branch in Me that beareth not fruit He taketh away: and every branch that beareth fruit, He purgeth it, that it may bring forth more fruit.

Now ye are clean through the word which I have spoken unto you.

Abide in Me, and I in you. As the branch cannot bear fruit of itself, except it abide in the vine; no more can ye, except ye abide in Me.

I am the vine, ye are the branches: he that abideth in Me, and I in him, the same bringeth forth much fruit: for without Me ye can do nothing.

If a man abide not in Me, he is cast forth as a branch, and is withered; and men gather them, and cast them into the fire, and they are burned.

If ye abide in Me, and My words abide in you, ye shall ask what ye will, and it shall be done unto you.

Herein is My Father glorified, that ye bear much fruit; so shall ye be My disciples.

As the Father hath loved Me, so have I loved you: continue ye in My love.

If ye keep My commandments, ye shall abide in My love; even as I have kept My Father's commandments, and abide in His love.

These things have I spoken unto you, that My joy might remain in you, and that your joy might be full.

This is My commandment, that ye love one another, as I have loved you.

Greater love hath no man than this, that a man lay down his life for his friends.

Ye are My friends, if ye do whatsoever I command you.

Henceforth I call you not servants; for the servant knoweth not what his lord doeth:

But I have called you friends; for all things that I have heard of My Father I have made known unto you.

Ye have not chosen Me, but I have chosen you, and ordained you, that ye should go and bring forth fruit, and that your fruit should remain: that whatsoever ye shall ask of the Father in My name, He may give it you.

These things I command you, that ye love one another.

John 15:1-17

650 THE LORD'S PRAYER

And when thou prayest, thou shalt not be as the hypocrites are: for they love to pray standing in the synagogues and in the corners of the streets, that they may be seen of men. Verily I say unto you, They have their reward.

But thou, when thou prayest, enter into thy closet, and when thou hast shut thy door, pray to thy Father which is in secret; and thy Father which seeth in secret shall reward thee openly.

But when ye pray, use not vain repetitions, as the heathen do: for they think that they shall be heard for their much speaking.

Be not ye therefore like unto them: for your Father knoweth what things ye have need of, before ye ask Him.

After this manner therefore pray ye: Our Father which art in heaven, Hallowed be Thy name.

Thy kingdom come. Thy will be done in earth, as it is in heaven.

Give us this day our daily bread.

And forgive us our debts, as we forgive our debtors.

And lead us not into temptation, but deliver us from evil:

For Thine is the kingdom, and the power, and the glory, for ever. Amen.

For if ye forgive men their trespasses, your heavenly Father will also forgive you:

But if ye forgive not men their trespasses, neither will your Father forgive your trespasses.

Matt. 6:5-15

651 DISCIPLESHIP

The disciple is not above his master, nor the servant above his lord.

It is enough for the disciple that he be as his master, and the servant as his lord.

If any man come to Me, and hate not his father, and mother, and wife, and children, and brethren, and sisters, yea, and his own life also, he cannot be My disciple.

And whosoever doth not bear his cross, and come after Me, cannot be My disciple.

Then spake Jesus again unto them, saying, I am the Light of the world: he that followeth Me shall not walk in darkness, but shall have the Light of Life.

Then said Jesus to those Jews which believed on Him, If ye continue in My word, then are ye My disciples indeed;

And ye shall know the truth, and the truth shall make you free.

A new commandment I give unto you, That ye love one another; as I have loved you, that ye also love one another.

By this shall all men know that ye are My disciples, if ye have love one to another.

Herein is My Father glorified, that ye bear much fruit; so shall ye be My disciples.

Matt. 10:24-25; Luke 14:26-27;
John 8:12,31-32; 13:34-35; 15:8

652 COMFORT

Let not your heart be troubled: ye believe in God, believe also in Me.

In My Father's house are many mansions: if it were not so, I would have told you. I go to prepare a place for you.

And if I go and prepare a place for you, I will come again, and receive you unto Myself; that where I am, there ye may be also.

If ye love Me, keep My commandments.

And I will pray the Father, and He shall give you another Comforter, that He may abide with you for ever;

Peace I leave with you, My peace I give unto you: not as the world giveth, give I unto you. Let not your heart be troubled, neither let it be afraid.

Blessed be God, even the Father of our Lord Jesus Christ, the Father of mercies, and the God of all comfort; who comforteth us in all our tribulation, that we may be able to comfort them which are in any trouble, by the comfort wherewith we ourselves are comforted of God.

For as the sufferings of Christ abound in us, so our consolation also aboundeth by Christ.

And whether we be afflicted, it is for your consolation and salvation, which is effectual in the enduring of the same sufferings which we also suffer: or whether we be comforted, it is for your consolation and salvation.

And our hope of you is stedfast, knowing, that as ye are partakers of the sufferings, so shall ye be also of the consolation.

John 14:1-3, 15-16, 27; 2 Cor. 1:3-7

653 GOD'S LOVE

For God so loved the world, that He gave His only begotten Son, that whosoever believeth in Him should not perish, but have everlasting life.

But God commendeth His love toward us, in that, while we were yet sinners, Christ died for us.

Behold, what manner of love the Father hath bestowed upon us, that we should be called the sons of God; therefore the world knoweth us not, because it knew Him not.

He that loveth not knoweth not God; for God is love.

In this was manifested the love of God toward us, because that God sent His only begotten Son into the world, that we might live though Him.

Herein is love, not that we loved God, but that He loved us, and sent His Son to be the propitiation for our sins.

Beloved, if God so loved us, we ought also to love one another.

No man hath seen God at any time. If we love one another, God dwelleth in us, and His love is perfected in us.

There is no fear in love; but perfect love casteth out fear: because fear hath torment. He that feareth is not made perfect in love.

We love Him, because He first loved us.

John 3:16; Rom. 5:8; 1 John 3:1; 4:8-12, 18-19

654 THE NEW BIRTH

There was a man of the Pharisees, named Nicodemus, a ruler of the Jews:

The same came to Jesus by night, and said unto Him, Rabbi, we know that Thou art a teacher come from God: for no man can do these miracles that Thou doest, except God be with Him.

Jesus answered and said unto him, Verily, verily, I say unto thee, Except a man be born again, he cannot see the kingdom of God.

Nicodemus saith unto Him, How can a man be born when he is old: can he enter the second time into his mother's womb, and be born?

Jesus answered, Verily, verily, I say unto thee, Except a man be born of water and of the Spirit, he cannot enter into the kingdom of God.

That which is born of the flesh is flesh; and that which is born of the Spirit is spirit.

Marvel not that I said unto thee, Ye must be born again.

The wind bloweth where it listeth, and thou hearest the sound thereof, but canst not tell whence it cometh, and whither it goeth: so is every one that is born of the Spirit.

And as Moses lifted up the serpent in the wilderness, even so must the Son of Man be lifted up: that whosoever believeth in Him should not perish, but have eternal life.

For God so loved the world, that He gave His only begotten Son, that whosoever believeth in Him should not perish, but have everlasting life.

For God sent not His Son into the world to condemn the world; but that the world through Him might be saved.

Therefore if any man be in Christ, he is a new creature: old things are passed away; behold, all things are become new.

John 3:1-8, 14-17; 2 Cor. 5:17

655 PRAYER

Ask, and it shall be given you; seek, and ye shall find; knock, and it shall be opened unto you:

For every one that asketh receiveth; and he that seeketh findeth; and to him that knocketh it shall be opened.

Or what man is there of you, whom if his son ask bread, will he give him a stone? Or if he ask a fish, will he give him a serpent? If ye then, being evil, know how to give good gifts unto your children, how much more shall your Father which is in heaven give good things to them that ask Him?

Therefore I say unto you, What things soever ye desire, when ye pray, believe that ye receive them and ye shall have them.

And when ye stand praying, forgive, if ye have ought against any: that your Father also which is in heaven may forgive you your trespasses.

And whatsoever ye shall ask in My name, that will I do, that the Father may be glorified in the Son. If ye shall ask

any thing in My name, I will do it.

Likewise the Spirit also helpeth our infirmities: for we know not what we should pray for as we ought: but the Spirit itself maketh intercession for us with groanings which cannot be uttered.

And He that searcheth the hearts knoweth what is the mind of the Spirit, because He maketh intercession for the saints according to the will of God.

Praying always with all prayer and supplication in the Spirit, and watching thereunto with all perseverance and supplication for all saints.

Seeing then that we have a great High Priest, that is passed into the heavens, Jesus the Son of God, let us hold fast our profession.

For we have not an High Priest which cannot be touched with the feeling of our infirmities; but was in all points tempted like as we are, yet without sin.

Let us therefore come boldly unto the throne of grace, that we may obtain mercy, and find grace to help in time of need.

And this is the confidence that we have in Him, that, if we ask any thing according to His will, He heareth us:

And if we know that He hear us, whatsoever we ask, we know that we have the petitions that we desired of Him.

Matt. 7:7-11; Mark 11:24-25; John 14:13-14; Rom. 8:26-27; Eph. 6:18; Heb. 4:14-16; 1 John 5:14-15

656 GIVING

Give, and it shall be given unto you; good measure, pressed down, and shaken together, and running over, shall men give into your bosom. For with the same measure that ye mete withal it shall be measured to you again.

I have shewed you all things, how that so labouring ye ought to support the weak, and to remember the words of the Lord Jesus, how He said, It is more blessed to give than to receive.

Upon the first day of the week let every one of you lay by him in store, as God hath prospered him, that there be no gatherings when I come.

Therefore, as ye abound in every thing, in faith, and utterance, and knowledge, and in all diligence, and in your love to us, see that ye abound in this grace also.

For ye know the grace of our Lord Jesus Christ, that, though He was rich, yet for your sakes He became poor, that ye through His poverty might be rich.

If there be first a willing mind, it is accepted according to that a man hath, and not according to that he hath not.

But this I say, He which soweth sparingly shall reap also sparingly; and he which soweth bountifully shall reap also bountifully. Every man according as he purposeth in his heart, so let him give; not grudgingly, or of necessity: for God loveth a cheerful giver.

Thanks be unto God for His unspeakable Gift.

*Luke 6:38; Acts 20:35; 1 Cor. 16:2;
2 Cor. 8:7,9,12; 9:6-7,15*

657 FAITHFULNESS

Who then is a faithful and wise servant, whom his lord hath made ruler over his household, to give them meat in due season?

Blessed is that servant, whom his lord when he cometh shall find so doing.

Verily I say unto you, That he shall make him ruler over all his goods.

His lord said unto him, Well done, thou good and faithful servant: thou hast been faithful over a few things, I will make thee ruler over many things: enter thou into the joy of thy lord.

He that is faithful in that which is least is faithful also in much: and he that is unjust in the least is unjust also in much.

If therefore ye have not been faithful in the unrighteous mammon, who will commit to your trust the true riches?

And if ye have not been faithful in that which is another man's, who shall give you that which is your own?

No servant can serve two masters: for either he will hate the one, and love the other; or else he will hold to the one, and despise the other. Ye cannot serve God and mammon.

It is required in stewards, that a man be found faithful.

The things that thou hast heard of Me among many witnesses, the same commit thou to faithful men, who shall be able to teach others also.

Fear none of those things which thou shalt suffer.

Be thou faithful unto death, and I will give thee a crown of life.

*Matt. 24:45-47; 25:21; Luke 16:10-13;
1 Cor. 4:2; 2 Tim. 2:2; Rev. 2:10*

658 ETERNAL LIFE

As Moses lifted up the serpent in the wilderness, even so must the Son of Man be lifted up: that whosoever believeth in Him should not perish, but have eternal life.

For God so loved the world, that He gave His only begotten Son, that whosoever believeth in Him should not perish, but have everlasting life.

He that believeth on the Son hath everlasting life: and he that believeth not the Son shall not see life; but the wrath of God abideth on him.

Verily, verily, I say unto you, He that heareth My word, and believeth on Him that sent Me, hath everlasting life, and shall not come into condemnation; but is passed from death unto life.

My sheep hear My voice, and I know them, and they follow Me: and I give unto them eternal life; and they shall never perish, neither shall any man pluck them out of My hand.

My Father, which gave them Me, is greater than all; and no man is able to pluck them out of My Father's hand.

This is the record, that God hath given to us eternal life, and this life is in His Son.

He that hath the Son hath life; and he that hath not the Son of God hath not life.

These things have I written unto you that believe on the name of the Son of God; that ye may know that ye have eternal life, and that ye may believe on the name of the Son of God.

We know that the Son of God is come, and hath given us an understanding, that we may know Him that is true, and we are in Him that is true, even in His Son Jesus Christ. This is the true God, and eternal life.

John 3:14-16, 36; 5:24; 10:27-29; 1 John 5:11-13,20

659 SALVATION BY GRACE

Of His fulness have all we received, and grace for grace. For the law was given by Moses, but grace and truth came by Jesus Christ.

Moreover the law entered, that the offence might abound. But where sin abounded, grace did much more abound: that as sin hath reigned unto death, even so might grace reign through righteousness unto eternal life by Jesus Christ our Lord.

But God, who is rich in mercy, for His great love wherewith He loved us, even when we were dead in sins, hath quickened us together with Christ, (by grace ye are saved;)

And hath raised us up together, and made us sit together in heavenly places in Christ Jesus: that in the ages to come He might shew the exceeding riches of His grace in His kindness toward us through Christ Jesus.

For by grace are ye saved through faith; and that not of yourselves: it is the gift of God: not of works, lest any man should boast.

The grace of God that bringeth salvation hath appeared to all men, teaching us that, denying ungodliness and worldly lusts, we should live soberly, righteously, and godly, in this present world.

After that the kindness and love of God our Saviour toward man appeared, not by works of righteousness which we have done, but according to His mercy He saved us, by the washing of regeneration, and renewing of the Holy Ghost;

Which He shed on us abundantly through Jesus Christ our Saviour; that being justified by His grace, we should be made heirs according to the hope of eternal life.

John 1:16-17; Rom. 5:20-21; Eph. 2:4-9; Titus 2:11-12; 3:4-7

660 REDEMPTION

For even the Son of Man came not to be ministered unto, but to minister, and to give His life a ransom for many.

But now the righteousness of God with

out the law is manifested, being witnessed by the law and the prophets;

Even the righteousness of God which is by faith of Jesus Christ unto all and upon all them that believe: for there is no difference.

For all have sinned, and come short of the glory of God; being justified freely by His grace through the redemption that is in Christ Jesus:

Whom God hath set forth to be a propitiation through faith in His blood, to declare His righteousness for the remission of sins that are past, through the forebearance of God;

To declare, I say, at this time, His righteousness: that He might be just, and the justifier of him which believeth in Jesus.

In whom we have redemption through His blood, the forgiveness of sins, according to the riches of His grace; wherein He hath abounded toward us in all wisdom and prudence.

For this cause He is the mediator of the new testament, that by means of death, for the redemption of the transgressions that were under the first testament, they which are called might receive the promise of eternal inheritance.

Forasmuch as ye know that ye were not redeemed with corruptible things, as silver and gold, from your vain conversation received by tradition from your fathers;

But with the precious blood of Christ, as of a lamb without blemish and without spot.

Mark 10:45; Rom. 3:21-26; Eph. 1:7-8;
Heb. 9:15; 1 Pet. 1:18-19

661   CHRISTIAN LOVE

Though I speak with the tongues of men and of angels, and have not charity, I am become as sounding brass, or a tinkling cymbal.

And though I have the gift of prophecy, and understand all mysteries, and all knowledge; and though I have all faith, so that I could remove mountains, and have not charity, I am nothing.

And though I bestow all my goods to feed the poor, and though I give my body to be burned, and have not charity, it profiteth me nothing.

Charity suffereth long, and is kind; charity envieth not; charity vaunteth not itself, is not puffed up;

Doth not behave itself unseemly, seeketh not her own, is not easily provoked, thinketh no evil;

Rejoiceth not in iniquity, but rejoiceth in the truth;

Beareth all things, believeth all things, hopeth all things, endureth all things.

Charity never faileth: but whether there be prophecies, they shall fail; whether there be tongues, they shall cease; whether there be knowledge, it shall vanish away.

For we know in part, and we prophesy in part. But when that which is perfect is come, then that which is in part shall be done away.

When I was a child, I spake as a child, I understood as a child, I thought as a child: but when I became a man, I put away childish things.

For now we see through a glass, darkly; but then face to face: now I know in part; but then shall I know even as also I am known.

And now abideth faith, hope, charity,

these three; but the greatest of these is charity.

1 Cor. 13

662 FAITH

Now faith is the substance of things hoped for, the evidence of things not seen.

For by it the elders obtained a good report.

Through faith we understand that the worlds were framed by the word of God, so that things which are seen were not made of things which do appear.

But without faith it is impossible to please Him: for he that cometh to God must believe that He is, and that He is a rewarder of them that diligently seek Him.

By faith Abraham, when he was called to go out into a place which he should after receive for an inheritance, obeyed; and he went out, not knowing whither he went.

By faith he sojourned in the land of promise, as in a strange country, dwelling in tabernacles with Isaac and Jacob, the heirs with him of the same promise.

For he looked for a city which hath foundations, whose builder and maker is God.

Through faith also Sara herself received strength to conceive seed, and was delivered of a child when she was past age, because she judged Him faithful who had promised.

Therefore sprang there even of one, and him as good as dead, so many as the stars of the sky in multitude, and as the sand which is by the sea shore innumerable.

By faith Abraham, when he was tried, offered up Isaac: and he that had re-ceived the promises offered up his only begotten son;

Of whom it was said, That in Isaac shall thy seed be called:

Accounting that God was able to raise him up, even from the dead; from whence also he received him in a figure.

Heb. 11:1-3, 6, 8-12, 17-19

663 FAMILY

Wives, submit yourselves unto your own husbands, as unto the Lord.

For the husband is the head of the wife, even as Christ is the head of the church: and He is the Saviour of the body.

Therefore as the church is subject unto Christ, so let the wives be to their own husbands in every thing.

Husbands, love your wives, even as Christ also loved the church, and gave Himself for it;

That He might sanctify and cleanse it with the washing of water by the word;

That He might present it to Himself a glorious church, not having spot, or wrinkle, or any such thing; but that it should be holy and without blemish.

So ought men to love their wives as their own bodies. He that loveth his wife loveth himself.

For no man ever yet hated his own flesh; but nourisheth and cherisheth it, even as the Lord the church:

For we are members of His body, of His flesh, and of His bones.

For this cause shall a man leave his father and mother, and shall be joined unto his wife, and they two shall be one flesh.

This is a great mystery: but I speak concerning Christ and the church.

Nevertheless let every one of you in particular so love his wife even as himself; and the wife see that she reverence her husband.

Children, obey your parents in the Lord: for this is right.

Honour thy father and mother; (which is the first commandment with promise;)

That it may be well with thee, and thou mayest live long on the earth.

And, ye fathers, provoke not your children to wrath: but bring them up in the nurture and admonition of the Lord.

Eph. 5:22-6:4

664 UNITY

I therefore, the prisoner of the Lord, beseech you that ye walk worthy of the vocation wherewith ye are called;

With all lowliness and meekness, with longsuffering, forbearing one another in love;

Endeavouring to keep the unity of the Spirit in the bond of peace.

There is one body, and one Spirit, even as ye are called in one hope of your calling;

One Lord, one faith, one baptism;

One God and Father of all, who is above all, and through all, and in you all.

If there be therefore any consolation in Christ, if any comfort of love, if any fellowship of the Spirit, if any bowels and mercies;

Fulfil ye my joy, that ye be like-minded, having the same love, being of one accord, of one mind.

Let nothing be done through strife or vainglory; but in lowliness of mind let each esteem other better than themselves.

Look not every man on his own things, but every man also on the things of others.

Eph. 4:1-6; Phil. 2:1-4

665 GOVERNMENT

Let every soul be subject unto the higher powers. For theirs is no power but of God: the powers that be are ordained of God.

Whosoever therefore resisteth the power, resisteth the ordinance of God: and they that resist shall receive to themselves damnation.

For rulers are not a terror to good works, but to the evil. Wilt thou then not be afraid of the power? do that which is good, and thou shalt have praise of the same.

He is the minister of God to thee for good. But if thou do that which is evil, be afraid; for he beareth not the sword in vain: for he is the minister of God, a revenger to execute wrath upon him that doeth evil.

Wherefore ye must needs be subject, not only for wrath, but also for conscience' sake.

For this cause pay ye tribute also: for they are God's ministers, attending continually upon this very thing.

Render therefore to all their dues: tribute to whom tribute is due; custom to whom custom; fear to whom fear; honour to whom honour.

Submit yourselves to every ordinance of man for the Lord's sake: whether it be to the king, as supreme; or unto governors, as unto them that are sent

by him for the punishment of evildoers, and for the praise of them that do well.

For so is the will of God, that with well doing ye may put to silence the ignorance of foolish men: as free, and not using your liberty for a cloak of maliciousness, but as the servants of God.

Honour all men. Love the brotherhood. Fear God. Honour the king.

Rom. 13:1-7; 1 Pet. 2:13-17

666 WORK

Now we command you, brethren, in the name of our Lord Jesus Christ, that ye withdraw yourselves from every brother that walketh disorderly, and not after the tradition which he received of us.

For yourselves know how ye ought to follow us: for we behaved not ourselves disorderly among you;

Neither did we eat any man's bread for nought; but wrought with labour and travail night and day, that we might not be chargeable to any of you.

Not because we have not power, but to make ourselves an ensample unto you to follow us.

For even when we were with you, this we commanded you, that if any would not work, neither should he eat.

For we hear that there are some which walk among you disorderly, working not at all, but are busybodies.

Now them that are such we command and exhort by our Lord Jesus Christ, that with quietness they work, and eat their own bread.

But ye, brethren, be not weary in well doing.

2 Thess. 3:6-13

667 THE CHRISTIAN'S RESURRECTION

If in this life only we have hope in Christ, we are of all men most miserable.

But now is Christ risen from the dead, and become the firstfruits of them that slept.

For since by man came death, by man came also the resurrection of the dead.

For as in Adam all die, even so in Christ shall all be made alive.

But some man will say, How are the dead raised up? and with what body do they come?

Thou fool, that which thou sowest is not quickened, except it die:

And that which thou sowest, thou sowest not that body that shall be, but bare grain, it may chance of wheat, or of some other grain.

But God giveth it a body as it hath pleased Him, and to every seed his own body.

So also is the resurrection of the dead. It is sown in corruption; it is raised in incorruption;

It is sown in dishonour; it is raised in glory: it is sown in weakness; it is raised in power.

It is sown a natural body; it is raised a spiritual body. There is a natural body, and there is a spiritual body.

For this corruptible must put on incorruption, and this mortal must put on immortality.

So when this corruptible shall have put on incorruption, and this mortal shall have put on immortality, then shall be brought to pass the saying that is written,

Death is swallowed up in victory. O death, where is thy sting? O grave, where is thy victory?

The sting of death is sin; and the strength of sin is the law. But thanks be to God, which giveth us the victory through our Lord Jesus Christ.

Therefore, my beloved brethren, be ye stedfast, unmoveable, always abounding in the work of the Lord, forasmuch as ye know that your labour is not in vain in the Lord.

1 Cor. 15:19-22, 35-38, 42-44, 53-58

668 JUSTIFICATION THROUGH FAITH

Therefore being justified by faith, we have peace with God through our Lord Jesus Christ:

By whom also we have access by faith into this grace wherein we stand, and rejoice in hope of the glory of God.

And not only so, but we glory in tribulations also: knowing that tribulation worketh patience;

And patience, experience; and experience, hope:

And hope maketh not ashamed; because the love of God is shed abroad in our hearts by the Holy Ghost which is given unto us.

For when we were yet without strength, in due time Christ died for the ungodly.

For scarcely for a righteous man will one die: yet peradventure for a good man some would even dare to die.

But God commendeth His love toward us, in that, while we were yet sinners, Christ died for us.

Much more then, being now justified by His blood, we shall be saved from wrath through Him.

For if, when we were enemies, we were reconciled to God by the death of His Son, much more, being reconciled, we shall be saved by His life.

And not only so, but we also joy in God through our Lord Jesus Christ, by whom we have now received the atonement.

Therefore as by the offence of one judgment came upon all men to condemnation; even so by the righteousness of one the free gift came upon all men unto justification of life.

Rom. 5:1-11,18

669 MATURITY

He gave some, apostles; and some, prophets; and some, evangelists; and some, pastors and teachers;

For the perfecting of the saints, for the work of the ministry, for the edifying of the body of Christ:

Till we all come in the unity of the faith, and of the knowledge of the Son of God, unto a perfect man, unto the measure of the stature of the fulness of Christ:

That we henceforth be no more children, tossed to and fro, and carried about with every wind of doctrine, by the sleight of men, and cunning craftiness, whereby they lie in wait to deceive;

But speaking the truth in love, may grow up into Him in all things, which is the head, even Christ:

From whom the whole body fitly joined together and compacted by that which every joint supplieth, according to the effectual working in the measure of

every part, maketh increase of the body unto the edifying of itself in love.

For when for the time ye ought to be teachers, ye have need that one teach you again which be the first principles of the oracles of God; and are become such as have need of milk, and not of strong meat.

For every one that useth milk is unskilful in the word of righteousness: for he is a babe.

But strong meat belongeth to them that are of full age, even those who by reason of use have their senses exercised to discern both good and evil.

Therefore leaving the principles of the doctrine of Christ, let us go on unto perfection.

Eph. 4:11-16; Heb. 5:12-6:1

670 CHRIST'S PRIESTHOOD

Wherefore, holy brethren, partakers of the heavenly calling, consider the Apostle and High Priest of our profession, Christ Jesus;

For we have not an High Priest which cannot be touched with the feeling of our infirmities; but was in all points tempted like as we are, yet without sin.

Let us therefore come boldly unto the throne of grace, that we may obtain mercy, and find grace to help in time of need.

But this Man, because He continueth ever, hath an unchangeable priesthood.

Wherefore He is able also to save them to the uttermost that come unto God by Him, seeing He ever liveth to make intercession for them.

For such an High Priest became us, who is holy, harmless, undefiled, sepa-

rate from sinners, and made higher than the heavens;

Who needeth not daily, as those high priests, to offer up sacrifice, first for His own sins, and then for the people's: for this He did once, when He offered up Himself.

And every priest standeth daily ministering and offering oftentimes the same sacrifices, which can never take away sins:

But this Man, after He had offered one sacrifice for sins for ever, sat down on the right hand of God; from henceforth expecting till His enemies be made His footstool.

For by one offering He hath perfected for ever them that are sanctified.

Having therefore, brethren, boldness to enter into the holiest by the blood of Jesus, by a new and living way, which He hath consecrated for us, through the veil, that is to say, His flesh; and having an High Priest over the house of God;

Let us draw near with a true heart in full assurance of faith, having our hearts sprinkled from an evil conscience, and our bodies washed with pure water.

Heb. 3:1; 4:15-16; 7:24-27; 10:11-14, 19-22

671 CHRIST'S TEMPTATION

Then was Jesus led up of the Spirit into the wilderness to be tempted of the devil.

And when He had fasted forty days and forty nights, He was afterward an hungered.

And when the tempter came to Him, he said, If Thou be the Son of God, command that these stones be made bread.

But He answered and said, It is written, Man shall not live by bread alone, but by every word that proceedeth out of the mouth of God.

Then the devil taketh Him up into the holy city, and setteth Him on a pinnacle of the temple,

And saith unto Him, If Thou be the Son of God, cast Thyself down: for it is written,

He shall give His angels charge concerning Thee: and in their hands they shall bear Thee up, lest at any time Thou dash Thy foot against a stone.

Jesus said unto him, It is written again, Thou shalt not tempt the Lord thy God.

Again, the devil taketh Him up into an exceeding high mountain, and sheweth Him all the kingdoms of the world, and the glory of them;

And saith unto Him, All these things will I give Thee, if Thou wilt fall down and worship me.

Then saith Jesus unto him, Get thee hence, Satan: for it is written, Thou shalt worship the Lord thy God, and Him only shalt thou serve.

Then the devil leaveth Him, and, behold, angels came and ministered unto Him.

Matt. 4:1-11

672 ASSURANCE

And we know that all things work together for good to them that love God, to them who are the called according to His purpose.

For whom He did foreknow, He also did predestinate to be conformed to the image of His Son, that He might be the firstborn among many brethren.

Moreover whom He did predestinate, them He also called: and whom He called, them He also justified: and whom He justified, them He also glorified.

What shall we then say to these things? If God be for us, who can be against us?

He that spared not His own Son, but delivered Him up for us all, how shall He not with Him also freely give us all things?

Who shall lay any thing to the charge of God's elect? It is God that justifieth.

Who is he that condemneth? It is Christ that died, yea rather, that is risen again, who is even at the right hand of God, who also maketh intercession for us.

Who shall separate us from the love of Christ? shall tribulation, or distress, or persecution, or famine, or nakedness, or peril, or sword?

As it is written, For Thy sake we are killed all the day long; we are accounted as sheep for the slaughter.

Nay, in all these things we are more than conquerors through Him that loved us.

For I am persuaded, that neither death, nor life, nor angels, nor principalities, nor powers, nor things present, nor things to come,

Nor height, nor depth, nor any other creature, shall be able to separate us from the love of God, which is in Christ Jesus our Lord.

Rom. 8:28-39

673 SANCTIFICATION

Likewise reckon ye also yourselves to be dead indeed unto sin, but alive unto God through Jesus Christ our Lord.

Let not sin therefore reign in your mortal body, that ye should obey it in the lusts thereof.

Neither yield ye your members as instruments of unrighteousness unto sin: but yield yourselves unto God, as those that are alive from the dead, and your members as instruments of righteousness unto God.

For sin shall not have dominion over you: for ye are not under the law, but under grace.

I speak after the manner of men because of the infirmity of your flesh: for as ye have yielded your members servants to uncleanness and to iniquity unto iniquity; even so now yield your members servants to righteousness unto holiness.

For when ye were the servants of sin, ye were free from righteousness.

What fruit had ye then in those things whereof ye are now ashamed? for the end of those things is death.

But now being made free from sin, and become servants to God, ye have your fruit unto holiness, and the end everlasting life.

Walk in the Spirit, and ye shall not fulfil the lust of the flesh.

For the flesh lusteth against the Spirit, and the Spirit against the flesh: and these are contrary the one to the other: so that ye cannot do the things that ye would.

But if ye be led of the Spirit, ye are not under the law.

Now the works of the flesh are manifest, which are these; Adultery, fornication, uncleanness, lasciviousness,

Idolatry, witchcraft, hatred, variance,

emulations, wrath, strife, seditions, heresies, envyings, murders, drunkenness, revellings, and such like:

Of the which I tell you before, as I have also told you in time past, that they which do such things shall not inherit the kingdom of God.

But the fruit of the Spirit is love, joy, peace, longsuffering, gentleness, goodness, faith,

Meekness, temperance: against such there is no law.

And they that are Christ's have crucified the flesh with the affections and lusts.

If we live in the Spirit, let us also walk in the Spirit.

Rom. 6:11-14, 19-22; Gal. 5:16-25

674 DEDICATED SERVICE

I beseech you therefore, brethren, by the mercies of God, that ye present your bodies a living sacrifice, holy, acceptable unto God, which is your reasonable service.

And be not conformed to this world: but be ye transformed by the renewing of your mind, that ye may prove what is that good, and acceptable, and perfect, will of God.

For I say, through the grace given unto me, to every man that is among you, not to think of himself more highly than he ought to think; but to think soberly, according as God hath dealt to every man the measure of faith.

For as we have many members in one body, and all members have not the same office: so we, being many, are one body in Christ, and every one members one of another.

Let love be without dissimulation.

Abhor that which is evil; cleave to that which is good.

Be kindly affectioned one to another with brotherly love; in honour preferring one another;

Not slothful in business; fervent in spirit; serving the Lord;

Rejoicing in hope; patient in tribulation; continuing instant in prayer;

Distributing to the necessity of saints; given to hospitality.

Bless them which persecute you: bless, and curse not.

Rejoice with them that do rejoice, and weep with them that weep.

Be of the same mind one toward another. Mind not high things, but condescend to men of low estate. Be not wise in your own conceits.

Recompense to no man evil for evil. Provide things honest in the sight of all men. If it be possible, as much as lieth in you, live peaceably with all men.

Be not overcome of evil, but overcome evil with good.

Rom. 12:1-5, 9-18, 21

675 PERSEVERANCE

Know ye not that they which run in a race run all, but one receiveth the prize? So run, that ye may obtain.

And every man that striveth for the mastery is temperate in all things. Now they do it to obtain a corruptible crown; but we an incorruptible.

I therefore so run, not as uncertainly; so fight I, not as one that beateth the air:

But I keep under my body, and bring it into subjection: lest that by any means, when I have preached to others, I myself should be a castaway.

Work out your own salvation with fear and trembling.

For it is God which worketh in you both to will and to do of His good pleasure.

But I follow after, if that I may apprehend that for which also I am apprehended of Christ Jesus.

Brethren, I count not myself to have apprehended: but this one thing I do, forgetting those things which are behind, and reaching forth unto those things which are before,

I press toward the mark for the prize of the high calling of God in Christ Jesus.

For we are made partakers of Christ, if we hold the beginning of our confidence stedfast unto the end.

Wherefore seeing we also are compassed about with so great a cloud of witnesses, let us lay aside every weight, and the sin which doth so easily beset us, and let us run with patience the race that is set before us,

Looking unto Jesus the author and finisher of our faith; who for the joy that was set before Him endured the cross, despising the shame, and is set down at the right hand of the throne of God.

For consider Him that endured such contradiction of sinners against Himself, lest ye be wearied and faint in your minds.

Take, my brethren, the prophets, who have spoken in the name of the Lord, for an example of suffering affliction, and of patience.

Behold we count them happy which endure. Ye have heard of the patience of Job, and have seen the end of the Lord; that the Lord is very pitiful, and of tender mercy.

Wherefore the rather, brethren, give diligence to make your calling and election sure: for if ye do these things, ye shall never fall:

For so an entrance shall be ministered unto you abundantly into the everlasting kingdom of our Lord and Saviour Jesus Christ.

But ye, beloved, building up yourselves on your most holy faith, praying in the Holy Ghost,

Keep yourselves in the love of God, looking for the mercy of our Lord Jesus Christ unto eternal life.

Now unto Him that is able to keep you from falling, and to present you faultless before the presence of His glory with exceeding joy, to the only wise God our Saviour, be glory and majesty, dominion and power, both now and ever. Amen.
1 Cor. 9:24-27; Phil. 2:12-13; 3:12-14; Heb. 3:14; 12:1-3; James 5:10-11; 2 Pet. 1:10-11; Jude 20-21, 24, 25

676 RIGHTEOUSNESS

And he believed in the Lord; and He counted it to him for righteousness.

Righteousness exalteth a nation: but sin is a reproach to any people.

For I am not ashamed of the gospel of Christ: for it is the power of God unto salvation to every one that believeth; to the Jew first, and also to the Greek.

For therein is the righteousness of God revealed from faith to faith: as it is written, The just shall live by faith.

Now we know that what things soever the law saith, it saith to them who are under the law: that every mouth may be stopped, and all the world may become guilty before God.

Therefore by the deeds of the law there shall no flesh be justified in His sight: for by the law is the knowledge of sin.

But now the righteousness of God without the law is manifested, being witnessed by the law and the prophets; Even the righteousness of God which is by faith of Jesus Christ unto all and upon all them that believe:

For there is no difference: For all have sinned, and come short of the glory of God: Being justified freely by His grace through the redemption that is in Christ Jesus: Whom God hath set forth to be a propitiation through faith in His blood,

To declare His righteousness for the remission of sins that are past, through the forbearance of God;

To declare, I say, at this time His righteousness: that He might be just, and the justifier of him which believeth in Jesus.

For the promise, that he should be the heir of the world, was not to Abraham, or to his seed, through the law, but through the righteousness of faith.

Therefore as by the offence of one judgment came upon all men to condemnation; even so by the righteousness of One the free gift came upon all men unto justification of life.

For as by one man's disobedience many were made sinners, so by the obedience of One shall many be made righteous.

Moreover the law entered, that the offence might abound. But where sin abounded, grace did much more abound: that as sin hath reigned unto death, even so might grace reign through righteousness unto eternal life by Jesus Christ our Lord.

Brethren, my heart's desire and prayer to God for Israel is, that they might be saved.

For I bear them record that they have a zeal of God, but not according to knowledge.

For they being ignorant of God's righteousness, and going about to establish their own righteousness, have not submitted themselves unto the righteousness of God.

For Christ is the end of the law for righteousness to every one that believeth.
Gen. 15:6; Prov. 14:34; Rom. 1:16-17; 3:19-26; 4:13; 5:18-21; 10:1-4

677 GLORIFICATION

For I reckon that the sufferings of this present time are not worthy to be compared with the glory which shall be revealed in us.

For the earnest expectation of the creature waiteth for the manifestation of the sons of God.

For the creature was made subject to vanity, not willingly, but by reason of Him who hath subjected the same in hope, because the creature itself also shall be delivered from the bondage of corruption into the glorious liberty of the children of God.

For we know that the whole creation groaneth and travaileth in pain together until now.

And not only they, but ourselves also, which have the firstfruits of the Spirit, even we ourselves groan within ourselves, waiting for the adoption, to wit, the redemption of our body.

For we are saved by hope: but hope that is seen is not hope: for what a man seeth, why doth he yet hope for?

But if we hope for that we see not, then do we with patience wait for it.

Likewise the Spirit also helpeth our infirmities: for we know not what we should

pray for as we ought: but the Spirit itself maketh intercession for us with groanings which cannot be uttered.

And He that searcheth the hearts knoweth what is the mind of the Spirit, because He maketh intercession for the saints according to the will of God.

And we know that all things work together for good to them that love God, to them who are the called according to His purpose.

For whom He did foreknow, He also did predestinate to be conformed to the image of His Son, that He might be the firstborn among many brethren.

Moreover whom He did predestinate, them He also called: and whom He called, them He also justified: and whom He justified, them He also glorified.
Rom. 8:18-30

678 GOD'S GOODNESS

O give thanks unto the Lord; for He is good; for His mercy endureth for ever.

Save us, O God of our salvation, and gather us together, and deliver us from the heathen, that we may give thanks to Thy holy name, and glory in Thy praise.

Blessed be the Lord God of Israel for ever and ever. And all the people said, Amen, and praised the Lord.

The Lord is good, a strong hold in the day of trouble; and He knoweth them that trust in Him.

Ye have heard that it hath been said, Thou shalt love thy neighbour, and hate thine enemy.

But I say unto you, Love your enemies, and pray for them which despitefully use you, and persecute you; that ye may be the children of your Father which is in heaven:

SCRIPTURE READINGS: RESPONSIVE

For He maketh His sun to rise on the evil and on the good, and sendeth rain on the just and on the unjust.

For if ye love them which love you, what reward have ye? do not even the publicans the same?

And if ye salute your brethren only, what do ye more than others? do not even the publicans so?

Be ye therefore perfect, even as your Father which is in heaven is perfect.

Or what man is there of you, whom if his son ask bread, will he give him a stone?

Or if he ask a fish, will he give him a serpent?

If ye then, being evil, know how to give good gifts unto your children, how much more shall your Father which is in heaven give good things to them that ask Him?

Therefore all things whatsoever ye would that men should do to you, do ye even so to them: for this is the law and the prophets.

And we know that all things work together for good to them that love God, to them who are the called according to His purpose.

For whom He did foreknow, He also did predestinate to be conformed to the image of His Son, that He might be the firstborn among many brethren.

Moreover whom He did predestinate, them He also called: and whom He called, them He also justified: and whom He justified, them He also glorified.

For every creature of God is good, and nothing to be refused, if it be received with thanksgiving.

Every good gift and every perfect gift is from above and cometh down from the Father of lights, with whom is no variableness, neither shadow of turning.

Ye have tasted that the Lord is gracious.
1 Chr. 16:34-36; Nah. 1:7; Matt. 5:43-48; 7:9-12; Rom. 8:28-30; 1 Tim. 4:4; James 1:17; 1 Pet. 2:3

679 WISDOM

The proverbs of Solomon the son of David, king of Israel; to know wisdom and instruction; to perceive the words of understanding;

To receive the instruction of wisdom, justice, and judgment, and equity;

To give subtilty to the simple, to the young man knowledge and discretion.

A wise man will hear, and will increase learning; and a man of understanding shall attain unto wise counsels:

To understand a proverb, and the interpretation; the words of the wise, and their dark sayings.

The fear of the Lord is the beginning of knowledge: but fools despise wisdom and instruction.

Happy is the man that findeth wisdom, and the man that getteth understanding.

For the merchandise of it is better than the merchandise of silver, and the gain thereof than fine gold.

The fear of the Lord is the beginning of wisdom: and the knowledge of the holy is understanding.

If any of you lack wisdom, let him ask of God, that giveth to all men liberally, and upbraideth not; and it shall be given him.

Who is a wise man and endued with knowledge among you? let him shew out of a good conversation his works with meekness of wisdom.

But if ye have bitter envying and strife in your hearts, glory not, and lie not against the truth.

This wisdom descendeth not from above, but is earthly, sensual, devilish.

For where envying and strife is, there is confusion and every evil work.

But the wisdom that is from above is first pure, then peaceable, gentle, and easy to be intreated, full of mercy and good fruits, without partiality, and without hypocrisy.

And the fruit of righteousness is sown in peace of them that make peace.

Prov. 1:1-7; 3:13-14; 9:10; James 1:5; 3:13-18

680   JOY

Although the fig tree shall not blossom, neither shall fruit be in the vines; the labour of the olive shall fail, and the fields shall yield no meat; the flock shall be cut off from the fold, and there shall be no herd in the stalls:

Yet I will rejoice in the Lord, I will joy in the God of my salvation.

I thank my God upon every remembrance of you.

Always in every prayer of mine for you all making request with joy,

For your fellowship in the gospel from the first day until now;

Being confident of this very thing, that He which hath begun a good work in you will perform it until the day of Jesus Christ.

Some indeed preach Christ even of envy and strife; and some also of good will:

The one preach Christ of contention, not sincerely, supposing to add affliction to my bonds:

But the other of love, knowing that I am set for the defence of the gospel.

What then? notwithstanding, every way, whether in pretence, or in truth, Christ is preached; and I therein do rejoice, yea, and will rejoice.

Therefore, my brethren dearly beloved and longed for, my joy and crown, so stand fast in the Lord, my dearly beloved.

Rejoice in the Lord alway: and again I say, Rejoice.

Hab. 3:17-18; Phil. 1:3-6, 15-18; 4:1, 4

681   RECONCILIATION

For if, when we were enemies, we were reconciled to God by the death of His Son, much more, being reconciled, we shall be saved by His life.

And not only so, but we also joy in God through our Lord Jesus Christ, by whom we have now received the atonement.

And all things are of God, who hath reconciled us to Himself by Jesus Christ, and hath given to us the ministry of reconciliation;

To wit, that God was in Christ, reconciling the world unto Himself, not imputing their trespasses unto them; and hath committed unto us the word of reconciliation.

Now then we are ambassadors for Christ, as though God did beseech you by us: we pray you in Christ's stead, be ye reconciled to God.

But now in Christ Jesus ye who sometimes were far off are made nigh by the blood of Christ.

For He is our peace, who hath made both one, and hath broken down the middle wall of partition between us;

having abolished in His flesh the enmity, even the law of commandments contained in ordinances; for to make in Himself of twain one new man, so making peace;

And that He might reconcile both unto God in one body by the cross, having slain the enmity thereby:

And came and preached peace to you which were afar off, and to them that were nigh.

For through Him we both have access by one Spirit unto the Father.

Rom. 5:10-11; 2 Cor. 5:18-20; Eph. 2:13-18

682 VICTORY OVER SIN

What shall we say then? Shall we continue in sin, that grace may abound?

God forbid. How shall we, that are dead to sin, live any longer therein?

Know ye not, that so many of us as were baptized into Jesus Christ were baptized into His death?

Therefore we are buried with Him by baptism into death: that like as Christ was raised up from the dead by the glory of the Father, even so we also should walk in newness of life.

For if we have been planted together in the likeness of His death, we shall be also in the likeness of His resurrection:

Knowing this, that our old man is crucified with Him, that the body of sin might be destroyed, that henceforth we should not serve sin.

For he that is dead is freed from sin.

Now if we be dead with Christ, we believe that we shall also live with Him: Knowing that Christ being raised from the dead dieth no more; death hath no more dominion over Him.

For in that He died, He died unto sin once: but in that He liveth, He liveth unto God.

Likewise reckon ye also yourselves to be dead indeed unto sin, but alive unto God through Jesus Christ our Lord.

Let not sin therefore reign in your mortal body, that ye should obey it in the lusts thereof.

Neither yield ye your members as instruments of unrighteousness unto sin: but yield yourselves unto God, as those that are alive from the dead, and your members as instruments of righteousness unto God.

Rom. 6:1-13

683 CHRIST, BREAD OF LIFE

And Jesus said unto them, I am the bread of life: he that cometh to Me shall never hunger; and he that believeth on Me shall never thirst.

But I said unto you, That ye also have seen Me, and believe not.

All that the Father giveth Me shall come to Me; and him that cometh to Me I will in no wise cast out.

For I came down from heaven, not to do Mine own will, but the will of Him that sent Me.

And this is the Father's will which hath sent Me, that of all which He hath given Me I should lose nothing, but should raise it up again at the last day.

And this is the will of Him that sent Me, that every one which seeth the Son, and believeth on Him, may have everlasting life: and I will raise him up at the last day.

The Jews then murmured at Him, because He said, I am the bread which came down from heaven.

And they said, Is not this Jesus, the son of Joseph, whose father and mother we know? how is it then that He saith, I came down from heaven?

Jesus therefore answered and said unto them, Murmur not among yourselves.

No man can come to Me, except the Father which hath sent Me draw him: and I will raise him up at the last day.

It is written in the prophets, And they shall be all taught of God. Every man therefore that hath heard, and hath learned of the Father, cometh unto Me.

Not that any man hath seen the Father, save He which is of God, He hath seen the Father.

Verily, verily, I say unto you, He that believeth on Me hath everlasting life.

I am that bread of life.

John 6:35-48

684 SPIRITUAL GIFTS

Now concerning spiritual gifts, brethren, I would not have you ignorant.

But the manifestation of the Spirit is given to every man to profit withal.

For to one is given by the Spirit the word of wisdom; to another the word of knowledge by the same Spirit;

To another faith by the same Spirit; to another the gifts of healing by the same Spirit;

To another the working of miracles; to another prophecy; to another discerning of spirits; to another divers kinds of tongues; to another the interpretation of tongues:

But all these worketh that one and the selfsame Spirit, dividing to every man severally as He will.

Now ye are the body of Christ, and members in particular.

And God hath set some in the church, first apostles, secondarily prophets, thirdly teachers, after that miracles, then gifts of healings, helps, governments, diversities of tongues.

Are all apostles? are all prophets?

Are all teachers? are all workers of miracles?

Have all the gifts of healing? do all speak with tongues? do all interpret?

But covet earnestly the best gifts: and yet shew I unto you a more excellent way.

Follow after charity, and desire spiritual gifts, but rather that ye may prophesy.

For he that speaketh in an unknown tongue speaketh not unto men, but unto God: for no man understandeth him; howbeit in the Spirit he speaketh mysteries.

But he that prophesieth speaketh unto men to edification, and exhortation, and comfort.

Let all things be done decently and in order.

1 Cor. 12:1, 7-11, 27-31; 14:1-3, 40

685 CHRISTIAN CONDUCT

If ye then be risen with Christ, seek those things which are above, where Christ sitteth on the right hand of God.

Set your affection on things above, not on things on the earth.

For ye are dead, and your life is hid with Christ in God.

When Christ, who is our life, shall ap-

pear, then shall ye also appear with Him in glory.

Mortify therefore your members which are upon the earth; fornication, uncleanness, inordinate affection, evil concupiscence, and covetousness, which is idolatry:

For which things' sake the wrath of God cometh on the children of disobedience:

In the which ye also walked some time, when ye lived in them.

But now ye also put off all these; anger, wrath, malice, blasphemy, filthy communication out of your mouth.

Lie not one to another, seeing that ye have put off the old man with his deeds; and have put on the new man, which is renewed in knowledge after the image of Him that created him:

Where there is neither Greek nor Jew, circumcision nor uncircumcision, Barbarian, Scythian, bond nor free: but Christ is all, and in all.

Col. 3:1-11

686 THE GOOD SAMARITAN

And, behold, a certain lawyer stood up, and tempted Him, saying, Master, what shall I do to inherit eternal life?

He said unto him, What is written in the law? how readest thou?

And he answering said, Thou shalt love the Lord thy God with all thy heart, and with all thy soul, and with all thy strength, and with all thy mind; and thy neighbour as thyself.

And He said unto him, Thou hast answered right: this do, and thou shalt live.

But he, willing to justify himself, said unto Jesus, And who is my neighbour?

And Jesus answering said, A certain man went down from Jerusalem to Jericho, and fell among thieves, which stripped him of his raiment, and wounded him, and departed, leaving him half dead.

And by chance there came down a certain priest that way: and when he saw him, he passed by on the other side.

And likewise a Levite, when he was at the place, came and looked on him, and passed by on the other side.

But a certain Samaritan, as he journeyed, came where he was: and when he saw him, he had compassion on him, and went to him, and bound up his wounds, pouring in oil and wine, and set him on his own beast, and brought him to an inn, and took care of him.

And on the morrow when he departed, he took out two pence, and gave them to the host, and said unto him, Take care of him; and whatsoever thou spendest more, when I come again, I will repay thee.

Which now of these three, thinkest thou, was neighbour unto him that fell among the thieves?

And he said, He that shewed mercy on him. Then said Jesus unto him, Go, and do thou likewise.

Luke 10:25-37

687 PASSOVER AND THE LAST SUPPER

Then came the Day of Unleavened Bread, when the Passover must be killed.

And He sent Peter and John, saying, Go and prepare us the Passover, that we may eat.

And they said unto Him, Where wilt Thou that we prepare?

And He said unto them, Behold, when ye are entered into the city, there shall a man meet you, bearing a pitcher of water; follow him into the house where he entereth in.

And ye shall say unto the goodman of the house, The Master saith unto thee, Where is the guestchamber, where I shall eat the Passover with My disciples?

And he shall shew you a large upper room furnished: there make ready.

And they went, and found as He had said unto them: and they made ready the Passover.

And when the hour was come, He sat down, and the twelve apostles with Him.

And He said unto them, With desire I have desired to eat this Passover with you before I suffer:

For I say unto you, I will not any more eat thereof, until it be fulfilled in the kingdom of God.

And He took the cup, and gave thanks, and said, Take this, and divide it among yourselves:

For I say unto you, I will not drink of the fruit of the vine, until the kingdom of God shall come.

And He took bread, and gave thanks, and brake it, and gave unto them, saying, This is My body which is given for you: this do in remembrance of Me.

Likewise also the cup after supper, saying, This cup is the new testament in My blood, which is shed for you.

Luke 22:7-20

688 THE CHRISTIAN'S BAPTISM

Go ye therefore, and teach all nations, baptizing them in the name of the Father, and of the Son, and of the Holy Ghost.

Repent, and be baptized every one of you in the name of Jesus Christ for the remission of sins, and ye shall receive the gift of the Holy Ghost.

Then he called for a light, and sprang in, and came trembling, and fell down before Paul and Silas,

And brought them out, and said, Sirs, what must I do to be saved?

And they said, Believe on the Lord Jesus Christ, and thou shalt be saved, and thy house.

And they spake unto him the word of the Lord, and to all that were in his house.

And he took them the same hour of the night, and washed their stripes; and was baptized, he and all his, straightway.

And when he had brought them into his house, he set meat before them, and rejoiced, believing in God with all his house.

Know ye not, that so many of us as were baptized into Jesus Christ were baptized into His death?

Therefore we are buried with Him by baptism into death: that like as Christ was raised up from the dead by the glory of the Father, even so we also should walk in newness of life.

In whom also ye are circumcised with the circumcision made without hands, in putting off the body of the sins of the flesh by the circumcision of Christ:

Buried with Him in baptism, wherein also ye are risen with Him through the faith of the operation of God, who hath raised Him from the dead.

<small>Matt. 28:29; Acts 2:38; 16:29-34;
Rom. 6:3-4; Col. 2:11-12</small>

689 FELLOWSHIP

That which was from the beginning, which we have heard, which we have seen with our eyes, which we have looked upon, and our hands have handled, of the Word of life;

For the life was manifested, and we have seen it, and bear witness, and shew unto you that eternal life, which was with the Father, and was manifested unto us;

That which we have seen and heard declare we unto you, that ye also may have fellowship with us: and truly our fellowship is with the Father, and with His Son Jesus Christ.

And these things write we unto you,

that your joy may be full.

This then is the message which we have heard of Him, and declare unto you, that God is Light, and in Him is no darkness at all.

If we say that we have fellowship with Him, and walk in darkness, we lie, and do not the truth:

But if we walk in the light, as He is in the light, we have fellowship one with another, and the blood of Jesus Christ His Son cleanseth us from all sin.

If we say that we have no sin, we deceive ourselves, and the truth is not in us.

If we confess our sins, He is faithful and just to forgive us our sins, and to cleanse us from all unrighteousness.

If we say that we have not sinned, we make Him a liar, and His word is not in us.

<small>1 John 1</small>

Worship & Celebrate

PSALMS FOR UNISON READING
OR PERSONAL MEDITATION

690 PSALM 1

Blessed is the man that walketh not in
the counsel of the ungodly, nor
standeth in the way of sinners, nor
sitteth in the seat of the scornful.
But his delight is in the law of the Lord;
and in His law doth he meditate day
and night.
And he shall be like a tree planted by
the rivers of water, that bringeth
forth his fruit in his season; his
leaf also shall not wither; and
whatsoever he doeth shall prosper.

The ungodly are not so: but are like the
chaff which the wind driveth away.
Therefore the ungodly shall not stand
in the judgment, nor sinners in the
congregation of the righteous.

For the Lord knoweth the way of the
righteous: but the way of the
ungodly shall perish.

691 PSALM 2

Why do the heathen rage, and the
people imagine a vain thing?
The kings of the earth set themselves,
and the rulers take counsel together,
against the Lord, and against His
Anointed, saying,
Let us break their bands asunder, and
cast away their cords from us.
He that sitteth in the heavens shall
laugh: the Lord shall have them in
derision.
Then shall He speak unto them in His
wrath, and vex them in His sore
displeasure.
Yet have I set My King upon My holy
hill of Zion.

I will declare the decree: the Lord hath
said unto Me, Thou art My Son; this
day have I begotten Thee.
Ask of Me, and I shall give Thee the
heathen for Thine inheritance, and
the uttermost parts of the earth for
Thy possession.
Thou shalt break them with a rod of
iron; Thou shalt dash them in pieces
like a potter's vessel.

Be wise now therefore, O ye kings: be
instructed, ye judges of the earth.
Serve the Lord with fear, and rejoice
with trembling.
Kiss the Son, lest He be angry, and ye
perish from the way, when His
wrath is kindled but a little. Blessed
are all they that put their trust in
Him.

692 PSALM 16

Preserve me, O God: for in Thee do I
put my trust.

O my soul, thou hast said unto the
Lord, Thou art my Lord: my
goodness extendeth not to Thee;
But to the saints that are in the earth,
and to the excellent, in whom is all
my delight.
Their sorrows shall be multiplied that
hasten after another god: their drink
offerings of blood will I not offer,
nor take up their names into my lips.
The Lord is the portion of mine
inheritance and of my cup: Thou
maintainest my lot.
The lines are fallen unto me in pleasant
places; yea, I have a goodly heritage.

I will bless the Lord, who hath given
me counsel: my reins also instruct
me in the night seasons.
I have set the Lord always before me:
because He is at my right hand, I
shall not be moved.

Therefore my heart is glad, and my
glory rejoiceth: my flesh also shall
rest in hope.

For Thou wilt not leave my soul in hell;
neither wilt Thou suffer Thine Holy
One to see corruption.
Thou wilt shew me the path of life: in
Thy presence is fulness of joy; at
Thy right hand there are pleasures
for evermore.

693 PSALM 19

The heavens declare the glory of God;
and the firmament sheweth His
handywork.
Day unto day uttereth speech, and
night unto night sheweth
knowledge.
There is no speech nor language, where
their voice is not heard.
Their line is gone out through all the
earth, and their words to the end of
the world.
In them hath He set a tabernacle for the
sun, which is as a bridegroom
coming out of his chamber, and
rejoiceth as a strong man to run a
race.
His going forth is from the end of the
heaven, and His circuit unto the ends
of it: and there is nothing hid from
the heat thereof.

The law of the Lord is perfect,
converting the soul: the testimony of
the Lord is sure, making wise the
simple.
The statutes of the Lord are right,
rejoicing the heart: the commandment
of the Lord is pure, enlightening
the eyes.
The fear of the Lord is clean, enduring
for ever: the judgments of the Lord
are true and righteous altogether.

More to be desired are they than gold,
yea, than much fine gold: sweeter
also than honey and the honeycomb.
Moreover by them is Thy servant
warned: and in keeping of them
there is great reward.

Who can understand his errors?
cleanse thou me from secret faults.

Keep back Thy servant also from
presumptuous sins; let them not
have dominion over me: then shall I
be upright, and I shall be innocent
from the great transgression.

Let the words of my mouth, and the
meditation of my heart, be
acceptable in Thy sight, O Lord, my
Strength, and my Redeemer.

694 PSALM 22

My God, my God, why hast Thou
forsaken me? why art Thou so far
from helping me, and from the
words of my roaring?
O my God, I cry in the daytime, but
Thou hearest not; and in the night
season, and am not silent.

But Thou art holy, O Thou that
inhabitest the praises of Israel.
Our fathers trusted in Thee: they
trusted, and Thou didst deliver
them.
They cried unto Thee, and were
delivered: they trusted in Thee, and
were not confounded.

Dogs have compassed me: the
assembly of the wicked have
enclosed me: they pierced my hands
and my feet.
I may tell all my bones: they look and
stare upon me.
They part my garments among them,
and cast lots upon my vesture.

But be not Thou far from me, O Lord:
O my strength, haste Thee to help
me.

Deliver my soul from the sword; my
darling from the power of the dog.
Save me from the lion's mouth: for
Thou hast heard me from the horns
of the unicorns.

I will declare Thy name unto my
brethren: in the midst of the
congregation will I praise Thee.

My praise shall be of Thee in the great
congregation: I will pay my vows
before them that fear Him.
The meek shall eat and be satisfied:
they shall praise the Lord that seek
Him: your heart shall live for ever.
All the ends of the world shall
remember and turn unto the Lord:
and all the kindreds of the nations
shall worship before Thee.
For the kingdom is the Lord's: and He
is the governor among the nations.

695 PSALM 23

The Lord is my shepherd; I shall not
want.
He maketh me to lie down in green
pastures: He leadeth me beside the
still waters.
He restoreth my soul: He leadeth me in
the paths of righteousness for His
name's sake.
Yea, though I walk through the valley
of the shadow of death, I will fear no
evil: for Thou art with me; Thy rod
and Thy staff they comfort me.

Thou preparest a table before me in the
presence of mine enemies: Thou
anointest my head with oil; my cup
runneth over.
Surely goodness and mercy shall
follow me all the days of my life: and
I will dwell in the house of the Lord
for ever.

696 PSALM 24

The earth is the Lord's, and the fulness
thereof; the world, and they that
dwell therein.
For He hath founded it upon the seas,
and established it upon the floods.

Who shall ascend into the hill of the
Lord? or who shall stand in His holy
place?
He that hath clean hands, and a pure
heart; who hath not lifted up his soul
unto vanity, nor sworn deceitfully.

He shall receive the blessing from the
Lord, and righteousness from the
God of his salvation.
This is the generation of them that seek
Him, that seek Thy face, O Jacob.
Lift up your heads, O ye gates; and be
ye lift up, ye everlasting doors; and
the King of glory shall come in.
Who is this King of glory? The Lord
strong and mighty, the Lord mighty
in battle.

Lift up your heads, O ye gates; even lift
them up, ye everlasting doors; and
the King of glory shall come in.
Who is this King of glory? The Lord of
hosts, He is the King of glory.

697 PSALM 27

The Lord is my light and my salvation;
whom shall I fear? the Lord is the
strength of my life; of whom shall I
be afraid?
When the wicked, even mine enemies
and my foes, came upon me to eat
up my flesh, they stumbled and fell.
Though an host should encamp against
me, my heart shall not fear; though
war should rise against me, in this
will I be confident.

One thing have I desired of the Lord,
that will I seek after; that I may
dwell in the house of the Lord all the
days of my life, to behold the beauty
of the Lord, and to inquire in His
temple.

Hear, O Lord, when I cry with my
voice: have mercy also upon me,
and answer me.
When Thou saidst, Seek ye My face;
my heart said unto Thee, Thy face,
Lord, will I seek.
Hide not Thy face far from me; put not
Thy servant away in anger: Thou
hast been my help; leave me not,
neither forsake me, O God of my
salvation.
When my father and my mother forsake
me, then the Lord will take me up.

Teach me Thy way, O Lord, and lead
me in a plain path, because of mine
enemies.

I had fainted, unless I had believed to
see the goodness of the Lord in the
land of the living.
Wait on the Lord: be of good courage,
and He shall strengthen thine heart:
wait, I say, on the Lord.

698 PSALM 32

Blessed is he whose transgression is
forgiven, whose sin is covered.
Blessed is the man unto whom the Lord
imputeth not iniquity, and in whose
spirit there is no guile.

When I kept silence, my bones waxed
old through my roaring all the day
long.
For day and night Thy hand was heavy
upon me: my moisture is turned into
the drought of summer.

I acknowledged my sin unto Thee, and
mine iniquity have I not hid. I said, I
will confess my transgressions unto
the Lord; and Thou forgavest the
iniquity of my sin.

For this shall every one that is godly
pray unto Thee in a time when Thou
mayest be found: surely in the floods
of great waters they shall not come
nigh unto him.
Thou art my hiding place; Thou shalt
preserve me from trouble; Thou
shalt compass me about with songs
of deliverance.

I will instruct thee and teach thee in the
way which thou shalt go: I will guide
thee with Mine eye.
Be ye not as the horse, or as the mule,
which have no understanding:
whose mouth must be held in with
bit and bridle, lest they come near
unto thee.
Many sorrows shall be to the wicked:

but he that trusteth in the Lord,
mercy shall compass him about.

Be glad in the Lord, and rejoice, ye
righteous: and shout for joy, all ye
that are upright in heart.

699 PSALM 33

Rejoice in the Lord, O ye righteous: for
praise is comely for the upright.
Sing unto Him a new song; play
skillfully with a loud noise.

For the word of the Lord is right; and
all His works are done in truth.
He loveth righteousness and judgment:
the earth is full of the goodness of
the Lord.

By the word of the Lord were the
heavens made; and all the host of
them by the breath of His mouth.
Let all the earth fear the Lord: let all the
inhabitants of the world stand in
awe of Him.
For He spake, and it was done; He
commanded, and it stood fast.
The Lord bringeth the counsel of the
heathen to nought: He maketh the
devices of the people of none effect.
The counsel of the Lord standeth for
ever, the thoughts of His heart to all
generations.

Our soul waiteth for the Lord: He is
our help and our shield.
For our heart shall rejoice in Him,
because we have trusted in His holy
name.
Let thy mercy, O Lord, be upon us,
according as we hope in Thee.

700 PSALM 40

I waited patiently for the Lord; and He
inclined unto me, and heard my cry.
He brought me up also out of an
horrible pit, out of the miry clay,
and set my feet upon a rock, and
established my goings.

And He hath put a new song in my mouth, even praise unto our God: many shall see it, and fear, and shall trust in the Lord.

Blessed is that man that maketh the Lord his trust, and respecteth not the proud, nor such as turn aside to lies.

Many, O Lord my God, are Thy wonderful works which Thou hast done, and Thy thoughts which are to us-ward: they cannot be reckoned up on order unto Thee: if I would declare and speak of them, they are more than can be numbered.

Sacrifice and offering Thou didst not desire; mine ears hast Thou opened: burnt offering and sin offering hast Thou not required.

Then said I, Lo, I come: in the volume of the book it is written of me,

I delight to do Thy will, O my God: yea, Thy law is within my heart.

I have preached righteousness in the great congregation: lo, I have not refrained my lips, O Lord, Thou knowest.

I have not hid Thy righteousness within my heart; I have declared Thy faithfulness and Thy salvation: I have not concealed Thy lovingkindness and Thy truth from the great congregation.

701 PSALM 42

As the hart panteth after the water brooks, so panteth my soul after Thee, O God.

My soul thirsteth for God, for the living God: when shall I come and appear before God?

My tears have been my meat day and night, while they continually say unto me, Where is thy God?

When I remember these things, I pour out my soul in me: for I had gone with the multitude, I went with them to the house of God, with the voice of joy and praise, with a multitude that kept holyday.

Why art thou cast down, O my soul? and why art thou disquieted in me? hope thou in God: for I shall yet praise Him for the help of His countenance.

O my God, my soul is cast down within me: therefore will I remember Thee from the land of Jordan, and of the Hermonites, from the hill Mizar.

Deep calleth unto deep at the noise of Thy waterspouts: all Thy waves and Thy billows are gone over me.

Yet the Lord will command His lovingkindness in the daytime, and in the night His song shall be with me, and my prayer unto the God of my life.

I will say unto God my Rock, Why hast Thou forgotten me? why go I mourning because of the oppression of the enemy?

As with a sword in my bones, mine enemies reproach me; while they say daily unto me, Where is thy God?

Why art thou cast down, O my soul? and why art thou disquieted within me? hope thou in God: for I shall yet praise Him, who is the health of my countenance, and my God.

702 PSALM 46

God is our refuge and strength, a very present help in trouble.

Therefore will not we fear, though the earth be removed, and though the mountains be carried into the midst of the sea;

Though the waters thereof roar and be troubled, though the mountains shake with the swelling thereof.

There is a river, the streams whereof shall make glad the city of God, the holy place of the tabernacles of the Most High.

God is in the midst of her; she shall not be moved: God shall help her, and that right early.

The heathen raged, the kingdoms were moved: He uttered His voice, the earth melted.

The Lord of hosts is with us; the God of Jacob is our refuge.

Come, behold the works of the Lord, what desolations He hath made in the earth.
He maketh wars to cease unto the end of the earth; He breaketh the bow, and cutteth the spear in sunder; He burneth the chariot in the fire.
Be still, and know that I am God: I will be exalted among the heathen, I will be exalted in the earth.

The Lord of hosts is with us; the God of Jacob is our refuge.

703 PSALM 51

Have mercy upon me, O God, according to Thy lovingkindness: according unto the multitude of Thy tender mercies blot out my transgressions.
Wash me thoroughly from mine iniquity, and cleanse me from my sin.

For I acknowledge my transgressions: and my sin is ever before me.
Against Thee, Thee only, have I sinned, and done this evil in Thy sight: that Thou mightest be justified when Thou speakest, and be clear when Thou judgest.
Behold, I was shapen in iniquity; and in sin did my mother conceive me.
Behold, Thou desirest truth in the inward parts: and in the hidden part Thou shalt make me to know wisdom.

Purge me with hyssop, and I shall be clean: wash me, and I shall be whiter than snow.
Make me to hear joy and gladness; that the bones which Thou hast broken may rejoice.

Hide Thy face from my sins, and blot out all mine iniquities.

Create in me a clean heart, O God; and renew a right spirit within me.
Cast me not away from Thy presence; and take not Thy Holy Spirit from me.
Restore unto me the joy of Thy salvation; and uphold me with Thy free spirit.

Then will I teach transgressors Thy ways; and sinners shall be converted unto Thee.
Deliver me from bloodguiltiness, O God, Thou God of my salvation: and my tongue shall sing aloud of Thy righteousness.
O Lord, open Thou my lips; and my mouth shall shew forth Thy praise.
For Thou desirest not sacrifice; else would I give it: Thou delightest not in burnt offering.
The sacrifices of God are a broken spirit: a broken and a contrite heart, O God, Thou wilt not despise.

704 PSALM 65

Praise waiteth for Thee, O God, in Sion: and unto Thee shall the vow be performed.
O Thou that hearest prayer, unto Thee shall all flesh come.
Iniquities prevail against me: as for our transgressions, Thou shalt purge them away.
Blessed is the man whom Thou choosest, and causest to approach unto Thee, that he may dwell in Thy courts: we shall be satisfied with the goodness of Thy house, even of Thy holy temple.

By terrible things in righteousness wilt Thou answer us, O God of our salvation; who art the confidence of all the ends of the earth, and of them that are afar off upon the sea.
They also that dwell in the uttermost parts are afraid at Thy tokens: Thou

makest the outgoings of the morning
and evening to rejoice.
Thou visitest the earth, and waterest it:
Thou greatly enrichest it with the
river of God, which is full of water:
Thou preparest them corn, when
Thou hast so provided for it.
Thou crownest the year with Thy
goodness; and Thy paths drop
fatness.
They drop upon the pastures of the
wilderness: and the little hills rejoice
on every side.

The pastures are clothed with flocks;
the valleys also are covered over
with corn; they shout for joy, they
also sing.

705   PSALM 84

How amiable are Thy tabernacles, O
Lord of hosts!
My soul longeth, yea, even fainteth for
the courts of the Lord: my heart and
my flesh crieth out for the living
God.

Yea, the sparrow hath found an house,
and the swallow a nest for herself,
where she may lay her young, even
Thine altars, O Lord of hosts, my
King, and my God.
Blessed are they that dwell in Thy
house: they will be still praising
Thee.

Blessed is the man whose strength is in
Thee; in whose heart are the ways of
them.
Who passing through the valley of
Baca make it a well; the rain also
filleth the pools.
They go from strength to strength,
every one of them in Zion appeareth
before God.

O Lord God of hosts, hear my prayer:
give ear, O God of Jacob.

For a day in Thy courts is better than a
thousand. I had rather be a door-

keeper in the house of my God, than
to dwell in the tents of wickedness.

For the Lord God is a sun and shield:
the Lord will give grace and glory:
no good thing will He withhold from
them that walk uprightly.
O Lord of hosts, blessed is the man that
trusteth in Thee.

706   PSALM 90

Lord, Thou hast been our dwelling
place in all generations.
Before the mountains were brought
forth, or ever Thou hadst formed the
earth and the world, even from everlasting to everlasting, Thou art God.
Thou turnest man to destruction; and
sayest, Return, ye children of men.
For a thousand years in Thy sight are
but as yesterday when it is past, and
as a watch in the night.

Thou hast set our iniquities before
Thee, our secret sins in the light of
Thy countenance.
For all our days are passed away in
Thy wrath: we spend our years as a
tale that is told.
The days of our years are threescore
years and ten; and if by reason of
strength they be fourscore years, yet
is their strength labour and sorrow;
for it is soon cut off, and we fly
away.
So teach us to number our days, that
we may apply our hearts unto
wisdom.

O satisfy us early with Thy mercy; that
we may rejoice and be glad all our
days.
Make us glad according to the days
wherein Thou hast afflicted us, and
the years wherein we have seen evil.

Let Thy work appear unto Thy
servants, and Thy glory unto their
children.

And let the beauty of the Lord our God

be upon us: and establish Thou the
work of our hands upon us; yea, the
work of our hands establish Thou it.

707 PSALM 91

He that dwelleth in the secret place of
the Most High shall abide under the
shadow of the Almighty.
I will say of the Lord, He is my refuge
and my fortress: my God; in Him
will I trust.

Surely He shall deliver thee from the
snare of the fowler, and from the
noisome pestilence.
He shall cover thee with His feathers,
and under His wings shalt thou trust:
His truth shall be thy shield and
buckler.
Thou shalt not be afraid for the terror
by night; nor for the arrow that
flieth by day;
Nor for the pestilence that walketh in
darkness; nor for the destruction
that wasteth at noonday.
A thousand shall fall at thy side, and
ten thousand at thy right hand; but it
shall not come nigh thee.
Only with thine eyes shalt thou behold
and see the reward of the wicked.

Because thou hast made the Lord,
which is my refuge, even the Most
High, thy habitation;
There shall no evil befall thee, neither
shall any plague come nigh thy
dwelling.
For He shall give His angels charge
over thee, to keep thee in all thy
ways.
They shall bear thee up in their hands,
lest thou dash thy foot against a
stone.

Because he hath set his love upon Me,
therefore will I deliver him: I will set
him on high, because he hath known
My name.
He shall call upon Me, and I will
answer him: I will be with him in
trouble; I will deliver him,

and honour him.
With long life will I satisfy him, and
shew him My salvation.

708 PSALM 95

O come, let us sing unto the Lord: let
us make a joyful noise to the Rock of
our salvation.
Let us come before His presence with
thanksgiving, and make a joyful
noise unto Him with psalms.

For the Lord is a great God, and a great
King above all gods.
In His hand are the deep places of the
earth: the strength of the hills is
His also.
The sea is His, and He made it: and His
hands formed the dry land.

O come, let us worship and bow down:
let us kneel before the Lord our
Maker.
For He is our God; and we are the
people of His pasture, and the sheep
of His hand.
To day if ye will hear His voice,

Harden not your heart, as in the
provocation, and as in the day of
temptation in the wilderness:
When your fathers tempted Me,
proved Me, and saw My work.
Forty years long was I grieved with this
generation, and said, It is a people
that do err in their heart, and they
have not known My ways:
Unto whom I sware in My wrath that
they should not enter into My rest.

709 PSALM 100

Make a joyful noise unto the Lord, all
ye lands.
Serve the Lord with gladness: come
before His presence with singing.
Know ye that the Lord He is God: it is
He that hath made us, and not we
ourselves; we are His people, and the
sheep of His pasture.

Enter into His gates with thanksgiving,
and into His courts with praise: be
thankful unto Him, and bless His
name.

For the Lord is good; His mercy is
everlasting; and His truth endureth
to all generations.

710 PSALM 103

Bless the Lord, O my soul, and all that
is within me, bless His holy name.

Bless the Lord, O my soul, and forget
not all His benefits:

Who forgiveth all thine iniquities; who
healeth all thy diseases;

Who redeemeth thy life from
destruction; who crowneth thee with
lovingkindness and tender mercies;

Who satisfieth thy mouth with good
things; so that thy youth is renewed
like the eagle's.

The Lord is merciful and gracious,
slow to anger, and plenteous in
mercy.

He will not always chide: neither will
He keep His anger for ever.

He hath not dealt with us after our
sins; nor rewarded us according to
our iniquities.

For as the heaven is high above the
earth, so great is His mercy toward
them that fear Him.

As far as the east is from the west, so
far hath He removed our
transgressions from us.

Like as a father pitieth his children, so
the Lord pitieth them that fear Him.

For He knoweth our frame; He
remembereth that we are dust.

As for man, his days are as grass: as a
flower of the field, so he flourisheth.

For the wind passeth over it, and it is
gone; and the place thereof shall
know it no more.

But the mercy of the Lord is from
everlasting to everlasting upon them that fear Him,
and His righteousness unto
children's children;

To such as keep His covenant, and to
those that remember His
commandments to do them.

The Lord hath prepared His throne in
the heavens; and His kingdom ruleth
over all.

Bless the Lord, O my soul.

711 PSALM 110

The Lord said unto my Lord, Sit Thou
at My right hand, until I make Thine
enemies Thy footstool.

The Lord shall send the rod of Thy
strength out of Zion: rule Thou in
the midst of Thine enemies.

Thy people shall be willing in the day
of Thy power, in the beauties of
holiness from the womb of the
morning: Thou hast the dew of Thy
youth.

The Lord hath sworn, and will not
repent, Thou art a priest for ever
after the order of Melchizedek.

The Lord at Thy right hand shall strike
through kings in the day of His
wrath.

He shall judge among the heathen, He
shall fill the places with the dead
bodies; He shall wound the heads
over many countries.

He shall drink of the brook in the way:
therefore shall He lift up the head.

712 PSALM 118

O give thanks unto the Lord; for He is
good: because His mercy endureth
for ever.

I called upon the Lord in distress: the
Lord answered me, and set me in a
large place.

The Lord is on my side; I will not fear:
what can man do unto me?

The Lord taketh my part with them
that help me: therefore shall I see my
desire upon them that hate me.

It is better to trust in the Lord than to
put confidence in man.

It is better to trust in the Lord than to
put confidence in princes.

Thou hast thrust sore at me that I
might fall: but the Lord helped me.

The Lord is my strength and song, and
is become my salvation.

The voice of rejoicing and salvation is
in the tabernacles of the righteous:
the right hand of the Lord doeth
valiantly.
The right hand of the Lord is exalted:
the right hand of the Lord doeth
valiantly.

I shall not die, but live, and declare the
works of the Lord.
The Lord hath chastened me sore: but
He hath not given me over unto
death.

Open to me the gates of righteousness:
I will go into them, and I will praise
the Lord:
This gate of the Lord, into which the
righteous shall enter.
I will praise Thee: for Thou hast heard
me, and art become my salvation.

The stone which the builders refused is
become the head stone of the corner.
This is the Lord's doing; it is marvellous
in our eyes.
This is the day which the Lord hath
made; we will rejoice and be glad
in it.

713 PSALM 121

I will lift up mine eyes unto the hills,
from whence cometh my help.
My help cometh from the Lord, which
made heaven and earth.

He will not suffer thy foot to be
moved: He that keepeth thee will not
slumber.
Behold, He that keepeth Israel shall
neither slumber nor sleep.
The Lord is thy keeper: the Lord is thy
shade upon thy right hand.
The sun shall not smite thee by day,
nor the moon by night.

The Lord shall preserve thee from all
evil: He shall preserve thy soul.

The Lord shall preserve thy going out
and thy coming in from this time
forth, and even for evermore.

714 PSALM 139

O Lord, Thou hast searched me, and
known me.
Thou knowest my downsitting and
mine uprising, Thou understandest
my thought afar off.
Thou compassest my path and my
lying down, and art acquainted with
all my ways.
For there is not a word in my tongue,
but, lo, O Lord, Thou knowest it
altogether.

Whither shall I go from Thy spirit? or
whither shall I flee from Thy
presence?
If I ascend up into heaven, Thou art
there: if I make my bed in hell,
behold, Thou art there.
If I take the wings of the morning, and
dwell in the uttermost parts of the sea;
Even there shall Thy hand lead me, and
Thy right hand shall hold me.

For Thou hast possessed my reins:
Thou hast covered me in my
mother's womb.
I will praise Thee; for I am fearfully
and wonderfully made: marvellous
are Thy works; and that my soul
knoweth right well.
My substance was not hid from Thee,
when I was made in secret, and
curiously wrought in the lowest
parts of the earth.
Thine eyes did see my substance, yet
being unperfect; and in Thy book all
my members were written, which in
continuance were fashioned, when
as yet there was none of them.

How precious also are Thy thoughts
unto me, O God! how great is the
sum of them!

If I should count them, they are more
in number than the sand: when I

awake, I am still with Thee.
Search me, O God, and know my
heart: try me, and know my
thoughts:
And see if there be any wicked way in
me, and lead me in the way
everlasting.

715 PSALM 145

I will extol Thee, my God, O King; and
I will bless Thy name for ever and
ever.

Great is the Lord, and greatly to be
praised; and His greatness is
unsearchable.
One generation shall praise Thy works
to another, and shall declare Thy
mighty acts.
They shall speak of the glory of Thy
kingdom, and talk of Thy power;
To make known to the sons of men His
mighty acts, and the glorious
majesty of His kingdom.
Thy kingdom is an everlasting
kingdom, and Thy dominion

endureth throughout all generations.

The Lord upholdeth all that fall, and
raiseth up all those that be bowed
down.
The eyes of all wait upon Thee; and
Thou givest them their meat in due
season.
Thou openest Thine hand, and
satisfiest the desire of every living
thing.

The Lord is righteous in all His ways,
and holy in all His works.
The Lord is nigh unto all them that call
upon Him, to all that call upon Him
in truth.

He will fulfill the desire of them that
fear Him: He also will hear their cry,
and will save them.
The Lord preserveth all them that love
Him: but all the wicked will He
destroy.

My mouth shall speak the praise of the
Lord: and let all flesh bless His holy
name for ever and ever.

Worship & Celebrate

AFFIRMATIONS OF FAITH AND TE DEUM

716 THE APOSTLES' CREED

I believe in God the Father Almighty, maker of heaven and earth:

And in Jesus Christ His only Son, our Lord; who was conceived by the Holy Spirit, born of the Virgin Mary, suffered under Pontius Pilate, was crucified, dead, and buried; He descended into hades; the third day He rose again from the dead; He ascended into heaven, and sitteth on the right hand of God, the Father Almighty; from thence He shall come to judge the quick and the dead.

I believe in the Holy Spirit, the holy Christian church, the communion of saints, the forgiveness of sins, the resurrection of the body, and the life ever-lasting. Amen.

717 THE NICENE CREED

I believe in one God the Father Almighty, Maker of heaven and earth, and of all things visible and invisible:

And in one Lord Jesus Christ, the only-begotten Son of God, begotten of His Father before all worlds, God of God, Light of Light, very God of very God, begotten, not made, being of one substance with the Father, by whom all things were made;
　　Who for us men and for our salvation came down from heaven,
　　　　and was incarnate by the Holy Spirit of the Virgin Mary,
　　　　and was made man, and crucified also for us under Pontius Pilate;
　　He suffered and was buried, and the third day He rose again
　　　　according to the Scriptures, and ascended into heaven,
　　　　and sitteth on the right hand of the Father;
　　And He shall come again with glory to judge both the quick
　　　　and the dead;
　　Whose kingdom shall have no end.

And I believe in the Holy Spirit, the Lord and Giver of life, who proceedeth from the Father and the Son, who with the Father and the Son together is worshiped and glorified; who spoke by the prophets. And I believe in one catholic and apostolic church; I acknowledge one baptism for the remission of sins, and I look for the resurrection of the dead, and the life of the world to come. Amen.

718   A CONTEMPORARY AFFIRMATION OF FAITH

We believe in Jesus Christ the Lord,
    Who was promised to the people of Israel,
    Who came in the flesh to dwell among us,
    Who announced the coming of the rule of God,
    Who gathered disciples and taught them,
    Who died on the cross to free us from sin,
    Who rose from the dead to give us life and hope,
    Who reigns in heaven at the right hand of God,
    Who comes to judge and bring justice to victory.

We believe in God His Father,
    Who raised Him from the dead,
    Who created and sustains the universe,
    Who acts to deliver His people in times of need,
    Who desires all men everywhere to be saved,
    Who rules over the destinies of men and nations,
    Who continues to love men even when they reject Him.

We believe in the Holy Spirit,
    Who is the form of God present in the church,
    Who moves men to faith and obedience,
    Who is the guarantee of our deliverance,
    Who leads us to find God's will in the Word,
    Who assists those whom He renews in prayer,
    Who guides us in discernment,
    Who impels us to act together.

We believe God has made us His people,
    To invite others to follow Christ,
    To encourage one another to deeper commitment,
    To proclaim forgiveness of sins and hope,
    To reconcile men to God through word and deed,
    To bear witness to the power of love over hate,
    To proclaim Jesus the Lord over all,
    To meet the daily tasks of life with purpose,
    To suffer joyfully for the cause of right,
        To the ends of the earth,
        To the end of the age,
        To the praise of His glory. Amen.

719 TE DEUM

We praise Thee, O God:
We acknowledge Thee to be the Lord.
All the earth doth worship Thee, the Father everlasting.
To Thee all angels cry aloud;
The heavens and all the powers therein.
To Thee cherubim and seraphim continually do cry:
Holy, Holy, Holy, Lord God of Sabaoth.
Heaven and earth are full of the majesty of Thy glory.
The glorious company of the apostles praise Thee.
The goodly fellowship of the prophets praise Thee.
The noble army of martyrs praise Thee.
The holy Church, throughout all the world, doth acknowledge Thee.
The Father of an infinite majesty;
Thine adorable, true, and only Son,
Also the Holy Spirit, the comforter.
Thou art the King of glory, O Christ.
Thou art the everlasting Son of the Father.
When Thou tookest upon Thee to deliver man,
Thou didst humble Thyself to be born of a virgin.
When Thou hadst overcome the sharpness of death,
Thou didst open the kingdom of heaven to all believers.
Thou sittest at the right hand of God, in the glory of the Father.
We believe that Thou shalt come to be our Judge.
We therefore pray Thee, help Thy servants,
Whom Thou hast redeemed with Thy precious blood.
Make them to be numbered with Thy saints in glory everlasting.
O Lord, save Thy people, and bless Thy heritage.
Govern them, and lift them up forever.
Day by day we magnify Thee;
And we worship Thy name ever, world without end.
Vouchsafe, O Lord, to keep us this day without sin.
O Lord, have mercy upon us, have mercy upon us.
O Lord, let Thy mercy be upon us, as our trust is in Thee.
O Lord, in Thee have I trusted;
Let me never be confounded.

INDEXES FOR
SCRIPTURAL RESOURCES

CONTENTS

ALPHABETICAL INDEX OF SCRIPTURE AND OTHER READINGS

TOPICAL INDEX OF SCRIPTURE AND OTHER READINGS

The subject headings for this index are coordinated with
the subject headings in the Topical Index of Hymns

SCRIPTURAL INDEX OF SCRIPTURE READINGS

Worship & Celebrate

INDEX OF SPOKEN CALLS TO WORSHIP AND BENEDICTIONS

INDEX OF NON-SCRIPTURAL READINGS

INDEXES
FOR THE HYMNS

CONTENTS

INDEX OF SCRIPTURE APPEARING
WITH HYMN TITLES

INDEX OF SCRIPTURE TEXTS AND ADAPTATIONS IN HYMNS

INDEX OF BRIEF SERVICES AND MEDLEYS

Brief Services

7 PRAISE GOD IN HIS SANCTUARY - A Brief Service of Worship and Exaltation
Theme: God Our Father - His Adoration and Praise
Selections included: *Praise to the Lord, the Almighty; Praise the Lord! Ye Heavens, Adore Him; O Worship the King*

28 HOW MAJESTIC IS YOUR NAME - A Brief Service in Recognition of God's Majesty and Power
Theme: God Our Father - His Majesty and Power
Selections included: *Glorify Thy Name; How Majestic Is Your Name; Great Is the Lord*

48 LEAD US, O GOD - A Brief Service of Prayer and Petition
Theme: God Our Father - His Guidance and Care
Selections included: *Lead Me, Lord; The Lord's My Shepherd, I'll Not Want; Guide Me, O Thou Great Jehovah; O God, Our Help in Ages Past*

86 GIVE HIM GLORY - A Brief Service Exalting Our Lord, Jesus Christ
Theme: Jesus Our Savior - His Adoration and Praise
Selections included: *May Jesus Christ Be Praised; Fairest Lord Jesus; Our Great Savior*

99 THE NAME OF JESUS - A Brief Service of Worship and Praise
Theme: Jesus Our Savior - His Adoration and Praise
Selections included: *There Is No Name So Sweet on Earth; His Name Is Wonderful; There's Something About That Name; Blessed Be the Name*

122 THE ADVENT OF OUR LORD - A Brief Service of Joyful Expectation
Theme: Jesus Our Savior - His Advent
Selections included: *O Come, O Come, Emmanuel; Come, Thou Long-Expected Jesus; Joy to the World!*

130 GLORIA IN EXCELSIS DEO - A Brief Service of Proclamation and Praise
Theme: Jesus Our Savior - His Birth
Selections included: *Angels from the Realms of Glory; Angels We Have Heard on High; Hark! the Herald Angels Sing*

142 FOR UNTO US A CHILD IS BORN - A Brief Service in Celebration of Our Lord's Birth
Theme: Jesus Our Savior - His Birth
Selections included: *Infant Holy, Infant Lowly; How Great Our Joy!; O Come, All Ye Faithful; For Unto Us a Child Is Born*

182 GLORY IN THE CROSS - A Brief Service of Reflection and Praise
Theme: Jesus Our Savior - His Cross
Selections included: *Beneath the Cross of Jesus; In the Cross of Christ I Glory; When I Survey the Wondrous Cross*

194 I KNOW A FOUNT - A Medley
Theme: Jesus Our Savior - His Blood
Selections included: *I Know a Fount; Nothing But the Blood*

200 GOD'S AMAZING GRACE - A Brief Service in Recognition of His Love and Provision
Theme: Jesus Our Savior - His Grace, Love and Mercy
Selections included: *Grace Greater Than Our Sin; Amazing Grace; And Can It Be?*

214 HE IS RISEN! ALLELUIA! - A Brief Service in Celebration of Our Lord's Resurrection
Theme: Jesus Our Savior - His Resurrection
Selections included: *Alleluia! Alleluia!; Christ Arose; Christ the Lord Is Risen Today*

290 THE LIVING CHURCH - A Brief Service of Prayer and Challenge
Theme: The Church - Renewal and Revival
Selections included: *O Breath of Life; God of Grace and God of Glory; Rise Up, O Church of God*

361 MY GOD, I LOVE THEE - A Brief Service of Adoration and Commitment
Theme: Life in Christ - Commitment and Consecration
Selections included: *I Love Thee; More Love to Thee; My Jesus, I Love Thee*

386 IN HIS IMAGE - A Brief Service of Aspiration and Hope
Theme: Life in Christ - Aspiration
Selections included: *O to Be Like Thee!; I Would Be Like Jesus; More About Jesus*

403 A LIVING HOPE - A Brief Service of Affirmation and Renewal
Theme: Life in Christ - Faith and Hope
Selections included: *The Solid Rock; My Faith Has Found a Resting Place; My Hope Is in the Lord*

459 THE LORD IS MY SHEPHERD - A Brief Service in Recognition of His Leadership
Theme: Life in Christ - Provision and Leading
Selections included: *All the Way My Savior Leads Me; He Leadeth Me; Savior, Like a Shepherd Lead Us*

476 SOLDIERS OF CHRIST, ARISE - A Brief Service of Challenge and Victory
Theme: Life in Christ - Spiritual Warfare
Selections included: *Stand Up, Stand Up for Jesus; Soldiers of Christ, Arise; Onward, Christian Soldiers*

491 PERFECT PEACE - A Brief Service in Recognition of His Provision
Theme: Life in Christ - Inner Peace and Joy
Selections included: *Thou Wilt Keep Him in Perfect Peace; It Is Well with My Soul; Like a River Glorious*

509 MY LIFE, MY JOY, MY ALL - A Brief Service of Testimony and Praise
Theme: Life in Christ - Testimony and Praise
Selections included: *Jesus Is All the World to Me; Now I Belong to Jesus; My Savior's Love; O, How He Loves You and Me*

540 AN UPWARD LOOK - A Brief Service of Joyful Anticipation
Theme: Life Everlasting
Selections included: *He the Pearly Gates Will Open; When We All Get to Heaven; When the Roll Is Called Up Yonder*

558 WITH A SONG OF THANKSGIVING - A Brief Service of Praise to God, the Creator
Theme: Thanksgiving
Selections included: *Come, Ye Thankful People, Come; For the Beauty of the Earth; We Gather Together*

570 ONE NATION, UNDER GOD - A Medley
Theme: Patriotic
Selections included: *My Country, 'Tis of Thee; America, the Beautiful; God of Our Fathers*

Medleys

55-56 Theme: God Our Father - His Guidance and Care
Selections included: *Day by Day - A Prayer*
Day by Day

152-153 Theme: Jesus Our Savior - His Birth
Selections included: *I Heard the Bells on Christmas Day*
Come On, Ring Those Bells

194-195 Theme: Jesus Our Savior - His Blood
Selections included: *I Know a Fount*
Nothing But the Blood

520-521 Theme: Life in Christ - Testimony and Praise
Selections included: *Redeemed (Ada)*
Redeemed (Kirkpatrick)

549-550 Theme: Life Everlasting
Selections included: *Face to Face*
Saved by Grace

570-573 Theme: Patriotic
Selections included: *My Country, 'Tis of Thee*
America, the Beautiful
God of Our Fathers

INDEX OF DESCANTS, LAST STANZA HARMONIZATIONS AND CHORAL ENDINGS

DESCANTS

Battle Hymn of the Republic, 569
Blessed Assurance, 345
Child of Love, 156
Faith of Our Fathers, 279
He Keeps Me Singing, 488
Holy God, We Praise Thy Name, 12
Holy, Holy, Holy, 262
Hosanna, Loud Hosanna, 174
I Will Call upon the Lord, 38
Jesus Shall Reign, 231
Like a River Glorious, 494

My Hope Is in the Lord, 406
O Worship the King, 10
Onward, Christian Soldiers, 479
Our Great Savior, 89
Pure and Holy, 437
Rejoice, the Lord Is King, 228
Rise Up, O Church (Men) of God, 293
Seek Ye First, 42
To God Be the Glory, 66
We Praise Thee, O God, Our Redeemer, 16

LAST STANZA HARMONIZATIONS AND SETTINGS

Alleluia, 91
Battle Hymn of the Republic, 569
Because He Lives, 213
Come, Thou Almighty King, 267
Crown Him with Many Crowns, 234
God of Our Fathers, 573
Hallelujah, What a Savior!, 175
How Great Thou Art, 4
I Sing the Mighty Power of God, 59
In the Name of the Lord, 90

Jesus Shall Reign, 231
Lead On, O King Eternal, 483
O For a Thousand Tongues, 76
O Worship the King, 10
Rise Up, O Church (Men) of God, 293
Take My Life and Let It Be, 379
We Gather Together, 561
We Will Glorify, 72
When I Survey the Wondrous Cross, 185

CHORAL ENDINGS

All Hail the Power of Jesus' Name (Coronation), 97
And Can It Be?, 203
Battle Hymn of the Republic, 569
Blessed Be the Name, 103
Christ the Lord Is Risen Today, 217
Come, Christians, Join to Sing, 108
Come, Thou Almighty King, 267
Crown Him with Many Crowns, 234
Faith of Our Fathers, 279
For Unto Us a Child Is Born, 146
Great Is the Lord, 31
Great Is Thy Faithfulness, 43
Hark! the Herald Angels Sing, 133
Hosanna, Loud Hosanna, 174
How Great Thou Art, 4
I Have Decided to Follow Jesus, 376
I Sing the Mighty Power of God, 59
I'll Fly Away, 554
In Remembrance, 322
Joy to the World!, 125

Lead On, O King Eternal, 483
Like a River Glorious, 494
Love Divine, All Loves Excelling, 92
More About Jesus, 389
My Hope Is in the Lord, 406
My Jesus, I Love Thee, 364
O For a Thousand Tongues, 76
O God, Our Help in Ages Past, 52
O, How He Loves You and Me, 513
Our Great Savior, 89
Rejoice, the Lord Is King, 228
Resurrection Canon, 221
Savior, Like a Shepherd Lead Us, 462
The Savior Is Waiting, 329
To God Be the Glory, 66
We Gather Together, 561
We Praise Thee, O God, Our Redeemer, 16
We Shall Behold Him, 237
When I Survey the Wondrous Cross, 185
When the Roll Is Called Up Yonder, 543

INDEX OF COPYRIGHT OWNERS

The use of the valid copyrights of the following publishers and individuals is gratefully acknowledged. In each case, rearranging, photocopying, or reproduction by any other means, as well as the use of the song in performance for profit, is specifically prohibited by law without the written permission of the copyright owner.

ALBERT E. BRUMLEY AND SONS, *Down In Memory Lane, Powell, MO 65730:* Selections 294, 473, 554

BIRDWING MUSIC/CHERRY LANE MUSIC PUB. CO., INC. *c/o Sparrow Corp., 9255 Deering Ave., Chatsworth, CA 91311:* Selections 15, 206

BROADMAN PRESS *The Sunday School Board, 127 Ninth Ave. North, Nashville, TN 37234:* Selections 85, 251, 302, 322, 360, 367, 408, 455, 520

BUG AND BEAR MUSIC (exclusive admin. by LCS MUSIC GROUP) *P.O. Box 7409, Dallas, TX 75209:* Selections 104, 272

CHANCEL MUSIC (a div. of WORD, INC.) *5221 N. O'Connor Blvd., Suite 1000, Irving, TX 75039:* Selection 456

CHERRY BLOSSOM MUSIC CO. *c/o Sparrow Corp., 9255 Deering Ave., Chatsworth, CA 91311:* Selection 411

CHRISTIAN ARTISTS MUSIC *P.O. Box 1984, Thousand Oaks, CA 91360:* Selection 134

CHRISTIAN PUBLICATIONS *3825 Hartzdale Dr., Camp Hill, PA 17011:* Selection 472

CHURCH HYMNAL CORP., THE *800 2nd Ave. (at 42nd St.) New York, NY 10017:* Selection 575

COVENANT PRESS (Covenant Book Concern) *5101 N. Francisco Ave. North, Chicago, IL 60625:* Selection 254

CRUMP, ELUNED AND DILYS EVANS *Tan-y-Coed, Uxbridge Square, Caernarvon, North Wales LL552:* Selections 211, 475

DUNAMIS MUSIC *8319 Lankershim Blvd., N. Hollywood, CA 91605:* Selection 115

DUNKERLEY, DESMOND *23 Haslemere Road, Southsea, Portsmouth, Hants PO4 8BB England:* Selection 285

EVANGELICAL COVENANT CHURCH, THE *5101 N. Francisco Ave. North, Chicago, IL 60625:* Selection 315

FAIRHILL MUSIC *P.O. Box 933, Newbury Park, CA 91320:* Selection 485

FARJEON, ELEANOR (see Harold Ober Associates, Inc.): Selection 60

FARJEON, GERVASE AND M.S.H. JONES (See Harold Ober Associates, Inc.): Selection 60

FARNSWORTH MUSIC (Division of Music by Hummingbird) *P.O. Box 120753, Nashville, TN 37212:* Selection 437

F.E.L. PUBLICATIONS, LTD. *2545 Chandler Ave., Suite 5, Las Vegas, NV 89120:* Selection 284

FOX PUBLICATIONS *P.O. Box 333, Tarzana, CA 91356:* Selection 300

FRED BOCK MUSIC COMPANY *P.O. Box 333, Tarzana, CA 91356:* Selections 73, 283, 536

G. SCHIRMER, INC. *866 3rd Ave., New York, NY 10022:* Selections 3, 139, 347, 426, 535

GAITHER MUSIC COMPANY (William J. Gaither) *P.O. Box 737, Alexandria, IN 46001:* Selections 90, 98, 102, 107, 114, 213, 238, 250, 282, 359, 446, 458, 504, 518, 519, 564

GOOD LIFE PUBLICATIONS *c/o Columbia Pictures Publications, P.O. Box 4340, Hialeah, FL 33041:* Selection 417

HAROLD OBER ASSOCIATES, INC. *40 East 49th Street, New York, NY 10017:* Selection 60

HILL AND RANGE SONGS, INC. (All rights controlled by Unichappel Music, Inc.—Rightsong Music, Publisher) *c/o Hal Leonard Pub. Corp., 8112 West Bluemound Rd., Milwaukee, WI 53213:* Selection 463

HIS EYE MUSIC *c/o Sparrow Corp., 9255 Deering Ave., Chatsworth, CA 91311:* Selection 411

HOLLIS MUSIC, INC. *c/o The Richman Organization, 10 Columbus Circle, New York, NY 10019:* Selection 150

HOPE PUBLISHING CO. *Carol Stream, IL 60188:* Selections 27, 43, 176, 198, 245, 429, 514, 568

HOUSE OF MERCY (admin. by Maranatha! Music) *P.O. Box 31050, Laguna Hills, CA 92654-1050:* Selection 80

HYMN SOCIETY OF AMERICA (represented by Hope Publishing Co.) *Carol Stream, IL 60188:* Selection 454

HYMNS ANCIENT AND MODERN, LTD. *St. Mary's Works, St. Mary's Plain, Norwich, Norfolk NR3 3BH, England:* Selection 304

INTERVARSITY CHRISTIAN FELLOWSHIP *InterVarsity Press, Box 1400, Downers Grove, IL 60515:* Selection 117

JOHN T. BENSON PUBLISHING CO. (The Benson Co., Inc.) *365 Great Circle Dr., Nashville, TN 37228:* Selections 179, 237

JOHN W. PETERSON MUSIC COMPANY *13610 N. Scottsdale Rd., #10-221, Scottsdale, AZ 85254:* Selections 239, 464, 495, 524

JOY OF THE LORD PUBLISHING *c/o Sparrow Corp., 9255 Deering Ave., Chatsworth, CA 91311:* Selection 411

LANNY WOLFE MUSIC *c/o Pathway Press, P.O. Box 2250, Cleveland, TN 37320:* Selection 255

LATTER RAIN MUSIC *c/o Sparrow Corp., 9255 Deering Ave., Chatsworth, CA 91311:* Selections 93, 222

LeFEVRE-SING PUBLISHING CO. *P.O. Box 460, Smyrna, GA 30081:* Selection 332

LEXICON MUSIC, INC. (Assigned to MacKenzie and Associates, Inc.), *23 Music Sq. E., Suite 101, Nashville, TN 37203:* Selections 11, 13, 23, 24, 40, 53, 256, 266, 309, 447, 516, 551, 626

LILLENAS PUBLISHING CO. *P.O. Box 527, Kansas City, MO 64141:* Selections 83, 165, 244, 281, 400, 415, 583

LIVING WAY MINISTRIES *14300 Sherman Way, Van Nuys, CA 91405-2499:* Selections 225, 407

Any omission or inaccuracy of copyright notices on individual hymns will be corrected in subsequent printings wherever valid information is offered by the claimants.

ALPHABETICAL INDEX OF TUNES

Worship & Celebrate

METRICAL INDEX OF TUNES

INDEX OF KEYS

Worship & Celebrate

INDEX OF AUTHORS, COMPOSERS, SOURCES, TRANSLATORS AND ARRANGERS

Lathbury, Mary Artemisia (1841-1913): 22, 274
Latin carol (14th century): 151
Latin hymn: 123, 145, 276
Latin poem, Medieval: 178
Leavitt, Joshua (1794-1873): 584
Leech, Bryan Jeffery (1931-   ): 283, 315, 456, 536
LeFevre, Mylon R. (1944-   ): 332
Lehman, Frederick M. (1868-1953): 67
Lemmel, Helen Howarth (1864-1961): 335
Liles, Dwight (1957-   ): 104
Lillenas, Haldor (1885-1959): 198
Linn, Joseph (1945-   ): 203
Lloyd, Eva B. (1912-   ): 455
Loizeaux, Alfred Samuel (1877-1962): 268
Long, Lela (19th century): 95
Longfellow, Henry Wadsworth (1807-1882): 152
Longstaff, William Dunn (1822-1894): 441, 442
Lowden, Carl Harold (1883-1963): 372
Lowell, James Russel (1819-1891): 475
Lowry, Robert (1826-1899): 195, 216, 428, 445, 460, 555
Luther, Martin (1483-1546): 26
Lutkin, Peter Christian (1858-1931): 607
Lvov, Alexis F. (1799-1870): 33
Lyon, Meyer (1751-1799): 34, 472
Lyra Davidica (1708), London: 217
Lyte, Henry Francis (1793-1847): 3, 377, 419

Mackay, William Paton (1839-1885): 295
Madan, Martin (1725-1790): 241
Main, Hubert Platt (1839-1925): 377
Maker, Frederick Charles (1844-1927): 183, 427
Malan, Henri Abraham César (1787-1864): 379
Malotte, Albert Hay (1895-1964): 426
Mann, Arthur Henry (1850-1929): 369
Maori melody: 438
Marsh, Charles Howard (1886-1956): 170, 236
Martin, Civilla Durfee (1869-1948): 47
Martin, Walter Stillman (1862-1935): 47
Mason, Lowell (1792-1872): 76, 110, 125, 185, 196, 286, 393, 410, 440, 448, 587
Matheson, George (1842-1906): 374
Matthews, Timothy Richard (1826-1910): 127
Mayfield, Larry (1944-   ): 592
McAfee, Cleland Boyd (1866-1944): 497
McClard, LeRoy (1926-   ): 360
McCutchan, Robert Guy (1877-1958): 593
McDaniel, Rufus Henry (1850-1940): 515
McFarland, John Thomas (1851-1913): 157, 158
McGee, Bob (1949-   ): 134
McGranahan, James (1840-1907): 289, 301, 409, 506
McGuire, Dony (1951-   ): 40
McHugh, Phill (1951-   ): 90, 197, 303
McIntosh, Rigdon McCoy (1836-1899): 552
McKinney, Baylus Benjamin (1886-1952): 85, 251, 367, 408, 544
Medema, Ken (1943-   ): 429, 591
Medley, Samuel (1738-1799): 110
Meece, David (1952-   ): 164, 209
Meineke, Christoph (1782-1850): 622
Melodia Sacra (1815), Weyman's: 135
Mendelssohn, Felix (1809-1847): 133, 269, 502, 556, 598
Merrill, William Pierson (1867-1954): 293
Messiter, Arthur Henry (1834-1916): 562
Mieir, Audrey (1916-   ): 101
Miles, C. Austin (1868-1946): 425
Miller, Rhea F. (1894-1966): 517
Millhuff, Charles (1938-   ): 238
Mills, Pauline M. (1898-   ): 73
Mitchell, Hubert (1907-   ): 415
Mitchell, Hugh (1914-   ): 69

Mohr, Joseph (1792-1848): 147
Monk, William Henry (1823-1889): 419, 560
Monsell, John Samuel Bewley (1811-1875): 165
Montgomery, James (1771-1854): 21, 131, 321
Moody, May Whittle (1870-1963): 351
Moore, Thomas (1779-1852): 416
Moore, William (19th century): 454, 585
Morris, Lelia Naylor (1862-1929): 245, 260, 392
Mote, Edward (1797-1874): 402, 404
Mountain, James (1844-1933): 315, 490, 494, 503
Mozart, Wolfgang Amadeus (1756-1791): 377, 584
Münster Gesangbuch (1677): 88
Murray, James Ramsey (1841-1905): 157

Naegeli, Johann Georg (1773-1836): 286
Neale, John Mason (1818-1866): 118, 123, 151, 173, 226, 276
Neander, Joachim (1650-1680): 8
Neidlinger, William Harold (1900-   ): 162
Nelson, Greg (1948-   ): 197, 303, 564
Netherlands Folk song: 16, 561
Netherlands Folk hymn: 561
Neumark, Georg (1621-1681): 600
Neuvermehrtes Gesangbuch (1693), Meiningen: 269
Newbolt, Michael R. (1874-1956): 304
Newell, William Reed (1868-1956): 338
Newton, John (1725-1807): 94, 202, 278, 608
Nichol, Henry Ernest (1862-1928): 296
Nicholson, James L. (1828-1876): 436
Nicholson, Sydney Hugo (1875-1947): 304
Niles, John Jacob (1892-1980): 139
Ninth Symphony (1839), Ludwig van Beethoven's: 1, 215
Noel, Caroline Maria (1817-1877): 235
Norris, John Samuel (1844-1907): 373
Nusbaum, Cyrus S. (1861-1937): 333

Oakeley, Frederick (1802-1880): 145
Oatman, Johnson, Jr. (1856-1922): 399, 422, 563
Oliver, Henry Kemble (1800-1885): 317
Olivers, Thomas (1725-1799): 34
Olson, Ernst William (1870-1958): 44
Orr, James Edwin (1912-   ): 438, 439
Ortlund, Anne (1923-   ): 316
O'Shields, Michael (1948-   ): 38
Osler, Edward (1798-1863): 9
Owens, Carol (1931-   ): 447
Owens, Jimmy (1930-   ): 23, 24, 256, 266, 626
Owens, Priscilla Jane (1829-1907): 306
Owens-Collins, Jamie (1955-   ): 485
Oxenham, John (1852-1941): 285

Palmer, Ray (1808-1887): 410, 501
Palmgren, Gerhard W. (1880-1959): 254
Paris, Twila (1958-   ): 72, 288
Parker, Debi J. (1961-   ): 63
Parker, Edwin Pond (1836-1925): 248
Parks, Joe Eldridge (1927-   ): 583
Parry, Joseph (1841-1903): 466
Patillo, Leon (1947-   ): 308
Peace, Albert Lister (1844-1912): 374
Pearce, Almeda J. (1893-   ): 240
Pennefather, William (1816-1873): 586
Perronet, Edward (1726-1792): 96, 97
Peterson, John Willard (1921-   ): 45, 239, 310. 417, 464, 495, 524
Phelps, Sylvanus Dryden (1816-1895): 445
Phillips, Keith (1941-   ): 206, 218, 272, 323, 564
Pierpoint, Folliott Sanford (1835-1917): 560
Pigott, Jean Sophia (1845-1882): 503

Worship & Celebrate

TOPICAL INDEX OF HYMNS

ADORATION AND PRAISE
God Our Father

A Mighty Fortress Is Our God, 26
Abba Father, 15
All Creatures of Our God and King, 64
All People That on Earth Do Dwell, 20
Be Exalted, O God, 5
Bless His Holy Name, 13
Children of the Heavenly Father, 44
Clap Your Hands, 24
Come Let Us Worship and Bow Down, 14
Come, Thou Almighty King, 267
Come, Thou Fount of Every Blessing, 2
Come, We That Love the Lord, 18
Doxology, 624
Doxology (Alternate Rhythm), 625
Doxology (Owens), 626
El Shaddai, 36
Father, I Adore You, 265
For the Beauty of the Earth, 560
Gloria Patri (Greatorex), 623
Gloria Patri (Meinecke), 622
Glorify Thy Name, 29
God Is So Good, 41
God, Our Father, We Adore Thee, 268
Great Are You, O Lord, 39
Great Is Thy Faithfulness, 43
Hallelujah Chorus, 37
Holy God, We Praise Thy Name, 12
Holy, Holy, 266
How Great Thou Art, 4
Isaiah 6:3, 22
It Is Good to Sing Thy Praises, 584
Joyful, Joyful, We Adore Thee, 1
Make a Joyful Noise, 23
My Tribute, 11
O God, Our Help in Ages Past, 52
O Worship the King, 10
Praise, My Soul, the King of Heaven, 3
Praise the Lord! Ye Heavens, Adore Him, 9
Praise to the Lord, the Almighty, 8
Praise Ye the Triune God, 264
Sing Praise to God Who Reigns Above, 6
Stand Up and Bless the Lord, 21
The God of Abraham Praise, 34
The Majesty and Glory of Your Name, 35
The Wonder of It All, 65
To God Be the Glory, 66
We Praise Thee, O God, Our Redeemer, 16
We Worship and Adore You, 19
Ye Servants of God, 17

ADORATION AND PRAISE
Jesus Our Savior

All for Jesus, 368

All Glory, Laud and Honor, 173
All Hail the Power of Jesus' Name (Coronation), 97
All Hail the Power of Jesus' Name (Diadem), 96
All That Thrills My Soul, 526
Alleluia, 91
Alleluia! Alleluia!, 215
Amazing Grace, 202
Blessed Assurance, 345
Blessed Be the Name, 103
Blessing and Honor, 78
Christ Is Made the Sure Foundation, 276
Christ, We Do All Adore Thee, 597
Come and Praise the Lord Our King, 171
Come, Christians, Join to Sing, 108
Fairest Lord Jesus, 88
Glorious Is Thy Name, 85
Glory to His Name, 527
Grace Greater Than Our Sin, 201
Hallowed Be the Name, 84
He Is Here, He Is Here, 256
He Is Lord, 105
He Touched Me, 504
His Name Is Life, 114
His Name Is Wonderful, 101
How Great Our Joy!, 144
How Sweet the Name of Jesus Sounds, 94
I Am His, and He Is Mine, 490
I Just Came to Praise the Lord, 113
I Love Thee, 362
I Love You, Lord, 80
I Will Sing of My Redeemer, 506
I'd Rather Have Jesus, 517
In the Name of the Lord, 90
Jesus, I Am Resting, Resting, 503
Jesus Is the Sweetest Name I Know, 95
Jesus, Name Above All Names, 112
Jesus, the Very Thought of Thee, 79
Jesus, Thou Joy of Loving Hearts, 501
Jesus, We Just Want to Thank You, 98
Join All the Glorious Names, 111
King of Heaven, Lord Most High, 104
King of Kings, 77
Let's Just Praise the Lord, 107
Lord, We Praise You, 83
Love Divine, All Loves Excelling, 92
Majestic Sweetness Sits Enthroned, 109
Majesty, 74
May Jesus Christ Be Praised, 87
My Jesus, I Love Thee, 364
O Come, Let Us Adore Him, 82
O Could I Speak the Matchless Worth, 110
O for a Thousand Tongues, 76
O the Deep, Deep Love of Jesus (Bunessan), 212
O the Deep, Deep Love of Jesus (Ebenezer), 211
Our Great Savior, 89
Praise Him! Praise Him!, 106
Praise the Name of Jesus, 93

Praise the Savior, 75
Sometimes "Alleluia", 115
Take the Name of Jesus with You, 116
There Is No Name So Sweet on Earth, 100
There's Something About That Name, 102
Thou Art Worthy, 73
We Come, O Christ, to You, 117
We Will Glorify, 72
What a Wonderful Savior!, 81

ADVENT
(see CHRIST - Advent)

AMENS
628

ASCENSION
(see CHRIST - Ascension and Reign)

ASPIRATION

A Charge to Keep I Have, 448
Aspiration Canon, 391
Be Thou My Vision, 382
Breathe on Me, 251
Breathe on Me, Breath of God, 259
Bring Back the Springtime, 396
Come, Thou Fount of Every Blessing, 2
Day by Day - A Prayer, 55
Dear Lord and Father of Mankind, 427
Draw Nigh to God, 397
Fill Me Now, 261
Fill My Cup, Lord, 398
Footsteps of Jesus, 470
Higher Ground, 399
I Am Thine, O Lord, 358
I Want to Be Like Jesus, 400
I Would Be Like Jesus, 388
In My Life Lord, Be Glorified, 394
Just a Closer Walk with Thee, 380
Lead Me to Calvary, 176
Make Me a Blessing, 452
May the Mind of Christ, My Savior, 390
More About Jesus, 389
More Love to Thee, 363
My Faith Looks Up to Thee, 410
Near the Cross, 385
Nearer, My God, to Thee, 393
Nearer, Still Nearer, 392
O for a Heart to Praise My God, 440
O to Be Like Thee!, 387
Open My Eyes, That I May See, 381
Open Our Eyes, Lord, 383
Psalm 42, 401
Search Me, 434
Set My Soul Afire, 294
Spirit of God, Descend upon My Heart, 249
Teach Me Thy Way, O Lord, 395
To Be Like Jesus, 384

ASSURANCE

A Child of the King, 352
A Mighty Fortress Is Our God, 26
A Shelter in the Time of Storm, 353
All the Way My Savior Leads Me, 460
Amazing Grace, 202
Be Calm My Soul, 421
Be Still and Know, 343
Be Still, My Soul, 347
Blessed Assurance, 345
Children of the Heavenly Father, 44
Christ Is Made the Sure Foundation, 276
Day by Day, 56
God Will Take Care of You, 47
Grace Greater Than Our Sin, 201
He Leadeth Me, 461
He Lives, 220
He's Got the Whole World in His Hands, 344
Hiding in Thee, 348
How Firm a Foundation, 275
I Am His, and He Is Mine, 490
I Am Trusting Thee, Lord Jesus, 346
I Know Whom I Have Believed, 409
Is It the Crowning Day?, 236
Jesus, I Am Resting, Resting, 503
Jesus Lives, and So Shall I, 224
Jesus Loves Even Me, 357
Leaning on the Everlasting Arms, 354
Moment by Moment, 351
My Faith Has Found a Resting Place, 405
My Hope Is in the Lord, 406
No, Not One!, 422
O God, Our Help in Ages Past, 52
Praise the Savior, 75
Standing on the Promises, 271
Surely Goodness and Mercy, 45
The Solid Rock (Melita), 402
The Solid Rock (Solid Rock), 404
This Is My Father's World, 58
'Tis So Sweet to Trust in Jesus, 350
Trust and Obey, 349
Trusting Jesus, 355
Under His Wings, 356
We Shall Behold Him, 237
We'll Understand It Better By and By, 544
Yesterday, Today and Tomorrow, 523

ATONEMENT

(see CHRIST - Atonement)

BABY DEDICATION

(see DEDICATION OF CHILDREN AND PARENTS)

BAPTISM

All the Way My Savior Leads Me, 460
Come Holy Spirit, Dove Divine, 320
I'll Live for Him, 370
Jesus, I My Cross Have Taken, 377
Just As I Am, 342
O Happy Day!, 532

O Master, Let Me Walk with Thee, 451
Take My Life and Let It Be, 379
Trust and Obey, 349
We Bless the Name of Christ, the Lord, 319
Where He Leads Me, 373
Wherever He Leads I'll Go, 367

BENEDICTIONS

Benediction, 612
Go Now and Live for the Savior, 610
Lord, Let Us Now Depart in Peace, 609
May the Grace of Christ, Our Savior, 608
Now unto the King, 611
The Lord Bless You and Keep You, 607

BIBLE

(see WORD OF GOD)

BLOOD OF CHRIST

(See CHRIST - Cleansing Blood)

BROTHERHOOD

(see SOCIAL CONCERN)

CALLS TO WORSHIP

(Choral)

Cast Thy Burden upon the Lord, 598
Christ, We Do All Adore Thee, 597
Now to the King of Heaven, 595
O Worship the Lord, 593
Praise Ye the Name of the Lord, 596
The Lord Is in His Holy Temple, 594

CALLS TO WORSHIP

(Spoken)

599

CANONS AND ROUNDS

A Doxology Canon, 627
Aspiration Canon, 391
Be Joyful, 223
Behold, What Manner of Love, 71
Blessing and Honor, 78
Clap Your Hands, 24
Father, I Adore You, 265
For God So Loved, 205
For Health and Strength, 566
Great Are You, O Lord, 39
He Is Coming, 246
His Way, 54
Holy Lord, 32
I Am a Soldier of the Cross!, 480
In His Cross I Glory, 187
Jesus Is Born, 149
Jesus Is King, 230
King of Kings, 77
Make a Joyful Noise, 23
Rejoice in the Lord Always, 489
Resurrection Canon, 221
Search Me, 434
Sing Praise, 263
We Thank You, Lord, 565

CHILDREN'S HYMNS

All Things Bright and Beautiful, 578
Children of the Heavenly Father, 44
Commit Thy Way, 581
Fairest Lord Jesus, 88
Gentle Shepherd, 458
God Leads Us Along, 46
Jesus Loves Even Me, 357
Jesus Loves Me, 579
Jesus Loves the Little Children, 580
Reach Your Hand, 582
Savior, Like a Shepherd Lead Us, 462
The Wise May Bring Their Learning, 583
This Is My Father's World, 58
Yesterday, Today and Tomorrow, 523

CHORUSES

(Scripture and Praise)

A Nativity Prayer, 126
A Perfect Heart, 40
Abba Father, Abba Father, 15
As for Me and My House, 537
Be Exalted, O God, 5
Bless His Holy Name, 13
Child of Love, 156
Come Celebrate Jesus, 324
Come Let Us Reason, 591
Come Let Us Worship and Bow Down, 14
Come on, Ring Those Bells, 153
Commit Thy Way, 581
Cover Me, 469
Day by Day - A Prayer, 55
Draw Nigh to God, 397
El Shaddai, 36
Emmanuel, 134
Gentle Shepherd, 458
Glorify Thy Name, 29
Go Ye into All the World, 301
God Is So Good, 41
Great Is the Lord, 31
Greater Is He That Is in Me, 255
He Careth for You, 57
He Is Lord, 105
He's Everything to Me, 516
His Name Is Life, 114
His Name Is Wonderful, 101
How Majestic Is Your Name, 30
I Know a Fount, 194
I Know That My Redeemer Liveth, 218
I Love You, Lord, 80
I Will Call upon the Lord, 38
I Will Serve Thee, 446
I Will Sing of the Mercies, 457
In My Life Lord, Be Glorified, 394
In the Name of the Lord, 90
In This Quiet Moment, 592
Isaiah 6:3, 22
Jesus Is the Sweetest Name I Know, 95
Jesus Loves the Little Children, 580
Jesus, Name Above All Names, 112
Lead Me, Lord, 49
Let's Just Praise the Lord, 107

Lord, Lay Some Soul upon My Heart, 313
Lord, Listen to Your Children Praying, 429
Majesty, 74
O, How He Loves You and Me, 513
Only Believe, 420
Open Our Eyes, Lord, 383
People Need the Lord, 303
Praise the Name of Jesus, 93
Saved by Grace, 550
Seek Ye First, 42
Something Beautiful, 519
Sometimes "Alleluia", 115
Spirit of the Living God, 247
Sweet, Sweet Spirit, 252
The Bond of Love, 281
The Family of God, 282
The King Is Coming, 238
The New 23rd, 53
The Trees of the Field, 244
There Is No Name So Sweet on Earth, 100
There's Something About That Name, 102
This Is the Day, 590
Thou Art Worthy, 73
Thou Wilt Keep Him in Perfect Peace, 492
Through It All, 507
Thy Loving Kindness, 69
Thy Word, 272
To Be Like Jesus, 384
Turn Your Eyes upon Jesus, 335
We Are the Reason, 209
We Will Stand, 474
We Worship and Adore You, 19
Welcome, Welcome, 260
What Can I Give Him?, 154
Where the Spirit of the Lord Is, 253
Worthy Is the Lamb, 180
Yesterday, Today and Tomorrow, 523

CHRIST - Adoration and Praise
(see ADORATION AND PRAISE - Jesus Our Savior)

CHRIST - Advent
(see also CHRIST - Birth)
Come, Thou Long-Expected Jesus, 124
Joy to the World!, 125
O Come, Let Us Adore Him, 82
O Come, O Come, Emmanuel, 123
O Thou Joyful, O Thou Wonderful 119
Of the Father's Love Begotten, 118
The Advent of Our God, 120
The Word Made Flesh, 121

CHRIST - Ascension and Reign
Alleluia! Sing to Jesus, 233
At the Name of Jesus, 235
Christ Arose, 216
Crown Him with Many Crowns, 234
Hail the Day That Sees Him Rise, 232

He Rose Triumphantly, 219
Jesus Is King, 230
Jesus Shall Reign, 231
Our God Reigns, 229
Rejoice, the Lord Is King, 228

CHRIST - Atonement, Crucifixion, Suffering and Death
A Perfect Heart, 40
Alas! and Did My Savior Bleed?, 208
Alleluia! Alleluia!, 215
Amazing Grace, 202
And Can It Be?, 203
Are You Washed in the Blood?, 190
At Calvary, 338
At the Cross, 188
Behold the Lamb, 179
Beneath the Cross of Jesus, 183
Calvary Covers It All, 189
For God So Loved, 205
Glory to His Name, 527
God So Loved the World, 207
Grace Greater Than Our Sin, 201
Hallelujah, What a Savior!, 175
He Is Lord, 105
He Rose Triumphantly, 219
He the Pearly Gates Will Open, 541
His Way with Thee, 333
I Am Thine, O Lord, 358
I Know a Fount, 194
I Lay My Sins on Jesus, 340
I Will Sing of My Redeemer, 506
I'll Live for Him, 370
In His Cross I Glory, 187
In the Cross of Christ I Glory, 184
Jesus Paid It All, 210
Jesus Saves!, 306
Jesus, Thy Blood and Righteousness, 193
Lead Me to Calvary, 176
Lift High the Cross, 304
Living for Jesus, 372
Near the Cross, 385
Nothing But the Blood, 195
O Sacred Head, Now Wounded, 178
One Day!, 170
Praise Him! Praise Him!, 106
Redeemed (Ada), 520
Redeemed (Kirkpatrick), 521
Rock of Ages, 204
Room at the Cross for You, 331
The Blood Will Never Lose Its Power, 192
The Old Rugged Cross, 186
The Unveiled Christ, 169
There Is a Fountain, 196
There Is a Redeemer, 206
There Is Power in the Blood, 191
'Tis So Sweet to Trust in Jesus, 350
We Are the Reason, 209
We Come, O Christ, to You, 117
Were You There?, 181
What a Wonderful Savior!, 81
What Wondrous Love Is This?, 177
When I Survey the Wondrous Cross, 185
Worthy Is the Lamb, 180

CHRIST - Birth
(see also CHRIST - Advent, CHRIST - Epiphany)
A Communion Hymn for Christmas, 140
A Nativity Prayer, 126
A Thousand Candles, 159
Angels from the Realms of Glory, 131
Angels We Have Heard on High, 132
Away in a Manger (Away in a Manger), 157
Away in a Manger (Cradle Song), 158
Break Forth, O Beauteous Heavenly Light, 129
Child of Love, 156
Come on, Ring Those Bells, 153
Emmanuel, 134
For Unto Us a Child Is Born, 146
Go, Tell It on the Mountain, 138
Good Christian Men, Rejoice, 151
Hark! the Herald Angels Sing, 133
How Great Our Joy!, 144
I Heard the Bells on Christmas Day, 152
I Wonder as I Wander, 139
Infant Holy, Infant Lowly, 143
It Came upon the Midnight Clear, 128
Jesus Is Born, 149
Joy to the World!, 125
Lo! How a Rose E'er Blooming, 160
O Come, All Ye Faithful, 145
O Hearken Ye, 150
O Holy Night!, 148
O Little Town of Bethlehem, 141
Once in Royal David's City, 155
Our Day of Joy Is Here Again, 161
Silent Night! Holy Night!, 147
The Birthday of a King, 162
The First Noel, 136
Thou Didst Leave Thy Throne, 127
What Can I Give Him?, 154
What Child Is This?, 137
While Shepherds Watched Their Flocks, 135

CHRIST - Cleansing Blood
(see CHRIST - Atonement)

CHRIST - Cross
(see CHRIST - Atonement)

CHRIST - Death
(see CHRIST - Atonement)

CHRIST - Epiphany
Adoration, 165
As with Gladness Men of Old, 163
Break Forth, O Beauteous Heavenly Light, 129
Fairest Lord Jesus, 88
Go, Tell It on the Mountain, 138
O Sing a Song of Bethlehem, 167
One Small Child, 164
We Three Kings, 166

HOLINESS AND PURITY

Cleanse Me (Ellers), 439
Cleanse Me (Maori), 438
Give Me Jesus, 443
O for a Heart to Praise My God, 440
Pure and Holy, 437
Search Me, 434
Take Time to Be Holy (Holiness), 441
Take Time to Be Holy (Slane), 442
Whiter Than Snow, 436

HOLY SPIRIT

Breathe on Me, 251
Breathe on Me, Breath of God, 259
Cleanse Me (Ellers), 439
Cleanse Me (Maori), 438
Come, Holy Spirit, 250
Come Holy Spirit, Dove Divine, 320
Fill Me Now, 261
Greater Is He That Is In Me, 255
He Is Here, He Is Here, 256
Heavenly Spirit, Gentle Spirit, 254
Holy Ghost, with Light Divine, 248
Jesus, Stand Among Us, 586
O Breath of Life, 291
Spirit of God, Descend upon My Heart, 249
Spirit of the Living God, 247
Sweet, Sweet Spirit, 252
The Comforter Has Come, 257
We Are Gathered for Thy Blessing, 258
Welcome, Welcome, 260
Where the Spirit of the Lord Is, 253

HOLY TRINITY
(see TRINITY)

HOME
(see FAMILY AND HOME)

HOPE
(see FAITH AND HOPE)

INVITATION AND ACCEPTANCE
(see also REPENTANCE AND FORGIVENESS)

All Your Anxiety, 418
Are You Washed in the Blood?, 190
Come, Ye Sinners, Poor and Needy, 334
Have You Any Room for Jesus?, 328
I Am Praying for You, 431
I Have Decided to Follow Jesus, 376
I Surrender All, 366
Jesus Calls Us, 375
Jesus, I Come, 336
Jesus Is Calling, 327
Just As I Am, 342
Lord, I'm Coming Home, 341
Only Trust Him, 330
Room at the Cross for You, 331
Softly and Tenderly, 326
The Savior Is Waiting, 329
Thou Didst Leave Thy Throne, 127
Turn Your Eyes upon Jesus, 335

JOY

Be Joyful, 223
Good Christian Men, Rejoice, 151
How Great Our Joy!, 144
Jesus, Thou Joy of Loving Hearts, 501
Joyful, Joyful, We Adore Thee, 1
Rejoice, the Lord Is King, 228
The Day of Resurrection, 226

JUDGMENT

Jesus, Thy Blood and Righteousness, 193
Lo, He Comes with Clouds Descending, 241

LEADING
(see PROVISION AND LEADING, GOD - Guidance and Care)

LIFE EVERLASTING

Beyond the Sunset, 548
Face to Face, 549
For All the Saints, 546
He Keeps Me Singing, 488
He the Pearly Gates Will Open, 541
I Am His, and He Is Mine, 490
I'll Fly Away, 554
Jesus Lives, and So Shall I, 224
Must Jesus Bear the Cross Alone?, 449
My Faith Looks Up to Thee, 410
O Could I Speak the Matchless Worth, 110
O That Will Be Glory, 539
On Jordan's Stormy Banks, 552
Saved by Grace, 550
Soon and Very Soon, 551
Sweet By and By, 553
The King of Love My Shepherd Is, 468
The Kingdom of God, 547
The New 23rd, 53
The Way of the Cross Leads Home, 471
We Shall See His Lovely Face, 545
We'll Understand It Better By and By, 544
We're Marching to Zion, 555
When I Can Read My Title Clear, 538
When the Roll Is Called Up Yonder, 543
When We All Get to Heaven, 542

LORD'S DAY
(see OPENING OF SERVICE)

LORD'S SUPPER
(see also CHRIST - Atonement)

A Communion Hymn for Christmas, 140
According to Thy Gracious Word, 321
Break Thou the Bread of Life, 274
Come Celebrate Jesus, 324
Here, O My Lord, I See Thee Face to Face, 325
In Remembrance, 322
Let Us Break Bread Together, 323

LOVE - God's Love
(see also GOD - Love and Mercy)

Children of the Heavenly Father, 44
For God So Loved, 205
God So Loved the World, 207
I Am His, and He Is Mine, 490
I Will Sing of My Redeemer, 506
In Heavenly Love Abiding, 502
Jesus, Lover of My Soul, 466
Jesus Loves Even Me, 357
Jesus Loves Me, 579
Joyful, Joyful, We Adore Thee, 1
Lavish Love, Abundant Beauty, 61
Love Divine, All Loves Excelling, 92
Love Lifted Me, 505
No One Ever Cared for Me Like Jesus, 528
O, How He Loves You and Me, 513
O Love That Will Not Let Me Go, 374
O the Deep, Deep Love of Jesus (Bunessan), 212
O the Deep, Deep Love of Jesus (Ebenezer), 211
Of the Father's Love Begotten, 118
Share His Love, 302
The Love of God, 67
Thy Loving Kindness, 69
When I Survey the Wondrous Cross, 185

LOVE - Our Love for God

Joyful, Joyful, We Adore Thee, 1
More Love to Thee, 363
My Jesus, I Love Thee, 364
O, How I Love Jesus, 529

LOVE - Our Love for Others

Blest Be the Tie That Binds, 286
Joyful, Joyful, We Adore Thee, 1
People Need the Lord, 303
The Bond of Love, 281
They'll Know We Are Christians by Our Love, 284

LOYALTY AND COURAGE
(see also SPIRITUAL WARFARE)

A Charge to Keep I Have, 448
Faith Is the Victory, 486
Greater Is He That Is In Me, 255
I Must Tell Jesus, 430
I Need Thee Every Hour, 428
Near the Cross, 385
O Jesus, I Have Promised, 369
Take the Name of Jesus with You, 116
Who Is on the Lord's Side?, 484

MARRIAGE
(see FAMILY AND HOME)

MEMORIAL DAY

America, the Beautiful, 572
Battle Hymn of the Republic, 569
God of Our Fathers, 573
Once to Every Man and Nation, 475
We Gather Together, 561

ALPHABETICAL INDEX OF HYMNS

Titles are in **bold face** type; First lines are in regular type.